Knowledge is Beautiful

Knowledge is Beautiful

David McCandless

WILLIAM
COLLINS

William Collins
An imprint of HarperCollins*Publishers*
1 London Bridge Street
London SE1 19GF
WilliamCollinsBooks.com

First published by William Collins in 2014

www.davidmccandless.com

A catalogue record for this book
is available from the British Library

ISBN 978-0-00-742792-5

Printed and bound in Spain

MIX
Paper from
responsible sources
FSC™ C007454

FSC™ is a non-profit international organisation established to promote the responsible management of the
world's forests. Products carrying the FSC label are independently certified to assure customers that they
come from forests that are managed to meet the social, economic and ecological needs of present and
future generations, and other controlled sources.

Find out more about HarperCollins and the environment at www.harpercollins.co.uk/green

To my girls, Holly & Kathryn

introduction

Funny. The more I visualise data, information and knowledge, the more I'm starting to feel and understand the differences between them.

Understanding really is the key. When you understand something, you're able to perceive its structure: its connections, its relationships, its significance relative to everything else. How it fits. You see–feel–intuit the fit. You know it. You know?

Context, I'm realising, is the field of these connections, the network we plug any new information into. That explains why, when something is contextualised, we can suddenly get it. It feels 'meaningful' to us because it fits into the network of what we already know and understand and can relate to. Our knowledge.

The more you understand information in this way, the more connected and contextualised it becomes, the more it starts to morph and grow into knowledge.

I'm finding it exhibits an organic vibe, like an organic network, with connections, roots and 'branches of knowledge'. It self-organises, becoming more cellular, organismic, with boundaries and perimeters, forming 'bodies of knowledge'. Its branches connect out horizontally, across subjects, ranging wide across the 'field of knowledge.' And it also sometimes sends roots out vertically, between domains of knowledge, both deeper and higher. When it does, we talk of 'deep understanding' and a 'depth of knowledge'.

Information focusses on the 'now' and the 'what'. News is a perfect example of information. In contrast, knowledge feels like it's more concerned with causes and consequences, past influences and future projections. The 'how' and the 'why'.

Some of the graphics in this book are complex, some deep. Not always because I wanted them to be. But more because the drive towards answering the how and why demanded a certain comprehensiveness. It just didn't feel like knowledge until I had the major questions covered.

This is when I often encountered 'The Never-Ending Graphic'. I'd start with one question which opened up three more. To answer those, I had to pull in information from another domain, which would trigger two or three more questions. Suddenly, one graphic had fanned out to become ten! That, I guess, is what's called the 'pursuit of knowledge' – bloody endless!

So, ultimately, every single graphic in the book is paired with an online dataset at the bottom of each page, a little 'font of knowledge'. You'll often find extra research and data going beyond what's in the visualisation. Sorry – sometimes it was difficult to stop! It's also why many of the graphics have – or will have – interactive versions online. Sift, filter and explore the richness of knowledge for yourself. See what you think. Drink it in. Hopefully, it will sate some of your 'thirst for knowledge'. Like it did for me.

David McCandless, June 2014

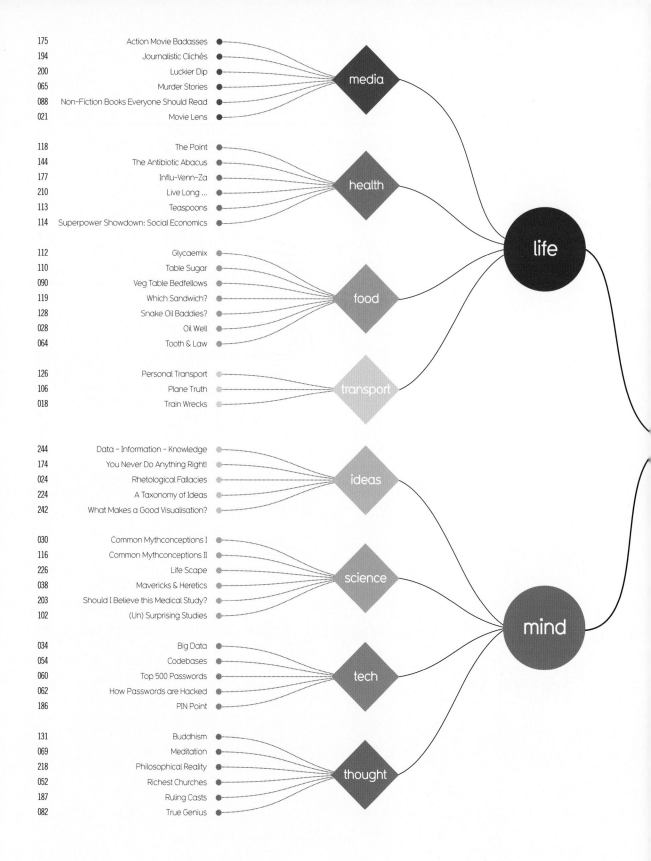

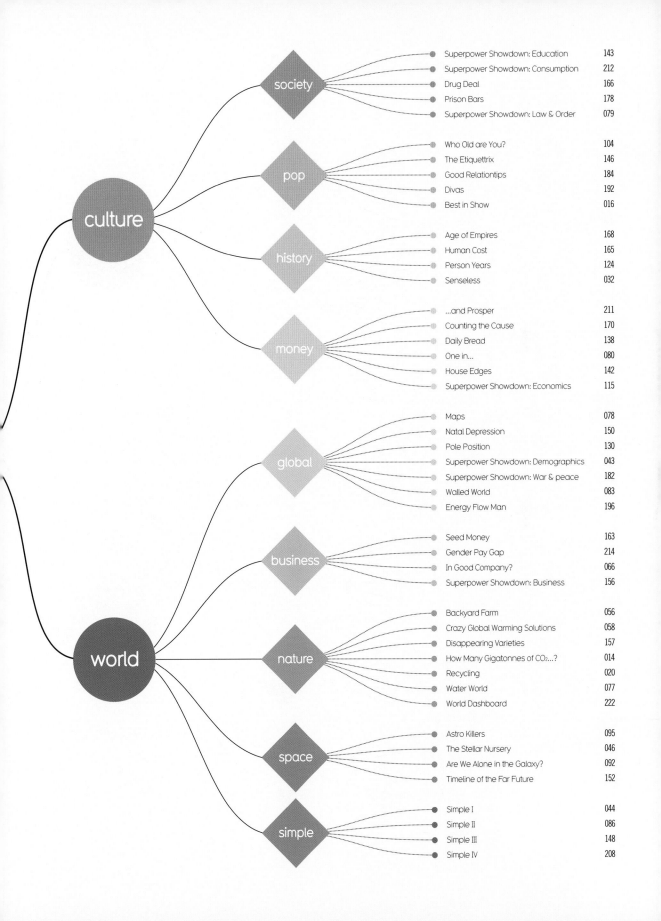

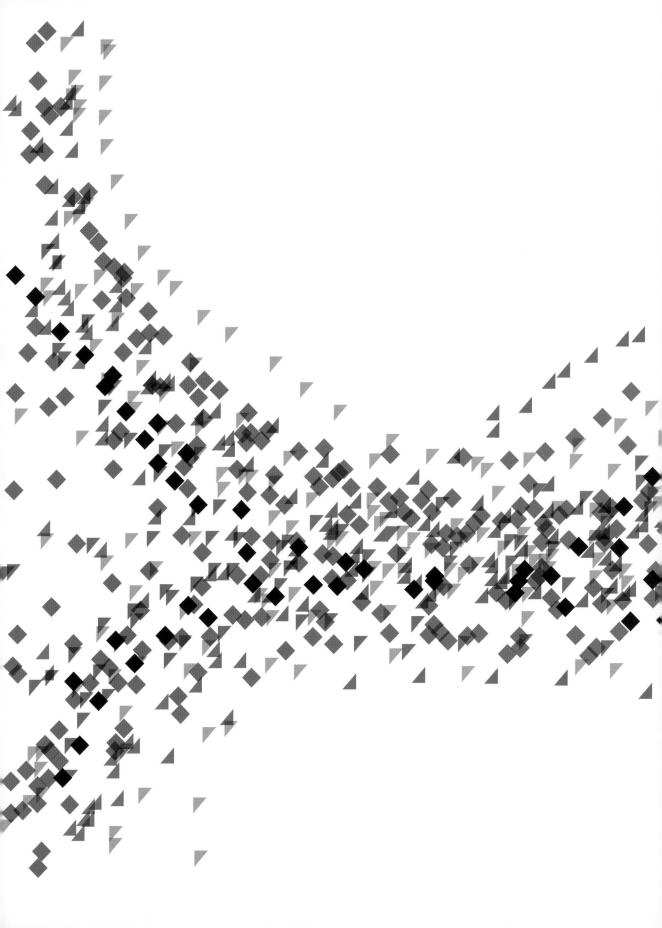

TYPE	**data**	structured **data**	**information**
ART	VISUALISATION		DESIGN

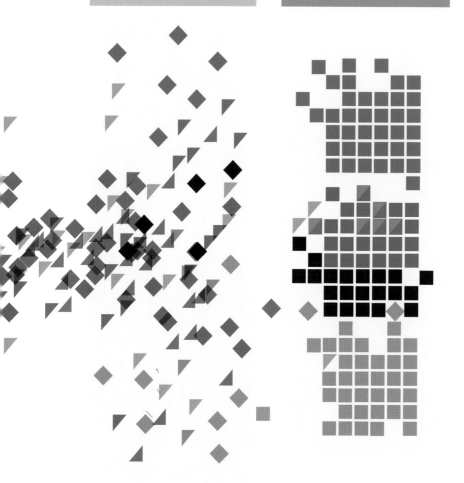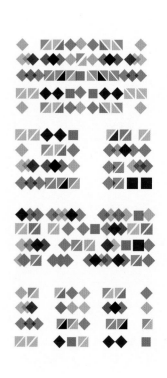

PROCESS	mine gather measure	examine recognise classify	filter interpret arrange

METAPHOR	atoms	molecules	DNA

linked

information   **knowledge**   inter-connected
knowledge

MAPPING

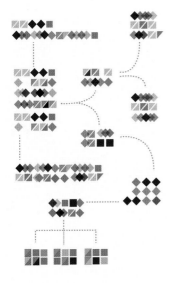
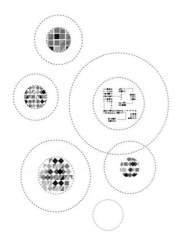
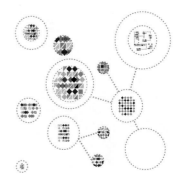

connect	evaluate	integrate
sequence	understand	extrapolate
condense	explain	generate

chromosomes   cells   organisms

How Many Gigatonnes of CO$_2$...?

...have we released to date?

1,565 GtCO$_2$
added 1850–2000

405
added since 2000

...more can we 'safely' release*?

850
our 'carbon budget'

...are left to release?

760
in fossil-fuel reserves of the top coal, oil & gas companies

780
remaining reserves that could be developed

2,860

+ **1,320**
other reserves including state-owned

* before 2050 and still have an 80% chance of staying below 2°C warming

39 gigatonnes
CURRENT HUMAN EMISSIONS PER YEAR

17 YEARS
average yearly emissions increase: 3%
TIME BEFORE WE BREAK OUR 'CARBON BUDGET'
if emissions continue to rise

over pre-industrial average temperature

relative to 1990 sea level

GLOBAL WARMING IF RELEASED	+0.8°C 1.4°F	+1.5°C 2.7°F	+2°C 3.6°F	+3-4°C 5.4-7.2°F	+5-6°C 9-10.8°F
SCENARIO	happened	inevitable	'safe' limit	tipping point	nightmare
SEA-LEVEL RISE BY 2100		0.85 m	1.04 m	1.24 m	1.43 m

DROWNING CITIES	Amsterdam	New York	Bangkok — knee-high flooding, serious inundation
OCEAN ACIDIFICATION	30% more acidic — CORAL stops growing	bleached	dead / 150% more acidic — oceans become more acidic as they absorb CO_2
HEAT	more severe heatwaves	every Euro summer a heatwave	Italy, Spain, Greece deserts / unknown
CORN & WHEAT YIELDS	-10%	-20%	-30 to -40% / unknown — US & Africa corn, Indian wheat
% MORE HEAVY RAIN OVER LAND	7%	13%	20-26% / 35-42% — compared to today
INCREASE IN HURRICANE DESTRUCTIVE POWER	+7.5%	+15%	+22.5-30% / +37.5-45%
SPECIES AT RISK OF EXTINCTION		30% up to	40%
REALLY SCARY THINGS		Greenland ice sheet starts to disintegrate. Will take 50,000 years with 2°C to melt but will raise sea levels by 6 m.	Risk of releasing huge amounts of CO_2 & methane released by melting permafrost in Siberia and Arctic. / Risk of ocean-floor methane release, causing runaway climate change. Possibility of mass extinction.

LAST TIME CO_2 LEVELS WERE THIS HIGH (398ppm)

3,500,000 YEARS AGO

TIME NEEDED TO RE-ABSORB ALL THIS CO_2 FROM ATMOSPHERE

300,000 YEARS

sources: Carbon Tracker Initiative, IPCC, National Research Council, International Energy Agency (IEA), National Oceanic & Atmospheric Administration (NOAA)
data: bit.ly/KIB_Gigatons

Best in Show
The ultimate datadog

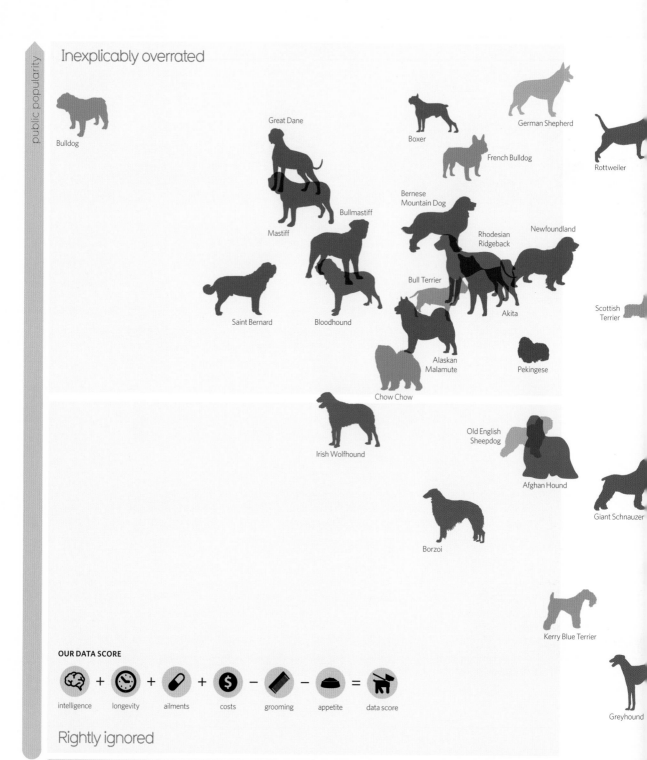

public popularity

Inexplicably overrated

Bulldog

Great Dane

Boxer

German Shepherd

French Bulldog

Rottweiler

Bernese Mountain Dog

Mastiff

Bullmastiff

Newfoundland

Rhodesian Ridgeback

Saint Bernard

Bloodhound

Bull Terrier

Akita

Scottish Terrier

Alaskan Malamute

Pekingese

Chow Chow

Irish Wolfhound

Old English Sheepdog

Afghan Hound

Giant Schnauzer

Borzoi

Kerry Blue Terrier

Greyhound

OUR DATA SCORE

intelligence + longevity + ailments + costs − grooming − appetite = data score

Rightly ignored

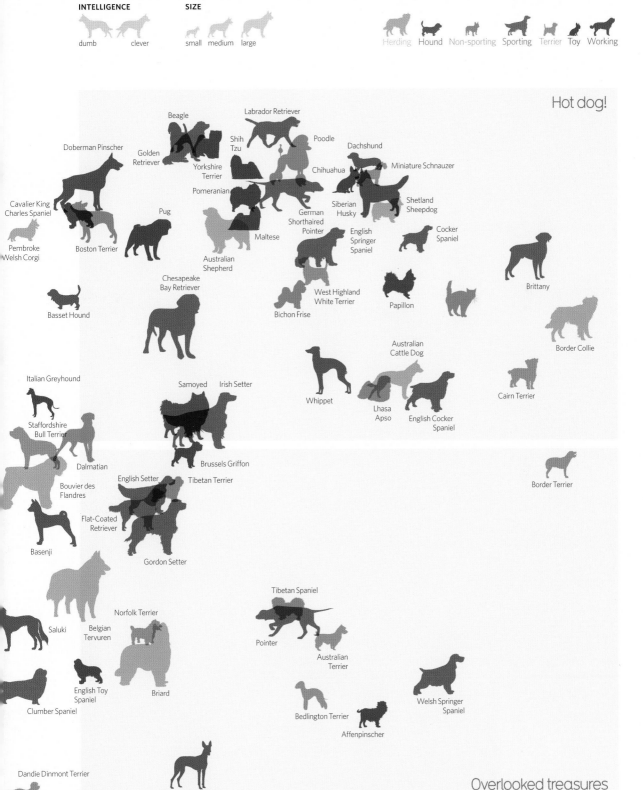

INTELLIGENCE
dumb   clever

SIZE
small   medium   large

Herding   Hound   Non-sporting   Sporting   Terrier   Toy   Working

Hot dog!

Doberman Pinscher
Cavalier King Charles Spaniel
Pembroke Welsh Corgi
Boston Terrier
Golden Retriever
Beagle
Pug
Yorkshire Terrier
Pomeranian
Basset Hound
Chesapeake Bay Retriever
Australian Shepherd
Maltese
Labrador Retriever
Shih Tzu
Poodle
Chihuahua
German Shorthaired Pointer
Bichon Frise
West Highland White Terrier
Dachshund
Miniature Schnauzer
Siberian Husky
Shetland Sheepdog
English Springer Spaniel
Papillon
Cocker Spaniel
Brittany
Border Collie

Italian Greyhound
Staffordshire Bull Terrier
Dalmatian
Basenji
Bouvier des Flandres
Flat-Coated Retriever
English Setter
Samoyed
Irish Setter
Whippet
Australian Cattle Dog
Lhasa Apso
English Cocker Spaniel
Cairn Terrier
Border Terrier
Brussels Griffon
Tibetan Terrier
Gordon Setter

Saluki
Belgian Tervuren
Norfolk Terrier
English Toy Spaniel
Briard
Clumber Spaniel
Tibetan Spaniel
Pointer
Australian Terrier
Bedlington Terrier
Affenpinscher
Welsh Springer Spaniel

Dandie Dinmont Terrier
Pharaoh Hound

Overlooked treasures

our data score

sources: American Kennel Club, Cassidy (2007), Canine Inherited Disorders Database, 'The Intelligence of Dogs', Stanley Coren
data: bit.ly/KIB_BestDogs

Train Wrecks
Best and worst railways

INFRASTRUCTURE					PASSENGERS		
Total length of track	Track per inhabitant	Spending per year	Amount spent per km of track	10-year rise in investment	Total journeys per year	Total journeys per year	10-year increase in journeys
'000 km	cm	$US billions	$US thousands	%	billions	% of population	%

Highest ranked

229 US	74	126	139	1,581	7.7	8	61
66 China	52	8.5	78	174	2.4	6	59
64 India	51	7	27	155	1.6	5	58
34 Germany	41	6	19	64	1.4	3	38
34 France	30	6	18	36	1.1	2	37
31 UK	7	2	12	-11	0.6	0.34	30
18 Italy	5	no data	0.9	no data	no data	0.03	28

Lowest ranked

China ● France ● Germany ● India ● Italy ● UK ● US

PASSENGERS

Rail passengers at busiest station	Yearly passenger distance	Journeys per person per year
% city population	billion km	average

MONEY

Gross revenue	Revenue per passenger journey	How far can you go for $1?
$US billions	$US	km

RANKING

Best & worst railways

total score

51
Frankfurt

975

29

132

92

57

1   China

22
Paris

816

22

54

63

19

2   Germany

17
Rome

85

17

47

39

9

3   UK

11
Mumbai

74

10

21

20

7

4   India

4
London

56

6

18

18

7

5   France

3
New York

39

1.2

11

11

6

6   Italy

1
Beijing

1.1

0.1

2.7

2.6

5

7   US

sources: CIA World Factbook, World Bank, Eurostat, United Nations Economic Commission for Europe, IndianRailways.gov
Data: bit.ly/KIB_TrainWrecks

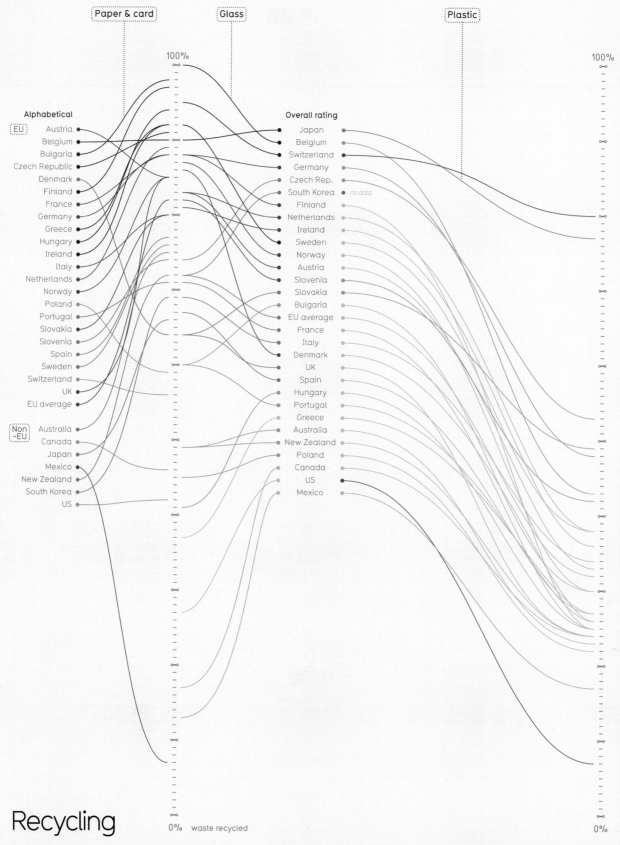

Paper & card   Glass   Plastic

100%   100%

Alphabetical   Overall rating

EU   Austria   Japan
      Belgium   Belgium
      Bulgaria   Switzerland
      Czech Republic   Germany
      Denmark   Czech Rep.
      Finland   South Korea   ● no data
      France   Finland
      Germany   Netherlands
      Greece   Ireland
      Hungary   Sweden
      Ireland   Norway
      Italy   Austria
      Netherlands   Slovenia
      Norway   Slovakia
      Poland   Bulgaria
      Portugal   EU average
      Slovakia   France
      Slovenia   Italy
      Spain   Denmark
      Sweden   UK
      Switzerland   Spain
      UK   Hungary
      EU average   Portugal
                                 Greece
Non   Australia   Australia
-EU   Canada   New Zealand
      Japan   Poland
      Mexico   Canada
      New Zealand   US
      South Korea   Mexico
      US

Recycling

0%   waste recycled   0%

020 | 021

sources: Eurostat, OECD, European Commission, BBC
data: bit.ly/Recycling

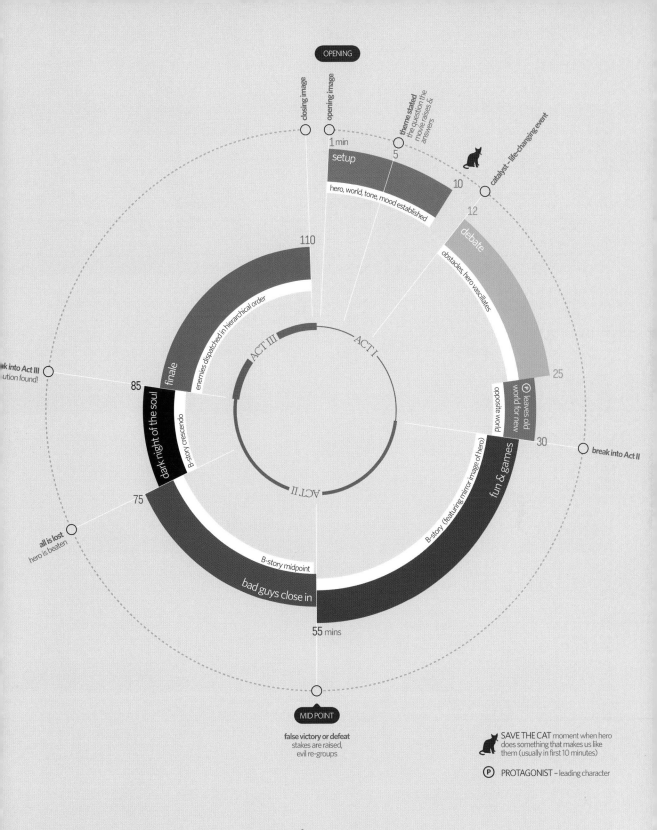

Movie Lens
The 'Save the Cat' screenwriting formula that underpins Hollywood

'Save the Cat!' Applied

| 1 min | 5 | 10 12 | | 25 | 30 |

setup — **debate** — ℗ **leaves old world for new** — **fun & games**

hero, world, tone, mood established — OPENING IMAGE — THEME STATED

obstacles, hero vascillates — CATALYST (LIFE-CHANGING EVENT)

opposite world — BREAK INTO ACT II — ℗ story (featuring mirror image of hero)

FALS
STAKES A.

MATRIX

℗ is a hacker who leads a double-life — will ℗ find out what the Matrix is? — enters the Matrix — ACT II — ℗ begins his training

dark, dystopian, shadowy world — COMPUTER SCREEN GREEN TEXT — THEME STATED

℗ is captured, bugged — ℗ MEETS TRINITY

'YOU EVER HAVE THAT FEELING, WHERE YOU'RE NOT SURE IF YOU'RE AWAKE OR STILL DREAMING?'

'fake' world — ℗ TAKES RED PILL — ℗ romance with Trinity / Cypher betrays them

N E
HE WILL H
MOI

The Hunger Games

℗ & her family are poor, destitute, barely surviving — has ℗ got what it takes to play the games? — opening ceremony — ACT II — ℗ begins training

dystopian, oppresive, hopeless world — COMFORTING HER TERRIFIED SISTER — THEME STATED

will ℗ survive the games? — THE REAPING — ℗ VOLUNTEERS IN HER SISTER'S PLACE

'WE COULD RUN OFF AND HIDE IN THE WOODS.' 'NO.'

'capitol' world — ℗ IS LOVED BY THE CROWD — ℗ cultivates a 'screen-romance' with Peeta

M

C
T

AVATAR

℗ is a crippled ex-marine with few options — will ℗ spy on the natives for the military? — ℗ is lost in the jungle — ACT II — ℗ gains the Tribe's trust, will be taught their ways

alien, beauty and raw danger — ℗ FACE WAKING UP — THEME STATED

'SOONER OR LATER YOU'VE GOT TO WAKE UP'

MEETS COLONEL, IS OFFERED HIS LEGS BACK

deadly alien world — LEAPS OFF CLIFF TO AVOID MONSTER — ℗ romance with Neytiri. ℗ learns to be a true warrior (with heart

THE KING'S SPEECH

℗ stammers, lacks leadership — will ℗ choose his saviour? — accepts — ℗ begins his bizarre training and shows improvemen

the pressures of life as a royal prince — HUMILIATION BEFORE CROWD

℗ doubts Lionel — MEETS SPEECH THERAPIST, LIONEL

Lionel's world — LISTENS TO RECORDING — ℗ relationship with his ailing father, the throne and his cocky bro

Lost in Translation

both characters lost in time & space — will they find each other? — accepts — he goes out with her

lonely, bored and unseen in an alien culture — HIM ASLEEP IN A CAB — SEE EACH OTHER IN LIFT

him busy, her empty

her world — SHE ASKS HIM OUT — their various relationship and existential crises

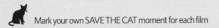 Mark your own SAVE THE CAT moment for each film

Each movie retimed to 110 minutes

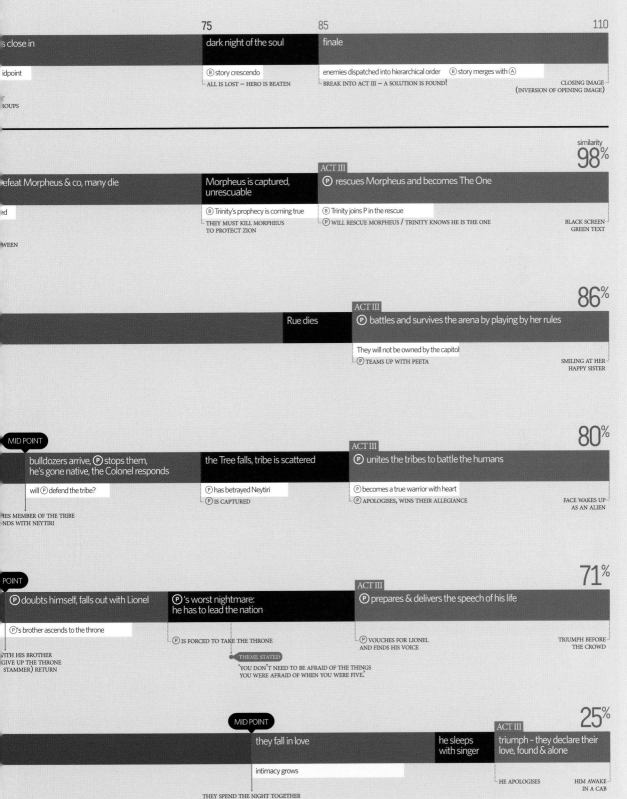

75 85 110

s close in | dark night of the soul | finale

idpoint

Ⓑ story crescendo | enemies dispatched into hierarchical order Ⓑ story merges with Ⓐ

ALL IS LOST — HERO IS BEATEN

BREAK INTO ACT III – A SOLUTION IS FOUND!

CLOSING IMAGE
(INVERSION OF OPENING IMAGE)

ROUPS

---

similarity
98%

efeat Morpheus & co, many die | Morpheus is captured, unrescuable | ACT III Ⓟ rescues Morpheus and becomes The One

ed

Ⓑ Trinity's prophecy is coming true | Ⓑ Trinity joins P in the rescue

THEY MUST KILL MORPHEUS
TO PROTECT ZION

Ⓟ WILL RESCUE MORPHEUS / TRINITY KNOWS HE IS THE ONE

BLACK SCREEN
GREEN TEXT

WEEN

86%

Rue dies | ACT III Ⓟ battles and survives the arena by playing by her rules

They will not be owned by the capitol

Ⓟ TEAMS UP WITH PEETA

SMILING AT HER
HAPPY SISTER

80%

MID POINT

bulldozers arrive, Ⓟ stops them, he's gone native, the Colonel responds | the Tree falls, tribe is scattered | ACT III Ⓟ unites the tribes to battle the humans

will Ⓟ defend the tribe?

Ⓟ has betrayed Neytiri | Ⓟ becomes a true warrior with heart

Ⓟ IS CAPTURED

Ⓟ APOLOGISES, WINS THEIR ALLEGIANCE

FACE WAKES UP
AS AN ALIEN

MES MEMBER OF THE TRIBE
NDS WITH NEYTIRI

71%

POINT

Ⓟ doubts himself, falls out with Lionel | Ⓟ's worst nightmare: he has to lead the nation | ACT III Ⓟ prepares & delivers the speech of his life

Ⓟ's brother ascends to the throne

Ⓟ IS FORCED TO TAKE THE THRONE | Ⓟ VOUCHES FOR LIONEL AND FINDS HIS VOICE

TRIUMPH BEFORE
THE CROWD

WITH HIS BROTHER
GIVE UP THE THRONE
STAMMER) RETURN

THEME STATED
'YOU DON'T NEED TO BE AFRAID OF THE THINGS
YOU WERE AFRAID OF WHEN YOU WERE FIVE.'

25%

MID POINT

ACT III

they fall in love | he sleeps with singer | triumph – they declare their love, found & alone

intimacy grows

HE APOLOGISES | HIM AWAKE IN A CAB

THEY SPEND THE NIGHT TOGETHER

sources: 'Save The Cat! The Last Book on Screenwriting You'll Ever Need', Blake Snyder (2005)
data: bit.ly/KIB_SaveTheCat

Appeal to the Emotions

Appeal to Consequences of a Belief
Arguing a belief is false because it implies something you'd rather not believe.

'That can't be the senator on that sex tape. If it were, he'd be lying about not knowing her. And he's not the kind of man who would lie.'

Appeal to Fear
An argument is made by increasing fear and prejudice towards the opposing side.

'Before you know it there will be more mosques than churches.'

Appeal to Flattery
Using an irrelevant compliment to slip in an unfounded claim that is accepted along with the compliment.

'Intelligent and sophisticated readers will of course recognise a fallacy like this when they read one.'

Appeal to Nature
Making your claim seem more true by drawing a comparison with the 'good' natural world.

'Of course homosexuality is unnatural. You don't see same-sex animals copulating.'

Appeal to Pity
Attempt to induce pity to sway opponents.

'The former dictator is an old, dying man. It's wrong to make him stand trial for these alleged offences.'

Appeal to Ridicule
Presenting the opponent's argument in a way that makes it appear absurd.

'Faith in God is like believing in Santa Claus and the Tooth Fairy.'

Appeal to Spite
Dismissing a claim by appealing to personal bias against the claimant.

'Don't you just hate how those rich liberal Hollywood actors go on TV to promote their agendas?'

Appeal to Wishful Thinking
Suggesting a claim is true or false just because you strongly hope it is.

'The president wouldn't lie. He's our leader and a good American.'

Garbled Cause & Effect

Affirming the Consequent
Assuming there's only one explanation for the observation you're making.

'Marriage often results in the birth of children. So that's the reason why it exists.'

Circular Logic
A conclusion is derived from a premise based on the conclusion.

'Stripping privacy rights only matters to those with something to hide. You must have something to hide if you oppose privacy protection.'

Cum Hoc Ergo Propter Hoc
Claiming two events that occur together must have a cause-and-effect relationship. (Correlation = cause)

'Teenagers in gangs listen to rap music with violent themes. Rap music inspires violence in teenagers.'

Denying the Antecedent
There isn't only one explanation for an outcome. So it's false to assume the cause based on the effect.

'If you get a degree, you'll get a good job. If you don't get a degree, you won't get a good job.'

Ignoring a Common Cause
Claiming one event must have caused the other when a third (unlooked-for) event is probably the cause.

'We had the 60s sexual revolution, and now people are dying of AIDS.'

Post Hoc Ergo Propter Hoc
Claiming that because one event followed another, it was also caused by it.

'Since the election of the president more people than ever are unemployed. Therefore the president has damaged the economy.'

Two Wrongs Make a Right
Assuming that if one wrong is committed, another wrong will cancel it out.

'Sure – the conditions in this prison are cruel and dehumanising. But these inmates are criminals!'

Rhetological Fallacies
Errors and manipulations of rhetoric and logical thought

Faulty Deduction

Anecdotal Evidence
Discounting evidence arrived at by systematic search or testing in favour of a few firsthand stories.

'I'm going to carry on smoking. My grandfather smoked 40 a day and he lived until he was 90!'

Composition
Assuming that characteristics or beliefs of some or all of a group apply to the entire group.

'Recent terrorist attacks have been carried out by radical Islamic groups. Therefore all Muslims are terrorists.'

Division
Assuming that characteristics or beliefs of a group automatically apply to any individual member.

'Many Conservatives wish to ban gay marriage, discredit climate change and deny evolution. Therefore all Conservatives are homophobic, anti-environmental creationists.'

Design Fallacy
Assuming that because something is nicely designed or beautifully visualised it's more true.

'Er....'

Gambler's Fallacy
Assuming the history of outcomes will affect future outcomes.

'I've flipped this coin 10 times in a row and it's been heads. Therefore the next coin flip is more likely to come up tails.'

Hasty Generalisation
Drawing a general conclusion from a tiny sample.

'I just got cut up by the woman driver in front. Women can't drive.'

Jumping to Conclusions
Drawing a quick conclusion without fairly considering relevant (and easily available) evidence.

'She wants birth control in her medical cover? She must be easy!!'

Middle Ground
Assuming because two opposing arguments have merit, the answer must lie somewhere between them.

'I rear-ended your car but I don't think I should pay for the damage. You think I should pay for all the damage. A fair compromise would be to split the bill in half.'

Perfectionist Fallacy
Assuming that the only option on the table is perfect success, then rejecting anything that will not work perfectly.

'What's the point of this anti-drink-driving campaign? People are still going to drink and drive no matter what.'

Relativist Fallacy
Rejecting a claim because of a belief that truth is relative to a person or group.

'That's perhaps true for you. But it's not true for me.'

Sweeping Generalisation
Applying a general rule too broadly.

'Those young men rioted because they lacked morally responsible fathers.'

Undistributed Middle
Assuming because two things share a property, that makes them the same thing.

'A theory can mean an unproven idea. Scientists use the term "evolutionary theory". Therefore evolution is an unproven idea.'

Spotlight
Assuming an observation from a small sample size applies to an entire group.

'This large shoe manufacturer employs children in sweatshops. Therefore all shoe companies are evil child-slave owners!'

sources: Fallacy Files, Internet Encyclopedia of Philosophy, Wikipedia, Skeptic Dictionary
data: bit.ly/KIB_Rhetological

Manipulating Content

Ad Hoc Rescue

Trying to save a cherished belief by repeatedly revising the argument to explain away problems.

'...But apart from better sanitation, medicine, education, irrigation, public health, roads, a freshwater system and public order... what have the Romans done for us?'

Begging the Question

A conclusion is derived from a statement based on the conclusion. Similar to circular logic, only with just one-step.

'Parallel lines will never meet, because they are parallel.'

On the Attack

Biased Generalising

Generalising from an unrepresentative sample to increase the strength of your argument.

'Our website poll found that 90% of internet users oppose online piracy laws.'

Ad Hominem

Bypassing the argument by launching an irrelevant attack on the person and not their claim.

'Anyone that says we should build the Ground Zero Mosque is an American-hating liberal.'

Confirmation Bias

Cherry-picking evidence that supports your idea while ignoring contradicting evidence.

'It's obvious 9/11 was a American-government-led conspiracy to justify war in Iraq and Afghanistan. No plane hit the Pentagon. The Twin Towers collapse was a controlled demolition...' etc.

Burden of Proof

I don't need to prove my claim – you must prove it is false.

'I maintain long-term solar cycles are the cause of global warming. Show me I'm wrong.'

False Dilemma

Presenting two opposing options as the only two options while hiding alternatives.

'We're going to have to cut the education budget or go deeper into debt. We can't afford to go deeper into debt. So we'll have to cut the education budget.'

Circumstance Ad Hominem

Stating a claim isn't credible only because of the advocate's interests in their claim.

'A study into the health risks of mobile-phone involved mobile phone companies. Therefore, the study cannot be trusted.'

Lie

An outright untruth repeated knowingly as a fact.

'I did not have sexual relations with that woman.'

Slippery Slope

Assuming a relatively small first step will inevitably lead to a chain of related (negative) events.

'If we legalise marijuana, more people will start using crack and heroin. Then we'd have to legalise those too.'

Misleading Vividness

Describing an occurrence in vivid detail, even if it is a rare occurrence, to convince someone that it is a problem.

'After a court decision to legalise gay marriage, school libraries were required to stock same-sex literature; primary-school children were given homosexual fairy stories and even manuals of explicit homosexual advocacy.'

Suppressed Evidence

Intentionally failing to use significant and relevant information that counts against one's own conclusion.

'The Iraqi regime possesses and produces chemical and biological weapons. It is seeking nuclear weapons.'

Red Herring

Introducing irrelevant material to the argument to distract and lead towards a different conclusion.

'The senator needn't account for irregularities in his expenses. After all, there are other senators who have done far worse things.'

Unfalsifiability

Offering a claim that cannot be proven false, because there is no way to check if it is false or not.

'He lied because he's possessed by demons.'

Appeal to the Mind

Appeal to Anonymous Authority

Using evidence from an unnamed 'expert' or 'study' or generalised group (like 'scientists') to claim something is true.

'They say that it takes 7 years to digest chewing gum.'

Appeal to Authority

Claiming something is true because an unqualified or untrustworthy 'expert' says it is.

'Over 400 prominent scientists and engineers dispute global warming.'

Appeal to Common Practice

Claiming something is true because it's commonly practised.

'This bank has some problems with corruption. But there's nothing going on here that doesn't go on in all the other banks.'

Genetic Fallacy

Attacking the cause or origin of a claim, rather than its substance.

'Of course, mainstream liberal media aren't going to say Barack Obama is a Muslim.'

Appeal to Ignorance

A claim is true simply because it has not been proven false (or false because it has not been proven true).

'Nobody has proved to me there is a God. So there is no God.'

Guilt by Association

Discrediting an idea or claim by associating it with an undesirable person or group.

'Oh, you want to relax the anti-terrorism laws, just like the terrorists want us to do. Are you saying you support terrorism?'

Straw Man

Creating a distorted or simplified caricature of your opponent's argument, and then arguing against that.

'You say Israel should stop building settlements on the West Bank in violation of international law. So you're saying Israel doesn't have the right to be a nation?'

Appeal to Incredulity

Because a claim sounds unbelievable, it must not be true.

'The eye is an incredibly complex biomechanical machine with thousands of interlocking parts. How could that exist without an intelligent designer?'

Appeal to Money

Supposing that, if someone is rich or something is expensive, then it affects the truth of the claim.

'If it costs more, it must be better.'

Appeal to Novelty

Supposing something is better because it is new or newer.

'Awesome! The latest version of this operating system is going to make my computer faster and better...'

Appeal to Popular Belief

Claiming something is true because the majority of people believe it.

'Milk is good for your bones.'

Appeal to Probability

$P(A \text{ or } B)$
$= P(A \cup B)$
$= P(A) + P(B)$

Assuming because something could happen, it will inevitably happen.

'There are billions of galaxies with billions of stars in the universe. So there must be another planet with intelligent life on it.'

Appeal to Tradition

Claiming something is true because it's (apparently) always been that way.

'Marriage is the union between man and woman. Therefore gay marriage is wrong.'

sources: Fallacy Files, Internet Encyclopedia of Philosophy, Wikipedia, Skeptic Dictionary
data: bit.ly/KIB_Rhetological

Oil Well

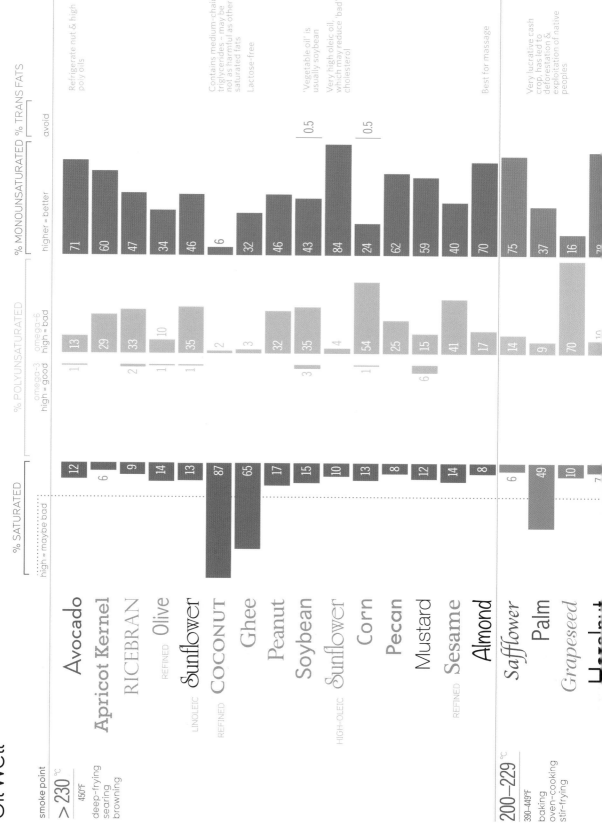

smoke point

>230 °C
450°F
deep-frying
searing
browning

% SATURATED
high = maybe bad

% POLYUNSATURATED
omega-3   omega-6
high = good   high = bad

% MONOUNSATURATED   % TRANS FATS
higher = better   avoid

Oil	Saturated	Polyunsaturated ω-3	Polyunsaturated ω-6	Monounsaturated
Avocado	12	1	13	71
Apricot Kernel	6		29	60
RICEBRAN	9	2	33	47
REFINED Olive	14	1	10	34
LINOLEIC Sunflower	13	1	35	46
REFINED COCONUT	87		2	6
Ghee	65		3	32
Peanut	17		32	46
Soybean	15	3	35	43
HIGH-OLEIC Sunflower	10		4	84
Corn	13	1	54	24
Pecan	8		25	62
Mustard	12	6	15	59
REFINED Sesame	14		41	40
Almond	8		17	70
Safflower	6		14	75
Palm	49		9	37
Grapeseed	10		70	16

Refrigerate nut & high poly oils

Contains medium-chain triglycerides – may be not as harmful as other saturated fats

Lactose-free

'Vegetable oil' is usually soybean

Very high oleic oil, which may reduce 'bad' cholesterol

0.5

0.5

Best for massage

200–229 °C
390-449°F
baking
oven-cooking
stir-frying

Very lucrative cash crop, has led to deforestation & exploitation of native peoples

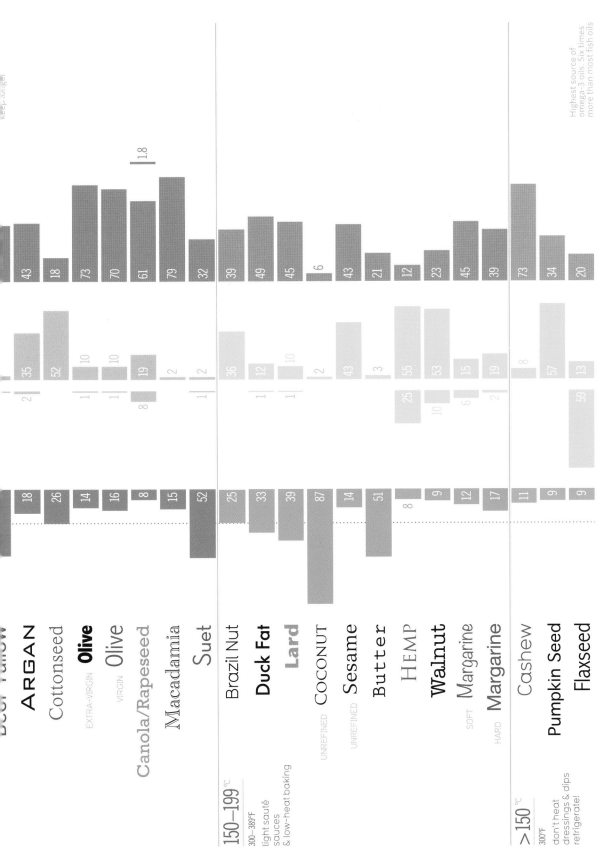

keep for gel

1.8

BEEF TALLOW

ARGAN	43	18	
Cottonseed	18	52	2
EXTRA-VIRGIN **Olive**	73	10	1
VIRGIN Olive	70	10	1
Canola/Rapeseed	61	19	8
Macadamia	79	2	
Suet	32	2	1

18
26
14
16
8
15
52

150–199°C

300–389°F
light sauté
sauces
& low-heat baking

Brazil Nut	39	36	
Duck Fat	49	12	1
Lard	45	10	1
UNREFINED COCONUT	6	2	
UNREFINED Sesame	43	43	
Butter	21	3	
HEMP	12	55	25
Walnut	23	53	10
SOFT Margarine	45	15	6
HARD **Margarine**	39	19	2

25
33
39
87
14
51
8
9
12
17

>150°C

300°F
don't heat
dressings & dips
refrigerate!

Cashew	73	8	
Pumpkin Seed	34	57	
Flaxseed	20	13	59

11
9
9

oil name colour = flavour: **strong** gentle neutral

Highest source of
omega-3 oils. Six times
more than most fish oils

sources: Nutrition Data, Cuinate.com, DiabetesinControl.com
data: bit.ly/KIB_OilWell

Common Mythconceptions I
Most contagious falsehoods

 Bubbles sized according to virulence of idea

The Vomitorium
Not a room Romans used for Bacchanalian binges, but the name for the entrance to a stadium.

Different tongue parts
There are no different sections for each taste: bitter, sour, salty, sweet & umami (savoury/meaty).

The first Thanksgiving
Celebrations were recorded 50 years before the 'first' Thanksgiving at Plymouth Colony.

Napoleon was short
A tall tale. At 5'7", he was actually above average height for a Frenchman of the time.

Bananas grow on trees
Actually grow on massive herbs that resemble trees. Bet you didn't know that.

Washington's wood teeth
No wood. A much more hygienic mix of gold, ivory & lead, plus horse & donkey teeth.

Great Wall of China
Not visible from space. Myth. Now stop saying it!

The 'Dark Ages'
A historical cliche. Era between the Roman Empire's decline & Renaissance not that backward.

US Cannabis Constitution
Written on parchment, not hemp, despite stoner revisionists claiming otherwise.

Bats are blind
Don't be fact-blind! Bats can not only see. They can also use echolocation. Awesome!

Vikings' horned helmets
Actually created by a costume designer for a 19th-century Wagner opera.

Salieri hated Mozart
Nothing like the film. They were composer friends with a little rivalry. Nothing more.

Einstein failed maths
Nope. He failed an entrance exam for a school but still excelled in maths.

Iron maidens
Never were medieval torture devices, but 18th-century fakes created for sensational circuses.

'Yes, I'm a cop'
US undercover police do not have to identify themselves as cops. A Hollywood-induced myth.

Evolution is a 'theory'
In science, the word 'theory' means anything more than a conjecture or proposition.

Medieval chastity belts
Not anti-adultery devices. Instead invented by prudes in the 19th century to prevent 'dangerous' masturbation.

Lincoln freed all slaves
He instigated the process but full abolition only happened 3 years later.

We evolved from chimps
No – they are our closest living genetic relatives. A shared ancestor lived 5–8 million years ago.

Pilgrims wore all black
Nope. They sported Elizabethan in-colours: reds, yellows, purples & greens. And no buckle hats!

Mussolini's trains never late
Fascist propaganda. They did run on time but only because of work done before his rule.

Sharks don't get cancer
Oh yes they do.
Particularly skin cancer.

Black holes
Not really 'holes' but hugely dense objects with massive gravitational pull.

Never wake a sleepwalker
They'll be really confused, but it's okay. They're more likely to hurt themselves if they're not awoken.

Missing persons reports
Police don't demand a 24-hour period before accepting a missing persons report.

Bulls hate red
Bulls are colour-blind. They actually react to motions of the bull fighter's cloth as a perceived threat.

Sleeping with an electric fan
Big myth in S. Korea that this is deadly. Very unlikely to harm you. Unless you put the fan in the bed.

Oil stops pasta sticking
Nope. But it can stop the water foaming or boiling over.

Dogs sweat by salivating
No. They regulate temperature through panting. They actually sweat through footpads.

Body heat & the head
Only in infants is most heat lost through the head. Or if the head is the only uncovered part of the body.

Cooking boils off alcohol
Partly true. But studies show not all burns off.

Don't touch baby birds!
Birds have a limited sense of smell so won't abandon babies who 'smell' of humans.

Don't eat before swim!
It's actually fine. It doesn't increase risk of cramps; alcohol is the biggest risk increaser.

MSG causes headaches
No proof, just anecdotal evidence implicating flavour 'enhancer' monosodium glutamate.

Goldfish 3-sec memory
While not the smartest, goldfish boast a memory span of 3 months – better than most politicans.

We have 5 senses
We actually have close to 20, including balance, pain, movement, hunger, thirst, etc.

Sushi is raw fish
Lost in translation. Sushi means 'sour rice' & does not always feature fish. Sashimi means 'raw'.

Humans & dinosaurs
Despite 59% of US adults thinking they coexisted, we actually missed each other by ~63 million years.

Shaving hair thickens it
Regrown hair isn't thicker, coarser or darker, it just appears so because it's no longer tapered.

The rule of thumb
Not from a law allowing a man to hit his wife with a stick no thicker than his thumb.

Glass is a liquid
'This is why stained-glass windows are thicker at the bottom.' Nope. It's just badly made glass.

Nails grow after death
The skin dries & shrinks away, giving the appearance of growth.

sources: NASA, NYTimes.com, Snopes.com, Wikipedia
data: bit.ly/KIB_Mythconception

Senseless

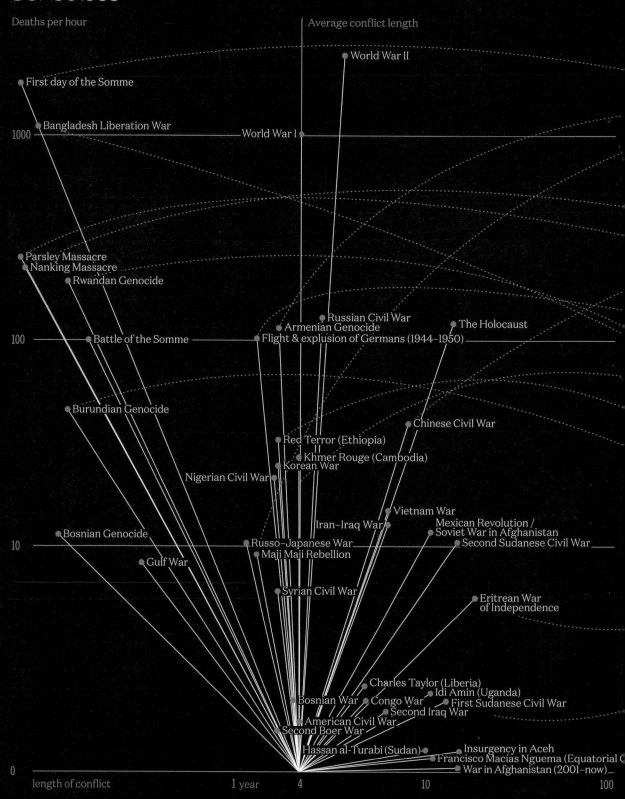

Deaths per hour

Average conflict length

- World War II
- First day of the Somme
- Bangladesh Liberation War
- World War I
- 1000
- Parsley Massacre
- Nanking Massacre
- Rwandan Genocide
- Russian Civil War
- Armenian Genocide
- The Holocaust
- Battle of the Somme
- Flight & explusion of Germans (1944–1950)
- 100
- Burundian Genocide
- Chinese Civil War
- Red Terror (Ethiopia)
- Khmer Rouge (Cambodia)
- Korean War
- Nigerian Civil War
- Vietnam War
- Mexican Revolution /
- Iran–Iraq War
- Soviet War in Afghanistan
- Bosnian Genocide
- Russo–Japanese War
- Second Sudanese Civil War
- 10
- Gulf War
- Maji Maji Rebellion
- Syrian Civil War
- Eritrean War of Independence
- Charles Taylor (Liberia)
- Idi Amin (Uganda)
- Bosnian War
- Congo War
- First Sudanese Civil War
- Second Iraq War
- American Civil War
- Second Boer War
- Hassan al-Turabi (Sudan)
- Insurgency in Aceh
- Francisco Macías Nguema (Equatorial C
- 0
- War in Afghanistan (2001–now)

length of conflict

1 year   4   10   100

Detail   Total deaths (million)

_____

                                                          0   0.5   1

1905 Violent uprising & resistance to
German colonial rule in East Africa.

1915 Systematic genocide of the Armenian
populace in the Ottoman Empire (Turkey) via
massacres, forced labour & death marches.

1 July 1916 Over 38,000 men died on
the first day of this battle. The British
lost 19,240 men in 16 hours.

1937 Battle between Communist Party
& Chinese government forces. In 1945 the
two sides formed a united army against
a Japanese invasion. Then recommenced
fighting a year after WWII.

1937 Invading Japanese army massacred
inhabitants of the (then) Chinese capital.

1937 The 'ethnic cleansing' of Haitians
living in the Dominican Republic. The way
you pronounced the word 'parsley'
determined whether you lived or died.

1944 The forced migration of millions
of Germans after WWII.

1955 Britain merged North & South Sudan
into one region without consultation, stoking
longstanding tensions & later triggering
a rebellion.

1961 Long conflict between the adjacent
East African states of Eritrea & Ethopia,
worsened by famine & brutal dictatorship.

1967 Battle between North & South triggered
by the attempted breakaway Nigerian state
of Biafra.

1971 A purge of Bangladeshi forces, religious
minorities & dissidents during a separatist
uprising in Pakistan.

1972 The systematic slaughter of Hutu
peoples by a Tutsi-controlled government.

1977 Brutal internal battle for power in the
vaccuum left by Emperor Haile Selassie.

1994 The genocidal mass slaughter of the
ethnic Tutsi people by the Hutu people
in Southeast Africa. Over 20% of the
population were slain.

sources: Wikipedia, Twentieth Century Atlas, University of Hawaii, Scaruffi.com
data: bit.ly/KIB_WarDeaths

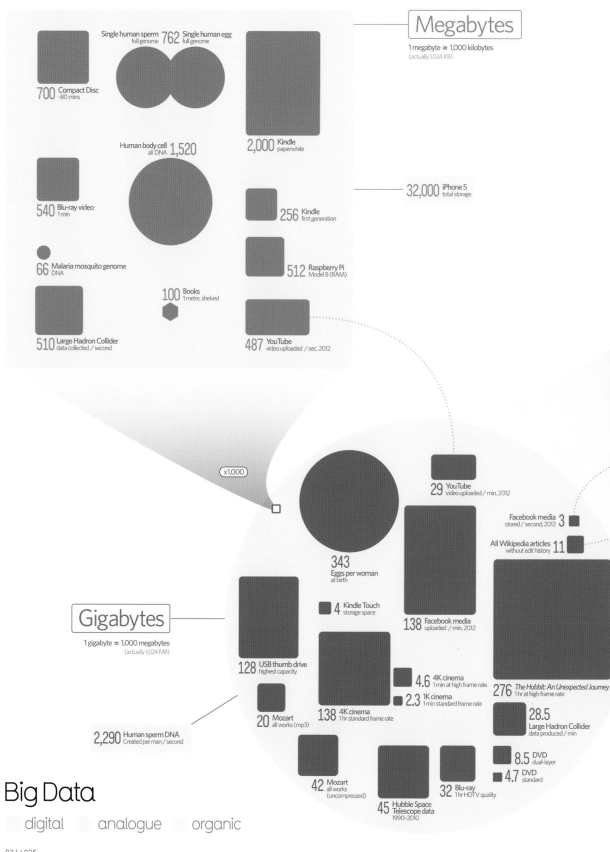

Megabytes
1 megabyte ≈ 1,000 kilobytes
(actually 1,024 KB)

762 Single human sperm / Single human egg
full genome

700 Compact Disc
~80 mins

2,000 Kindle
paperwhite

Human body cell 1,520
all DNA

540 Blu-ray video
1 min

256 Kindle
first generation

66 Malaria mosquito genome
DNA

512 Raspberry Pi
Model B (RAM)

100 Books
1 metre, shelved

510 Large Hadron Collider
data collected / second

487 YouTube
video uploaded / sec, 2012

32,000 iPhone 5
total storage

×1,000

29 YouTube
video uploaded / min, 2012

Facebook media 3
stored / second, 2012

All Wikipedia articles 11
without edit history

343 Eggs per woman
at birth

4 Kindle Touch
storage space

138 Facebook media
uploaded / min, 2012

Gigabytes
1 gigabyte ≈ 1,000 megabytes
(actually 1,024 MB)

128 USB thumb drive
highest capacity

4.6 4K cinema
1 min at high frame rate

2.3 1K cinema
1 min standard frame rate

276 The Hobbit: An Unexpected Journey
1 hr at high frame rate

28.5 Large Hadron Collider
data produced / min

20 Mozart
all works (mp3)

138 4K cinema
1 hr standard frame rate

2,290 Human sperm DNA
Created per man / second

8.5 DVD
dual-layer

4.7 DVD
standard

42 Mozart
all works
(uncompressed)

45 Hubble Space
Telescope data
1990–2010

32 Blu-ray
1 hr HDTV quality

Big Data

digital   analogue   organic

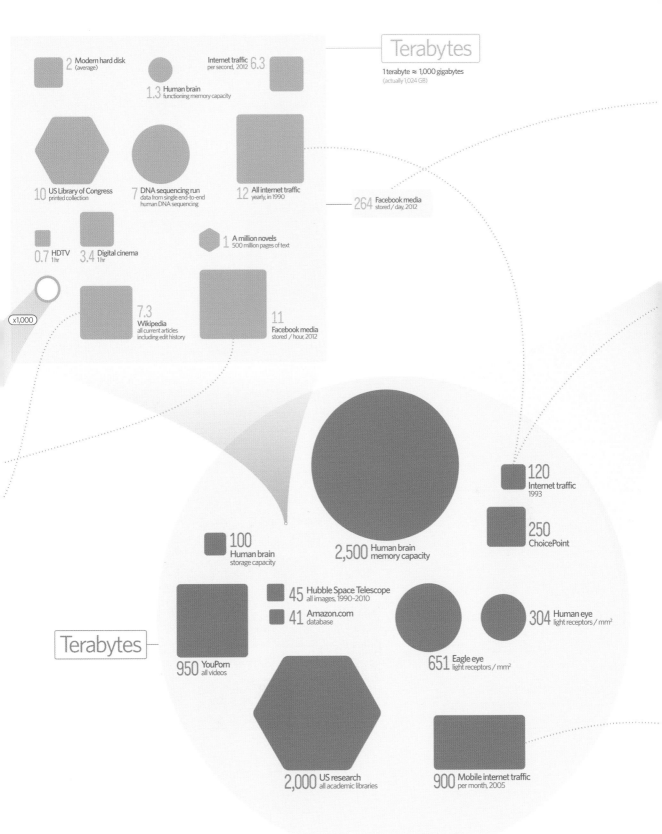

Terabytes

1 terabyte ≈ 1,000 gigabytes
(actually 1,024 GB)

2 Modern hard disk (average)

1.3 Human brain functioning memory capacity

Internet traffic per second, 2012 6.3

10 US Library of Congress printed collection

7 DNA sequencing run data from single end-to-end human DNA sequencing

12 All internet traffic yearly, in 1990

264 Facebook media stored / day, 2012

0.7 HDTV 1hr

3.4 Digital cinema 1hr

1 A million novels 500 million pages of text

x1,000

7.3 Wikipedia all current articles including edit history

11 Facebook media stored / hour, 2012

Terabytes

100 Human brain storage capacity

2,500 Human brain memory capacity

120 Internet traffic 1993

250 ChoicePoint

45 Hubble Space Telescope all images, 1990–2010

41 Amazon.com database

304 Human eye light receptors / mm²

950 YouPorn all videos

651 Eagle eye light receptors / mm²

2,000 US research all academic libraries

900 Mobile internet traffic per month, 2005

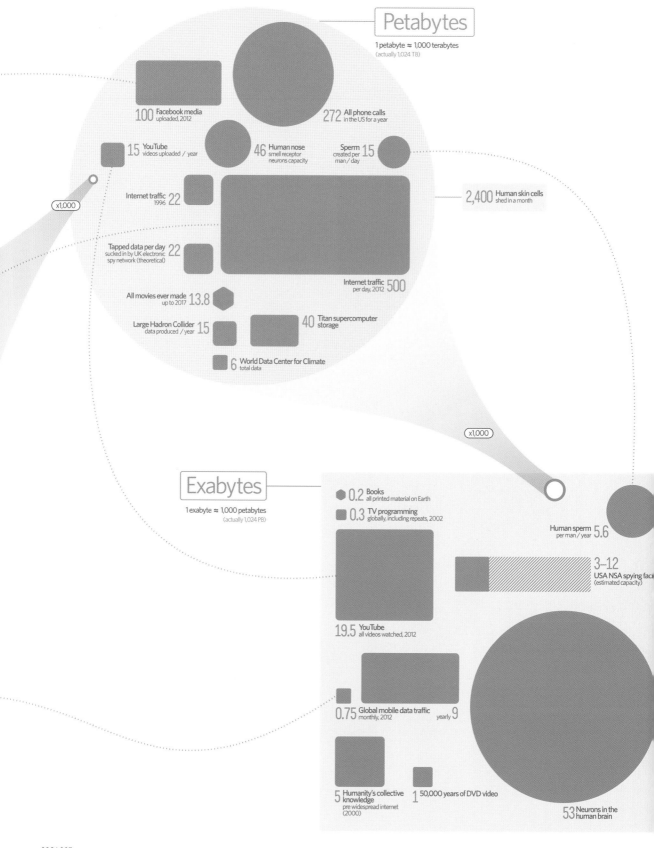

Petabytes

1 petabyte ≈ 1,000 terabytes
(actually 1,024 TB)

100 Facebook media
uploaded, 2012

272 All phone calls
in the US for a year

15 YouTube
videos uploaded / year

46 Human nose
smell receptor
neurons capacity

15 Sperm
created per
man / day

Internet traffic **22**
1996

2,400 Human skin cells
shed in a month

Tapped data per day **22**
sucked in by UK electronic
spy network (theoretical)

Internet traffic **500**
per day, 2012

All movies ever made **13.8**
up to 2017

Large Hadron Collider **15**
data produced / year

40 Titan supercomputer
storage

6 World Data Center for Climate
total data

×1,000

×1,000

Exabytes

1 exabyte ≈ 1,000 petabytes
(actually 1,024 PB)

0.2 Books
all printed material on Earth

0.3 TV programming
globally, including repeats, 2002

Human sperm **5.6**
per man / year

3–12
USA NSA spying facil
(estimated capacity)

19.5 YouTube
all videos watched, 2012

0.75 Global mobile data traffic
monthly, 2012

9 yearly

5 Humanity's collective
knowledge
pre widespread internet
(2000)

1 50,000 years of DVD video

53 Neurons in the
human brain

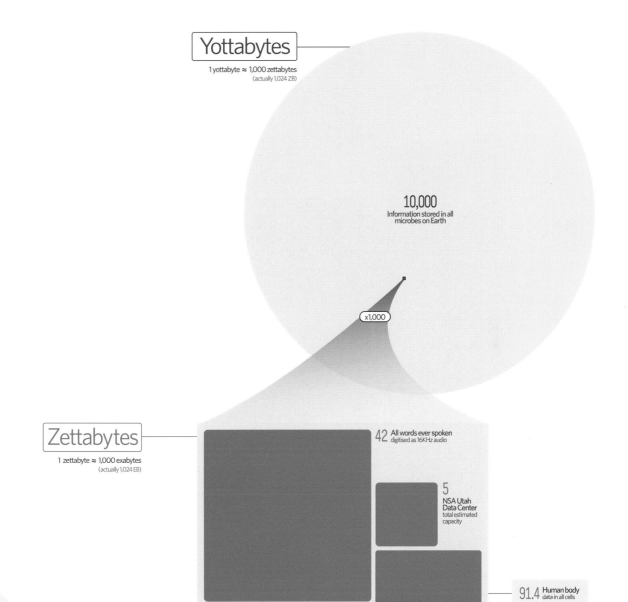

Yottabytes

1 yottabyte ≈ 1,000 zettabytes
(actually 1,024 ZB)

10,000
Information stored in all
microbes on Earth

x1,000

Zettabytes

1 zettabyte ≈ 1,000 exabytes
(actually 1,024 EB)

42 All words ever spoken
digitised as 16KHz audio

5
NSA Utah
Data Center
total estimated
capacity

91.4 Human body
data in all cells

All data created & stored globally

0.5	0.8	1.2	1.8	2.8
2008	2009	2010	2011	2012

All data
2020 prediction **30**

x1,000

330 Internet traffic
2011

⬛ digital ⬤ analogue ⬤ organic

sources: UC Berkeley, ExtremeTech.com, Wikipedia, Morton (1991), MaximumPC.com, Cnet.com, Britannica, NASA, IDC
data: bit.ly/KIB_BigData

Mavericks & Heretics

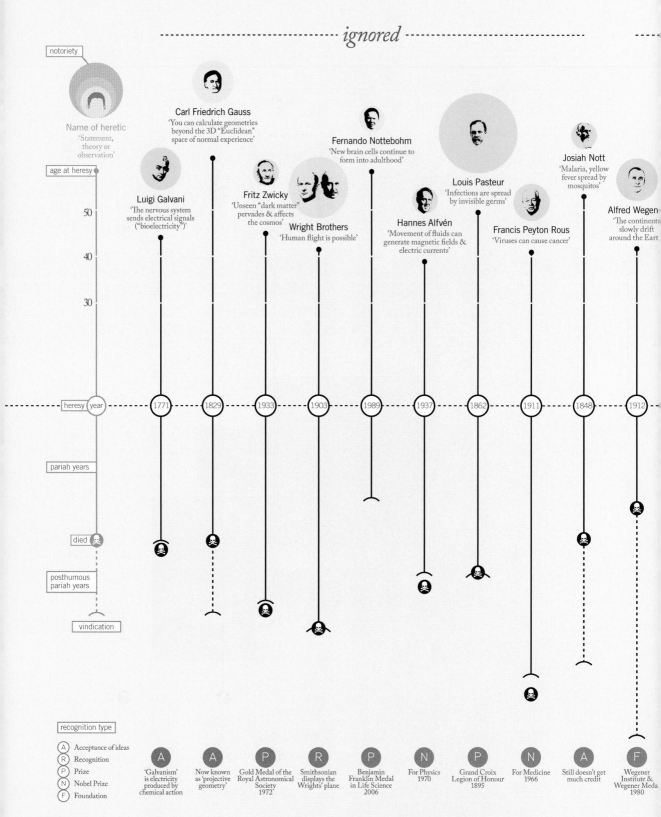

notoriety

Name of heretic
'Statement,
theory or
observation'

age at heresy

Carl Friedrich Gauss
'You can calculate geometries
beyond the 3D "Euclidean"
space of normal experience'

Fernando Nottebohm
'New brain cells continue to
form into adulthood'

Josiah Nott
'Malaria, yellow
fever spread by
mosquitos'

Luigi Galvani
'The nervous system
sends electrical signals
("bioelectricity")'

Fritz Zwicky
'Unseen "dark matter"
pervades & affects
the cosmos'

Wright Brothers
'Human flight is possible'

Louis Pasteur
'Infections are spread
by invisible germs'

Hannes Alfvén
'Movement of fluids can
generate magnetic fields &
electric currents'

Francis Peyton Rous
'Viruses can cause cancer'

Alfred Wegen
'The continents
slowly drift
around the Eart'

50

40

30

heresy | year   1771   1829   1933   1903   1989   1937   1862   1911   1848   1912

pariah years

died

posthumous
pariah years

vindication

recognition type

(A) Acceptance of ideas
(R) Recognition
(P) Prize
(N) Nobel Prize
(F) Foundation

(A)
'Galvanism'
is electricity
produced by
chemical action

(A)
Now known
as 'projective
geometry'

(P)
Gold Medal of the
Royal Astronomical
Society
1972

(R)
Smithsonian
displays the
Wrights' plane

(P)
Benjamin
Franklin Medal
in Life Science
2006

(N)
For Physics
1970

(P)
Grand Croix
Legion of Honour
1895

(N)
For Medicine
1966

(A)
Still doesn't get
much credit

(F)
Wegener
Institute &
Wegener Meda
1980

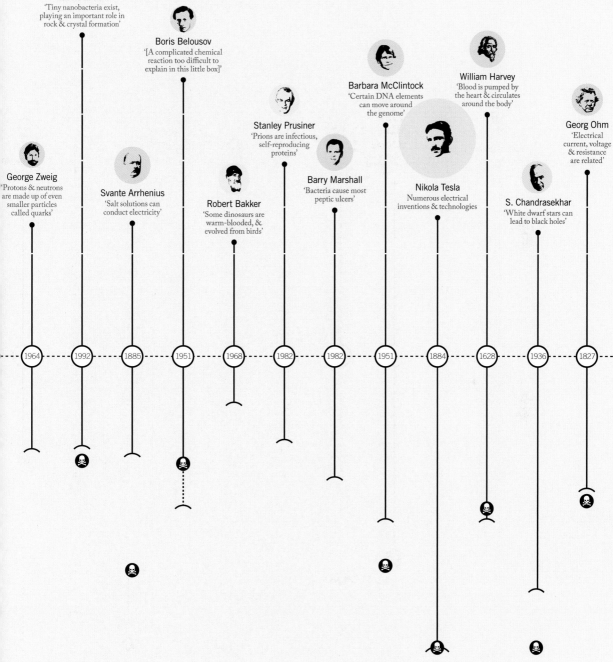

Astronomy   Biology   Engineering   Maths   Medicine   Philosophy   Physical
                                                                          sciences

------ *rejected* --- -- *discredited* --

Robert L. Folk
'Tiny nanobacteria exist,
playing an important role in
rock & crystal formation'

Boris Belousov
'[A complicated chemical
reaction too difficult to
explain in this little box]'

Barbara McClintock
'Certain DNA elements
can move around
the genome'

William Harvey
'Blood is pumped by
the heart & circulates
around the body'

Stanley Prusiner
'Prions are infectious,
self-reproducing
proteins'

Georg Ohm
'Electrical
current, voltage
& resistance
are related'

George Zweig
'Protons & neutrons
are made up of even
smaller particles
called quarks'

Svante Arrhenius
'Salt solutions can
conduct electricity'

Robert Bakker
'Some dinosaurs are
warm-blooded, &
evolved from birds'

Barry Marshall
'Bacteria cause most
peptic ulcers'

Nikola Tesla
Numerous electrical
inventions & technologies

S. Chandrasekhar
'White dwarf stars can
lead to black holes'

1964   1992   1885   1951   1968   1982   1982   1951   1884   1628   1936   1827

P	A	N	P	R	N	N	N	R	A	N	R
MacArthur Prize Fellowship 1981	Still some controversy	For Chemistry 1903	Lenin Prize 1980	Triggered 'dino renaissance'	For Physiology 1997	For Medicine 2005	For Medicine 1983	Regarded as one of the greatest inventors of all time	Theories confirmed	For Physics 1983	Academic role at Munich University

Astronomy   Biology   Engineering   Maths   Medicine   Philosophy   Physical sciences

------------ *ridiculed* ------------   ----- *beaten* -----

notoriety

Name of heretic
'Statement, theory or observation'

Avenzoar (Ibn Zuhr)
'The earth evolves & is self-renewing'

age at heresy

50

40

30

Binnig, Rohrer, Gimzeski
'A scanning tunnelling microscope can image surfaces at an atomic level'

Ernst Chladni
'Meteorites fall from outer space, not volcanoes'

John Logie Baird
'Radio waves can be used to create a visual broadcast'

Robert Goddard
'Spaceships can be powered by liquid-fuelled rockets'

J. Harlen Bretz
'The Scabland deserts in Washington State were created by massive flooding'

Al-Razi
'Fever is a natural defence mechanism' & other medical insights

Marcello Malpighi
'Tiny blood cells circulate in the blood stream'

Galileo Galilei
'The Earth is not the centre of the solar system – the Sun is'

heresy | year   1141   1982   1794   1925   1909   1923   895   1660   1616

pariah years

death

posthumous pariah years

vindication

recognition type

(A) Acceptance of ideas
(R) Recognition
(P) Prize
(N) Nobel Prize
(F) Foundation

| (A) Early ideas on evolution adopted | (N) For Physics 1986 | (A) Theory confirmed | (A) The BBC adopted his system | (A) Launch of Apollo 11 in 1969 | (P) Penrose Medal 1979 | (A) Considered the father of paediatrics | (A) Member of the Royal Society | (A) Model of solar system confirmed |

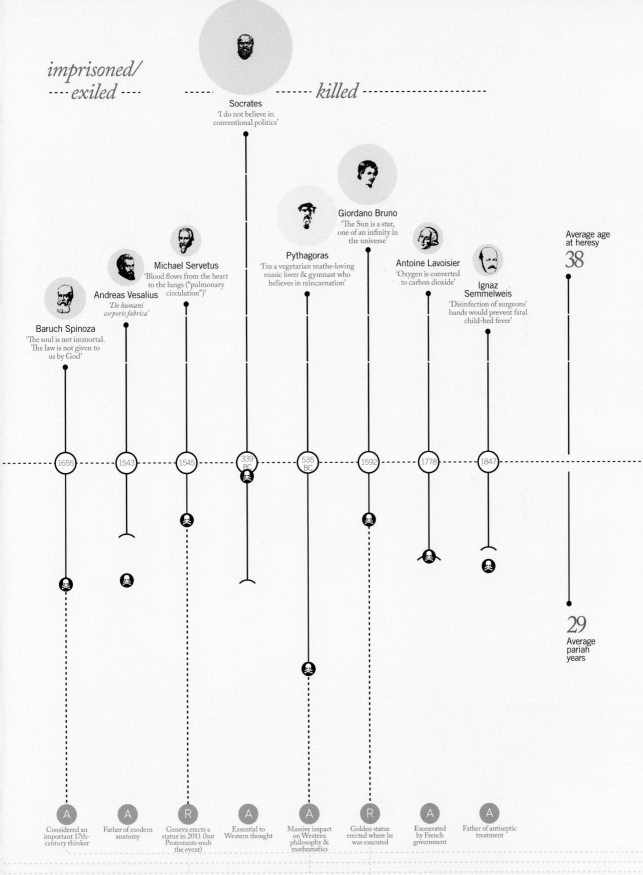

imprisoned/
--- *exiled* ---

killed -----------------

Socrates
'I do not believe in
conventional politics'

Giordano Bruno
'The Sun is a star,
one of an infinity in
the universe'

Michael Servetus
'Blood flows from the heart
to the lungs ("pulmonary
circulation")'

Pythagoras
'I'm a vegetarian maths-loving
music lover & gymnast who
believes in reincarnation'

Antoine Lavoisier
'Oxygen is converted
to carbon dioxide'

Andreas Vesalius
*'De humani
corporis fabrica'*

**Ignaz
Semmelweis**
'Disinfection of surgeons'
hands would prevent fatal
child-bed fever'

Baruch Spinoza
'The soul is not immortal.
The law is not given to
us by God'

Average age
at heresy
38

1655   1543   1545   339 BC   535 BC   1592   1778   1847

29
Average
pariah
years

A — Considered an important 17th-century thinker

A — Father of modern anatomy

R — Geneva erects a statue in 2011 (but Protestants snub the event)

A — Essential to Western thought

A — Massive impact on Western philosophy & mathematics

R — Golden statue erected where he was executed

A — Exonerated by French government

A — Father of antiseptic treatment

sources: Annals of Clinical and Laboratory Science, Wikipedia, New Scientist, Rockfeller Institute, NY Times
data: bit.ly/KIB_Mavericks

Mavericks & Heretics

Making amends trends

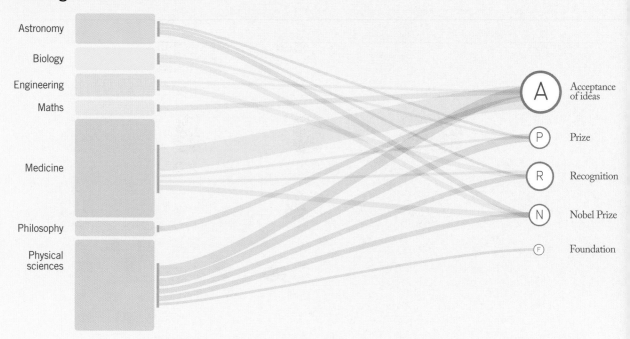

Astronomy	A	Acceptance of ideas
Biology	P	Prize
Engineering	R	Recognition
Maths	N	Nobel Prize
Medicine	F	Foundation
Philosophy		
Physical sciences		

Most vicious domains?

	Philosophy	Maths	Biology	Engineering	Astronomy	Physical Sciences	Medicine
ignored	○○○○○	◐○○○○	◐○○○○	○○○○○	●◐○○○	●◐○○○	●●●●◐
rejected	○○○○○	○○○○○	◐◐○○○	●○○○○	○○○○○	●●●●●	●●○○○
discredited	○○○○○	○○○○○	○○○○○	○○○○○	◐○○○○	○○○○○	○○○○○
ridiculed	○○○○○	○○○○○	○○○○○	◐○○○○	○○○○○	●●●●●	○○○○○
imprisoned	●○○○○	○○○○○	○○○○○	○○○○○	○○○○○	◐◐○○○	●●◐○○
beaten	○○○○○	○○○○○	○○○○○	○○○○○	○○○○○	○○○○○	◐●●○○
killed	●○○○○	◐○○○○	○○○○○	○○○○○	◐○○○○	○○○○○	●●●●◐

Spinoza 245 pariah years
Galileo 219
Al-Razi 384
Pythagoras 435
Servetus 466
Bruno 297

source: calculated from our Mavericks data

Superpower Showdown
Demographics

	China	EU	India	USA
TOTAL POPULATION MILLIONS	1,355	509	1,236	319
SURFACE AREA MILLION KM²	9,600	4,300	3,300	9,800
PEOPLE PER KM²	141	118	376	32
% URBAN / RURAL	48 / 52	73 / 27	32 / 68	82 / 18
GENDER DISPARITY MILLION MORE MEN	+49	-12	+42	-0.5
BIRTH RATE YEARLY PER 1,000 WOMEN	12.1	10.4	19.9	13.4
DEATH RATE DEATHS PER 1,000 PEOPLE	7.4	9.6	7.3	8.1
DEGREE OF MIGRATION MIGRANTS PER 1,000 PEOPLE	-0.32	1.8	-0.05	2.5
% MIGRANT POPULATION	0.05%	9.3%	0.4%	13.8%
% DEPENDENT POPULATION UNDER 15, OVER 64	37%	26%	52%	50%
MEDIAN AGE	37	41	27	37
SCORE	3	1	4	4

GENDER DISPARITY: FEWER MEN — MORE MEN

% MIGRANT POPULATION: 1970 — 2010

INDIA & USA DRAW!

sources: CIA World Factbook, World Bank, Eurostat
data: bit.ly/KIB_Superpowers

Simple I

Organic Shopping
Price of vital body parts ($1,000s)

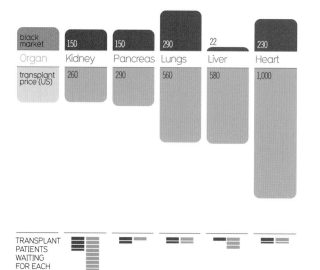

black market	Organ	transplant price (US)
	Kidney	
150		260
150	Pancreas	290
290	Lungs	560
22	Liver	580
230	Heart	1,000

TRANSPLANT PATIENTS WAITING FOR EACH ORGAN
UK   US

sources: Wired, Havascope.com, Telegraph.co.uk

Child Killers
Main causes of death

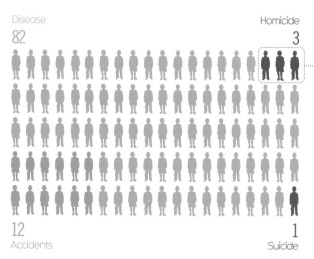

Disease
82

Homicide
3

12
Accidents

1
Suicide

source: US Centers for Disease Control and Prevention, US Data (2010)

Salt

| body needs | 2 grams per day | 5 | 6 1 teaspoon | worldwide average intake | 10 |

Sodium

| Avg bag of crisps | 0.8 grams | World Health Organisation intake target for 2025 | 2 | 2.4 Most governments' current daily guideline | 4 |

sources: World Health Organisation, Institute of Food Research, Campbell et al (2012)

Big Country

Antarctica

the Moon

source: NASA, Google Maps

Child Murderers
Who does it?

Parent / step-parent
60

Stranger
15

Friend / other relative
2

23
Unknown

source: UK Office of National Statistics, 2011–12. Warning: small sample size

Times Tables Times
Error rate

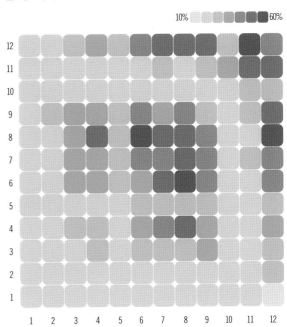

10% ▢▢▢▢▢▢▢ 60%

source: private study by Caddington School of 232 children, 5-8 years old

Pass the Salt

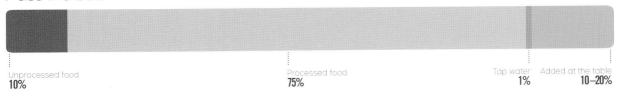

Unprocessed food
10%

Processed food
75%

Tap water
1%

Added at the table
10–20%

Death Rows Total cost of death penalty for California 1978–2010

$1,940m
Death-penalty trials

$1,020m
Incarceration costs

$925m
State appeals

$156m Federal appeals

Executions
13

Cost per execution
$310m

source: 'Executing the Will of the Voters', Alarcón & Mitchell (2010)

The Stellar Nursery

- ● Star
- ○ 'Exotic' Star
- ● Galaxy object
- ● Exploding object (nova)
- ● Black Hole-type object
- ● Cloud

Young Stellar Object

A star in an early stage of evolution.

Main Sequence Star

Stars in the hydrogen-burning main phase of their life. Often called dwarves.

Brown Dwarf

Lacks the bulk to trigger reactions necessary to shine. Often a companion to a larger star.

Planetary Nebula

A glowing shell of electrified gas expanding from a dying star.

Protoplanetary Nebula

A glowing shell of electrified gas generated as a star runs out of nuclear fuel.

Protostar

A contraction in a molecular cloud that precedes the birth of a star.

Herbig Ae/Be Star

Young star inside a gas-dust envelope.

Magnetar

Small, ultra-dense star with gigantic magnetic field spinning 100's of times per second.

Giant

Large hydrogen-fusing star a few hundred times the radius of the Sun.

Sub Giant

Bright & on its way to becoming a supergiant. Rich in metals & often with planets.

T. Tauri

A proto-star about 100 million years into its growth, before it becomes a full star.

Bright Giants

Somewhere in between giants & supergiants, very bright but not overly massive.

Blue Straggler

Slightly mysterious stars that don't follow the usual curve of star evolution.

Neutron Star

Rapidly spinning collapsed core of a massive star, dense & made mostly of neutrons.

Dwarf Nova

A small dwarf star sucking material from a giant star, causing flares & belches.

Luminous Red/Blue Nova

Explosion caused by the collossal merging of two stars.

Supergiant

Biggest & brightest of stars. Massive, hot & destined to explode into supernovae.

Hyper Giant

Short-lived but incredibly bright & massive stars, shedding huge amounts of mass.

Flare Star

Type of flickering star with very unpredictable & dramatic increases in brightness.

Peculiar Star

Stars unusually high in metals such as mercury & manganese.

Supernova

Exploding star, often briefly outshining the brightness of a entire galaxy.

Hypernova

Massively high-energy stellar explosion. May create deadly gamma-ray bursts.

Pulsating / Variable Star

Brightness appears to flicker & fluctuate as seen from Earth.

Wolf-Rayet Star

Massive, very bright old stars shedding massive layers of their mass.

Galactic Cluster

Unimaginably huge collections of thousands of galaxies bound together.

Open Star Cluster

Group of a few thousand stars of the same age, formed from the same cloud.

Spiral Galaxy

Billions of stars collected in a flat, rotating disc with a distinctive central 'bulge'.

Barred Spiral Galaxy

Common version, featuring a central bar-shaped structure made of stars.

Globular Cluster

Spherical group of stars orbiting in the outer halo of a galaxy.

Elliptical Galaxy

Oval masses of old stars without discs & with little new star formation.

Quasar

Very energetic & active nucleus of a galaxy – the brightest objects in the universe.

Blazar

Very compact quasar shooting two massive jets of energy from its poles.

COMMON ←

SMALL

Pulsar

Highly magnetic neutron star emitting pulsed beams of light like a lighthouse.

Supernova Imposter

A massive stellar explosion that has not destroyed its parent sun.

Soft Gamma Repeater

Unknown object emitting large, irregular bursts of gamma radiation & X-rays.

Extreme Helium Star

Very rare stellar entity, with almost no hydrogen, the most common element.

Gravastar

A gravitational vacuum star – a theoretical alternative to black holes.

Dark Energy Star

Black-hole replacement made from vacuum or maybe dark energy.

Dark Star (Dark Matter)

Theoretical object that may have existed in the early universe before normal stars formed.

Stellar Black Hole

Ultra-dense object formed when a massive star gravitationally collapses on itself.

Bok Globule

Dense dark cloud of cosmic dust & gas-like cocoons where stars can be born.

Supernova Remnant

A star in mid-explosion, forming a bubble-like shockwave.

Cataclysmic Variable Star

Two stars, a white dwarf & a very close 'donor' star that feeds the host dwarf star.

Dark Star (Newtonian)

An alternative & more stable object than a traditional black hole.

Preon Star

Small, compact star made of theoretical particles.

Electroweak star

I can't explain this one. It's far too complicated for this little box.

Molecular Cloud or H2 Region

Large interstellar cloud & often stellar nurseries where stars are birthed.

Compact Star

Very massive unknown type of star at the end of its life.

Micro Quasar

A very small quasar only a few times bigger than the Sun.

Luminous Blue Variable

Very large & unstable star prone to dramatic energetic outbursts.

Iron Star

Complex quantum effects turn light into iron inside this object, creating a metal star.

Quark Star

Massive neutron star so dense that the neutrons break down into 'strange matter'.

Thorne–Żytkow Object

Giant star with a second object, a neutron star, at its core.

Lenticular Galaxy

Old, thin galaxies with both a bulge & a disk, but only very vague spiral arms.

White Dwarf

The burnt-out remains of a star once it's used up all its hydrogen.

Supermassive Black Hole

Over 1–10,000 million times bigger than a normal black hole.

Ultramassive Black Hole

Even bigger – a mere 10–40,000 million times bigger than your average black hole.

MASSIVE

Black Dwarf

When a white dwarf sufficiently cools & no longer emits heat or light.

Planck Star

Microscopic star residing at the centre of a black hole.

→ RARE

——————————————— THEORETICAL

sources: NASA, Space.com, Wikipedia
data: bit.ly/KIB_Stellar

Stellar Constellations

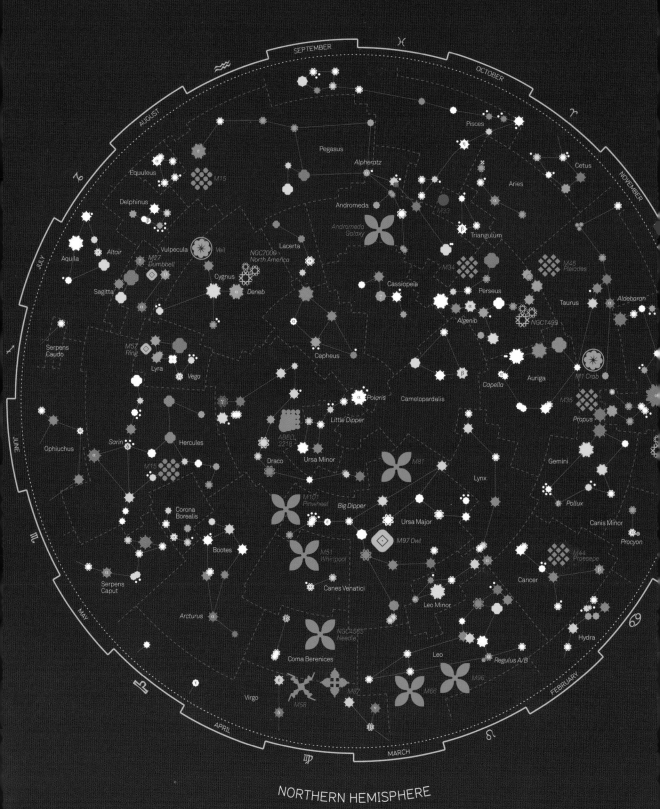

NORTHERN HEMISPHERE

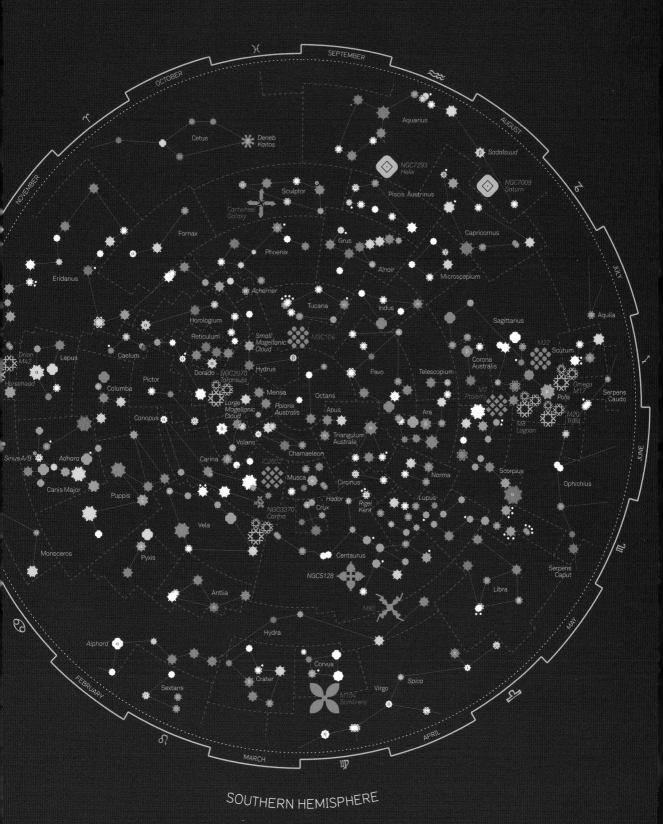

SOUTHERN HEMISPHERE

sources: SIMBAD Astronomical Database, James Kaler: University of Illinois, Wikipedia
data: bit.ly/KIB_Stellar

The Milky Way
% composition

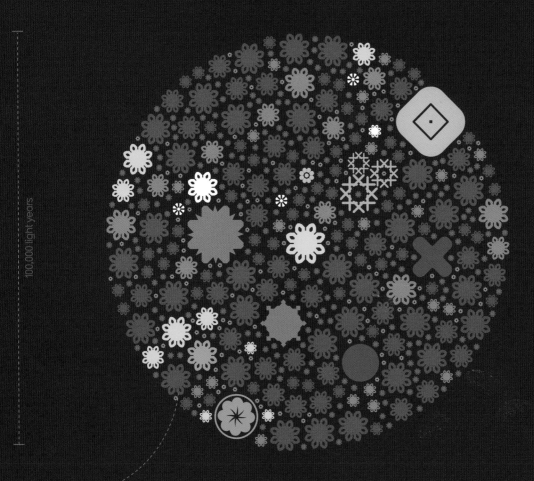

100,000 light years

very ancient galaxy, formed
just after the birth of the universe

mostly red-dwarf stars

13.6 billion years ago

9

 Giant star   Main sequence star

The Andromeda Galaxy

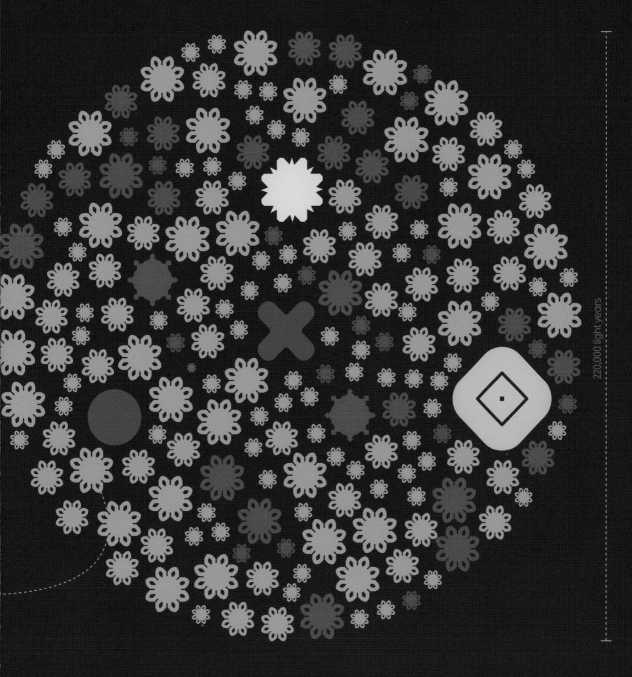

220,000 light years

our nearest galactic neighbour
formed by the merger of two galaxies

mostly hot young blue stars

age of the universe

now

Molecular cloud Planetary nebula Pulsar Stellar black hole Supergiant star Supermassive black hole Supernova remnant White dwarf

sources: 'Atlas of the Universe', Wikipedia, HubbleSite.org, NASA
data: bit.ly/KIB_Stellar

Richest Churches
Belief system

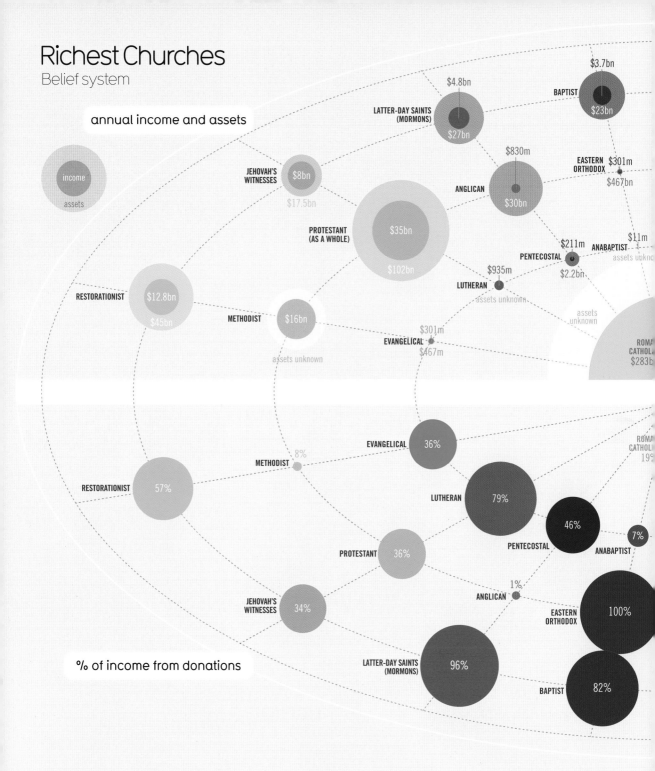

annual income and assets

income
assets

$4.8bn
LATTER-DAY SAINTS
(MORMONS)
$27bn

$3.7bn
BAPTIST
$23bn

$830m
ANGLICAN
$30bn

EASTERN
ORTHODOX $301m
$467bn

JEHOVAH'S
WITNESSES $8bn
$17.5bn

PROTESTANT
(AS A WHOLE) $35bn
$102bn

$211m
ANABAPTIST
assets unkno

$11m
assets unknown

PENTECOSTAL
$2.2bn

$935m
LUTHERAN
assets unknown

RESTORATIONIST $12.8bn
$45bn

METHODIST $16bn

assets
unknown

ROMA
CATHOL
$283b

EVANGELICAL
$301m
$467m

assets unknown

% of income from donations

EVANGELICAL 36%

METHODIST 8%

ROMA
CATHOL
19%

RESTORATIONIST 57%

LUTHERAN 79%

46%
PENTECOSTAL
ANABAPTIST 7%

PROTESTANT 36%

1%
ANGLICAN

EASTERN
ORTHODOX 100%

JEHOVAH'S
WITNESSES 34%

LATTER-DAY SAINTS
(MORMONS) 96%

BAPTIST 82%

DENOMINATION	ANABAPTIST	ANGLICAN	BAPTIST	CATHOLIC	E. ORTHODOX	EVANGELICAL
Key aspects and distinctive qualities	True baptism = a public confession of sin and faith by an adult. Infants not punishable for sin. Christ's return imminent.	Mixes Catholic beliefs with Protestant-style services. Uses the Book of Common Prayer. No central authority.	Baptism = conscious, public display of faith – adults only. No: fixed worship, prayer books. Direct experience of God. Heated preaching (evangelism).	Pope is infallible. Big focus on prayer, confession of sins. Acts of mercy expected to help the needy. Patron saints. Judgement Day. And **GUILT**.	Jesus had one nature (divine) not two (human and divine). Holy Spirit flows not from the Father and the Son – just from the Father. Oh, and lots of icons.	Preach New Testament in order to convert. Bible is Word of God and sole basis for faith. Emphasis on personal conversion experience.

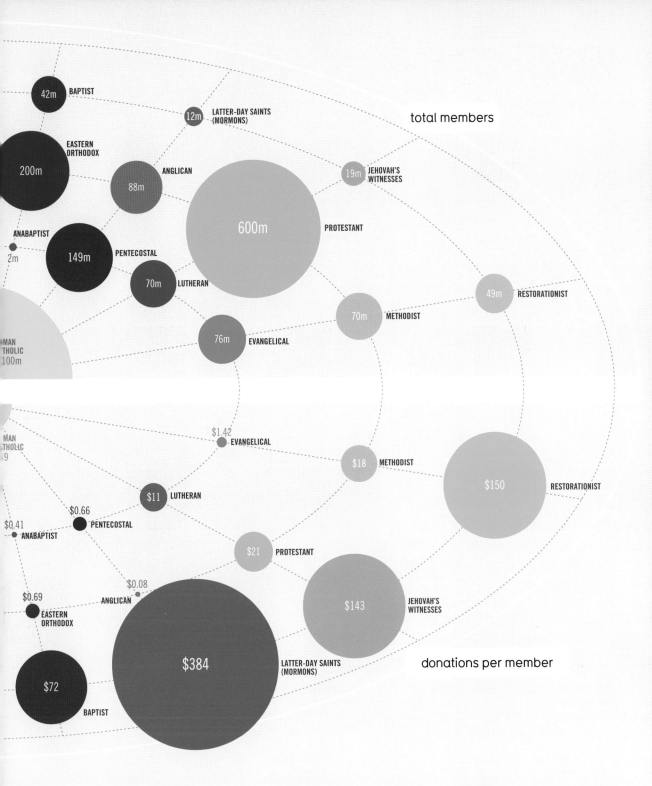

total members

42m BAPTIST

12m LATTER-DAY SAINTS (MORMONS)

EASTERN ORTHODOX
200m

ANGLICAN
88m

19m JEHOVAH'S WITNESSES

600m PROTESTANT

ANABAPTIST
2m

149m PENTECOSTAL

70m LUTHERAN

49m RESTORATIONIST

MAN THOLIC 100m

70m METHODIST

76m EVANGELICAL

$1.42 EVANGELICAL

$18 METHODIST

MAN THOLIC 9

$150 RESTORATIONIST

$11 LUTHERAN

$0.66
$0.41 PENTECOSTAL
ANABAPTIST

$21 PROTESTANT

$0.08 ANGLICAN

$143 JEHOVAH'S WITNESSES

$0.69 EASTERN ORTHODOX

$384 LATTER-DAY SAINTS (MORMONS)

$72 BAPTIST

donations per member

JEHOVAH'S WITNESS
nd of Days imminent.
eject: Holy Trinity,
ministers, churches,
irthdays, Christmas.
ed by Watchtower
ible and Tract Society,
ew York.

LUTHERAN
Authority of scripture
is paramount. Salvation
(or 'justification') by
faith alone, through
God's grace, NOT by
good deeds.

METHODIST
Use 'method' in Bible for
life guidance. Concern
for social welfare, justice,
public morals. Encourage
faculty of 'reason' to
interpret scripture and
practise faith correctly.

MORMON
Bible and the Book of
Mormon. All are spirit-
children of God.
Polygamy, chastity, health
(no alcohol etc.). Living
prophets and apostles
guide the church.

PENTECOSTAL
Faith is about experience,
not ritual nor thinking.
God felt directly through
'gifts of the Spirit' –
speaking in tongues,
prophecies and
healing.

PROTESTANT
Back to basics. Bible
itself, rather than
interpretation, is the
source of religious
truth. The faithful, as
well as priests, should
run the Church.

RESTORATIONIST
Early Christianity
abandoned true
teachings of Jesus, Paul
and apostles. Aims to
restore Christianity to
its purer, more primitive
form.

sources: Charity Commission, Wikipedia, The Economist, BBC News, TIME, Guardian, various annual reports
data: bit.ly/KIB_RichChurches

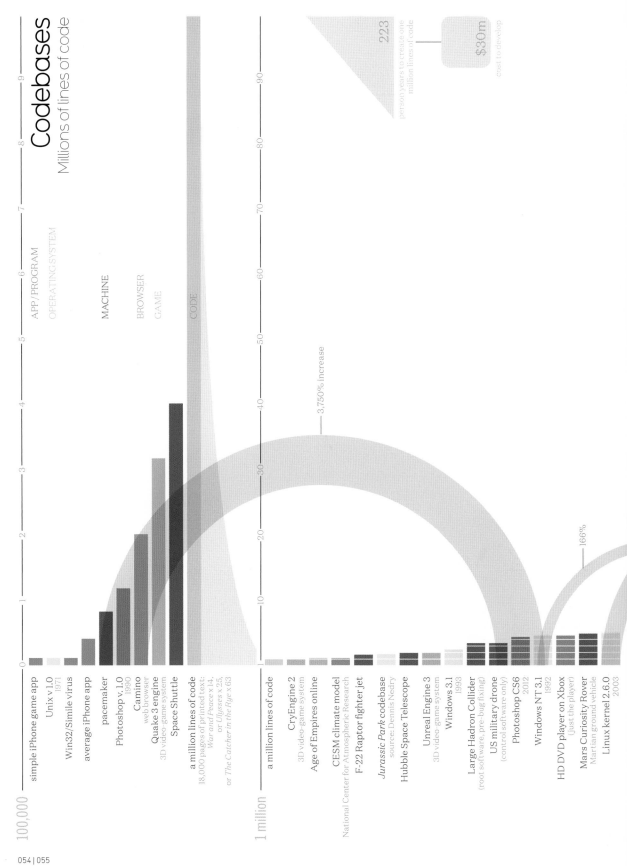

Codebases

Millions of lines of code

100,000

APP / PROGRAM
OPERATING SYSTEM
MACHINE
BROWSER
GAME
CODE

simple iPhone game app
Unix v 1.0 — 1971
Win32/Simile virus
average iPhone app
pacemaker
Photoshop v. 1.0 — 1990
Camino — web browser
Quake 3 engine — 3D video-game system
Space Shuttle
a million lines of code
18,000 pages of printed text:
War and Peace x 14,
or *Ulysses* x 25,
or *The Catcher in the Rye* x 63

1 million

a million lines of code
CryEngine 2 — 3D video-game system
Age of Empires online
CESM climate model — National Center for Atmospheric Research
F-22 Raptor fighter jet
Jurassic Park codebase — source: Dennis Nedry
Hubble Space Telescope
Unreal Engine 3 — 3D video-game system
Windows 3.1 — 1993
Large Hadron Collider — (root software, pre-bug fixing)
US military drone — (control software only)
Photoshop CS6 — 2012
Windows NT 3.1 — 1992
HD DVD player on Xbox — (just the player)
Mars Curiosity Rover — Martian ground vehicle
Linux kernel 2.6.0 — 2003

3,750% increase

223 — person years to create one million lines of code

$30m — cost to develop

166%

054 | 055

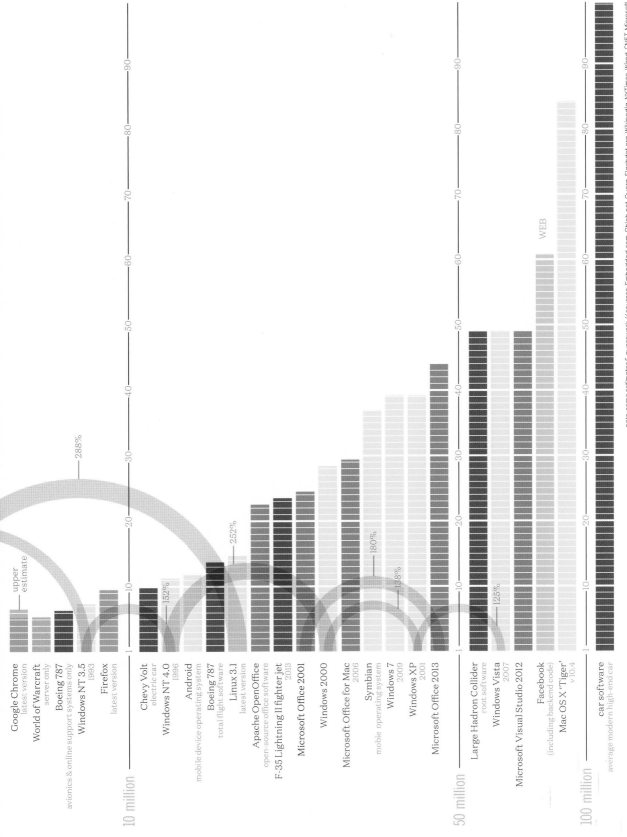

Google Chrome
latest version

World of Warcraft
server only

Boeing 787
avionics & online support systems only

Windows NT 3.5
1993

Firefox
latest version

Chevy Volt
electric car

Windows NT 4.0
1996

Android
mobile device operating system

Boeing 787
total flight software

Linux 3.1
latest version

Apache OpenOffice
open-source office software

F-35 Lightning II fighter jet
2013

Microsoft Office 2001

Windows 2000

Microsoft Office for Mac
2006

Symbian
mobile operating system

Windows 7
2009

Windows XP
2001

Microsoft Office 2013

Large Hadron Collider
root software

Windows Vista
2007

Microsoft Visual Studio 2012

Facebook
(including backend code)

Mac OS X "Tiger"
v 10.4

car software
average modern high-end car

288%

152%

252%

180%

138%

125%

WEB

10 million

50 million

100 million

note: some estimates & guesswork // sources: Embedded.com, Ohloh.net, Quora, Slashdot.org, Wikipedia, NYTimes, Wired, CNET, Microsoft
data: bit.ly/KIB_CodeBases

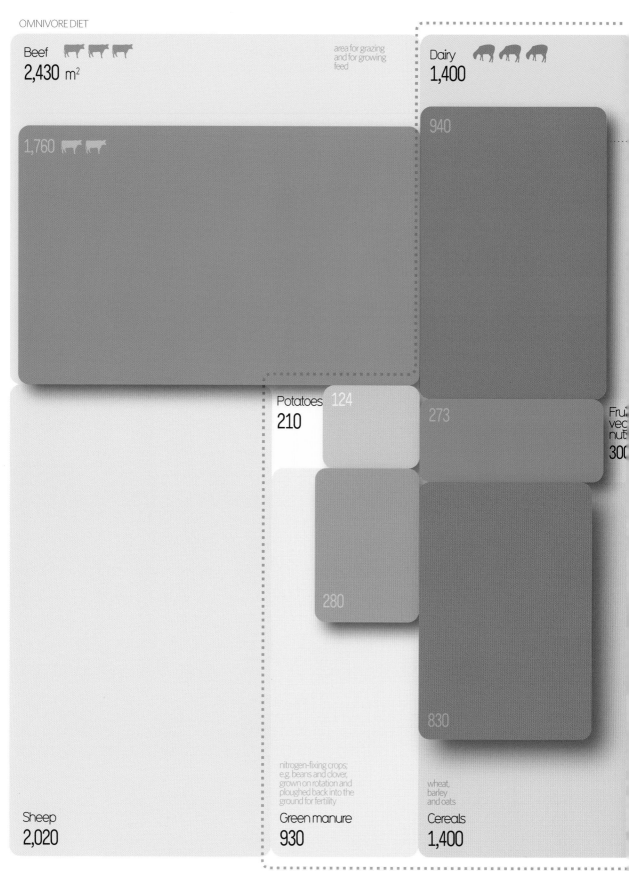

Beef
2,430 m²

area for grazing
and for growing
feed

Dairy
1,400

1,760

940

Potatoes
210

124

273

Fru…
veg…
nut…
300

280

830

nitrogen-fixing crops;
e.g. beans and clover,
grown on rotation and
ploughed back into the
ground for fertility

wheat,
barley
and oats

Sheep
2,020

Green manure
930

Cereals
1,400

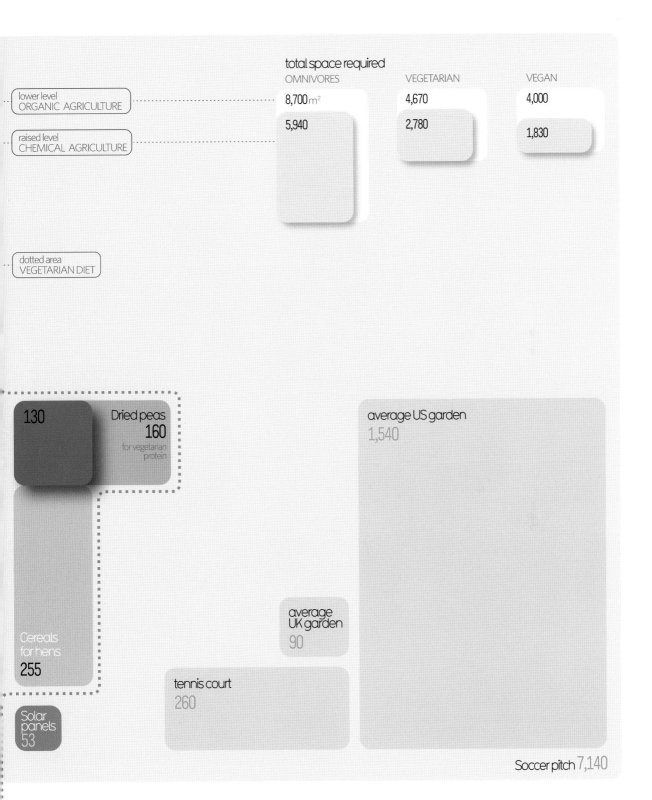

total space required

OMNIVORES	VEGETARIAN	VEGAN

lower level
ORGANIC AGRICULTURE

8,700 m²   4,670   4,000

raised level
CHEMICAL AGRICULTURE

5,940   2,780   1,830

dotted area
VEGETARIAN DIET

130

Dried peas
160
for vegetarian protein

average US garden
1,540

Cereals
for hens
255

average
UK garden
90

tennis court
260

Solar
panels
53

Soccer pitch 7,140

Backyard Farm
Surface area required for a family of four to live off the land

sources: 'Can Britain Feed Itself?' Simon Fairlie (2007), Penn State University, UKAgriculture.com
data: bit.ly/KIB_BackyardFarm

Crazy Global Warming Solutions
Current best ideas on the table

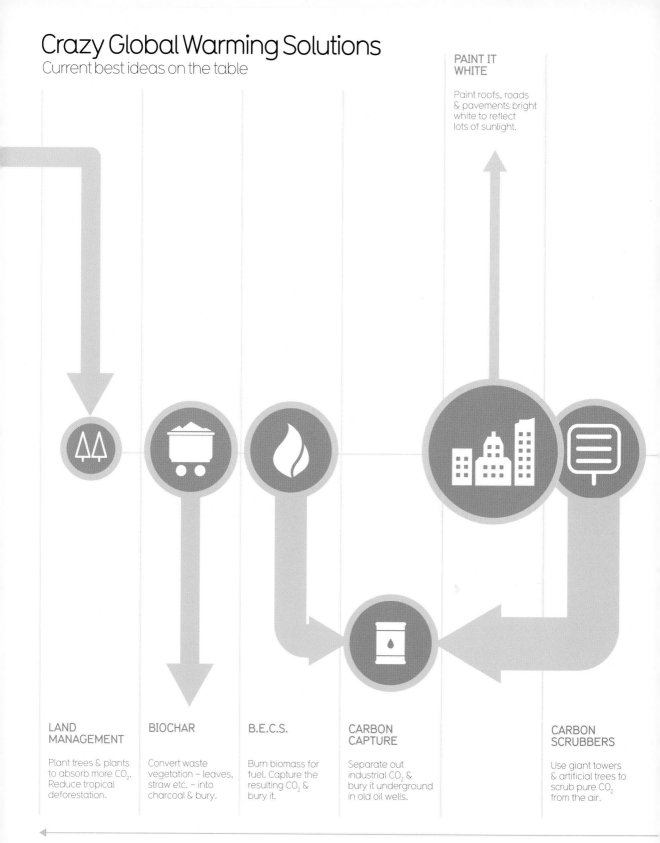

PAINT IT
WHITE

Paint roofs, roads
& pavements bright
white to reflect
lots of sunlight.

LAND
MANAGEMENT

Plant trees & plants
to absorb more CO_2.
Reduce tropical
deforestation.

BIOCHAR

Convert waste
vegetation – leaves,
straw etc. – into
charcoal & bury.

B.E.C.S.

Burn biomass for
fuel. Capture the
resulting CO_2 &
bury it.

CARBON
CAPTURE

Separate out
industrial CO_2 &
bury it underground
in old oil wells.

CARBON
SCRUBBERS

Use giant towers
& artificial trees to
scrub pure CO_2
from the air.

LIKELY

CLOUD WHITENING

Air-spray particles of sea salt to make clouds whiter & reflect more sunlight.

STRATOSPHERIC AEROSOLS

Scatter sulphate particles high in the atmosphere to reflect sunlight & lower heat.

SPACE REFLECTORS

Launch thousands of orbiting mirrors to divert sunlight away from the surface.

DESERT REFLECTORS

Cover vast areas of unused land with foil. No, seriously.

ALL-OUT NUCLEAR WAR

Fill the atmosphere with terratonnes of soot, dropping temperatures by 10°C.

ENHANCED LAND WEATHERING

Accelerate natural CO_2 absorption by rocks by adding minerals to soil.

ENHANCED OCEAN WEATHERING

Stir megatonnes of limestone into oceans so more CO_2 is absorbed by less acidic waters.

OCEAN FERTILISATION

Add iron filings to surface water & boost growth of CO_2-absorbing algae.

$trillions

$billions

$millions

EXPENSE

EFFECTIVENESS

UNLIKELY

sources: Royal Society, 'Geoengineering the Climate' (2009), Carbon Tracker
data: bit.ly/KIB_ClimateFixes

Top 500 Passwords Is yours here?

FREQUENCY

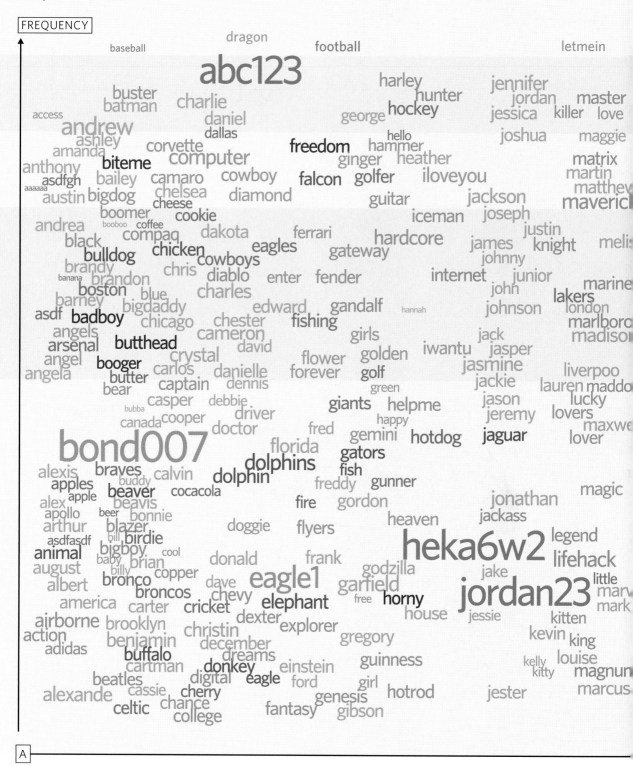

A

THEMES 6%   ANIMAL COOL/MACHO   FLUFFY   FOOD NAME   NERDY

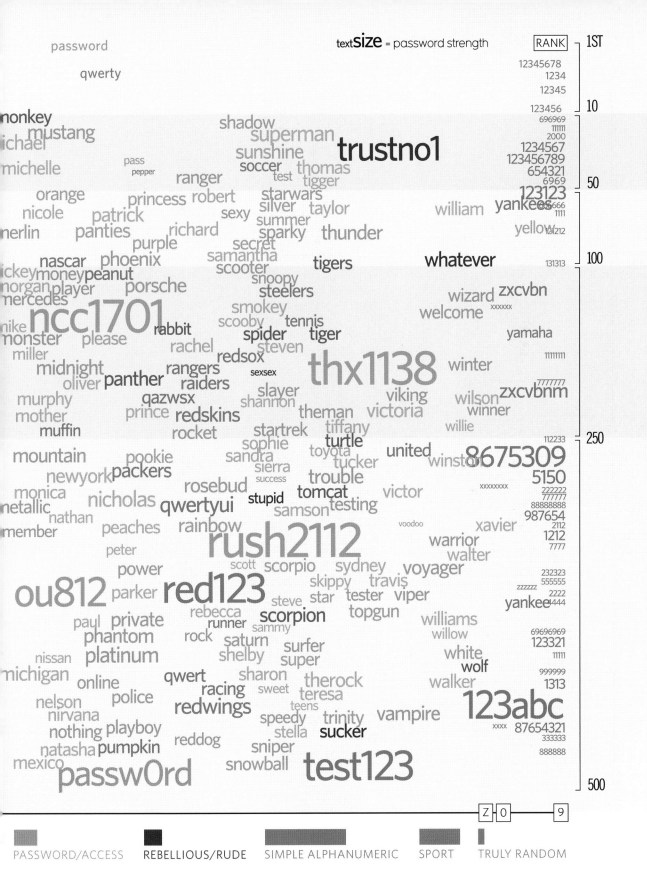

textSize = password strength

RANK

1ST

password

12345678
1234
12345

qwerty

monkey
mustang
ichael
michelle
pass
pepper
ranger
orange
nicole
patrick
merlin
panties
purple
princess robert
sexy
silver
summer
secret
richard
sparky
thunder
samantha
scooter
snoopy
steelers
smokey
scooby
rabbit
please
rachel
redsox
rangers
raiders
slayer
shannon
prince
redskins
rocket
sophie
sandra
sierra
success
rosebud
nicholas
peaches
rainbow
scott scorpio
skippy
star
scorpion
rebecca
runner sammy
rock saturn
shelby
sharon
sweet
racing
teresa
teens
stella
sniper
snowball

shadow
superman
sunshine
soccer thomas
test tigger
starwars
taylor
tigger
secret
tigers
spider
steven
tiger
sexsex
theman
victoria
tiffany
turtle
toyota
tucker
trouble
tomcat
testing
samson
stupid
victor
voodoo
scott scorpio sydney voyager
tester viper
topgun
steve star
therock
trinity vampire
sucker
test123

trustno1
whatever
wizard zxcvbn
welcome
xxxxxx
yamaha
thx1138
winter
zxcvbnm
wilson
winner
willie
united
winston 8675309
5150
xxxxxxx
222222
777777
88888888
987654
2112
1212
7777
warrior
walter
xavier
williams
willow
white
wolf
walker
123abc
xxxx 87654321
333333
888888

696969
11111
2000
1234567
123456789
654321
6969
123123
yankees 55666
1111
yellow 121212
131313
monster
miller
midnight
oliver panther
murphy
mother
muffin
mountain
newyork packers
monica
metallic
nathan
member
peter
ou812 parker red123
paul private
phantom
platinum
nissan
michigan
online
nelson police
nirvana
nothing playboy
natasha pumpkin
mexico passw0rd

nascar phoenix
ickeymoneypeanut
norganplayer porsche
mercedes
nike
ncc1701
qazwsx
panther
qwertyui
qwert
power
rush2112
rush2112

111111
1111111
7777777

112233

232323
zzzzzz 555555
2222
yankee 4444

69696969
123321
1111

999999
1313

PASSWORD/ACCESS   REBELLIOUS/RUDE   SIMPLE ALPHANUMERIC   SPORT   TRULY RANDOM

Z 0 9

sources: various data breaches, Xato.net, TroyHunt.com
data: bit.ly/KIB_Passwords

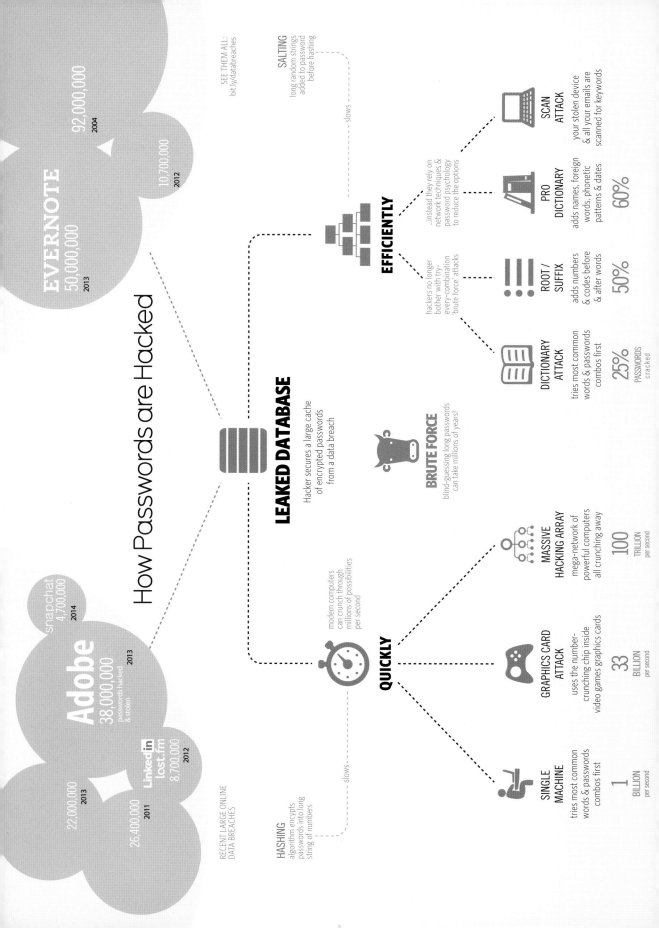

How Passwords are Hacked

RECENT LARGE ONLINE
DATA BREACHES

SEE THEM ALL:
bit.ly/databreaches

Adobe
38,000,000
passwords hacked
& stolen
2013

snapchat
4,700,000
2014

22,000,000
2013

Linked in
last.fm
8,700,000
2012

26,400,000
2011

EVERNOTE
50,000,000
2013

92,000,000
2004

10,700,000
2012

LEAKED DATABASE

Hacker secures a large cache
of encrypted passwords
from a data breach

HASHING
algorithm encypts
passwords into long
string of numbers

SALTING
long random strings
added to password
before hashing

slows

slows

BRUTE FORCE

blind-guessing long passwords
can take millions of years!

modern computers
can crunch through
millions of possibilities
per second

QUICKLY

SINGLE MACHINE
tries most common
words & passwords
combos first

1
BILLION
per second

GRAPHICS CARD ATTACK
uses the number-
crunching chip inside
video games graphics cards

33
BILLION
per second

MASSIVE HACKING ARRAY
mega-network of
powerful computers
all crunching away

100
TRILLION
per second

hackers no longer
bother with try-
every-combination
brute force attacks

...instead they rely on
network techniques &
password psychology
to reduce the options

EFFICIENTLY

DICTIONARY ATTACK
tries most common
words & passwords
combos first

25%
PASSWORDS
cracked

ROOT / SUFFIX
adds numbers
& codes before
& after words

50%

PRO DICTIONARY
adds names, foreign
words, phonetic
patterns & dates

60%

SCAN ATTACK
your stolen device
& all your emails are
scanned for keywords

the majority of passwords crackable in

under 3 hours

Create a Bullet-Proof Password

'When I was seven, my sister threw my stuffed rabbit in the toilet'

'Wow, does that couch smell terrible'

'A long time ago in a galaxy far, far away'

W1w7,mstmsritt...

Wow..doestcst

Alltime@ago-inag-ffa

CONVERT A MEMORABLE SENTENCE

take a sentence that you will remember and convert it into a passcode

pioneered by security researcher Bruce Schneier

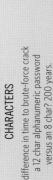

TWO FACTOR AUTHENTICATION

Google & many other sites allow you to use your mobile device to enter a second password

tips

AT LEAST TWELVE CHARACTERS

difference in time to brute-force crack a 12 char alphanumeric password versus an 8 char? 200 years.

RANDOM ALPHANUMERIIC

created by a password generator & handled by a password manager

e.g. $9Eh7*8lim0p&

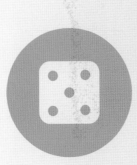

NEVER RE-USE A GOOD PASSWORD

use unique passwords for your core services & high-level data

sources: BoingBoing.net, Arstechnica
data: bit.ly/KIB_Passwords

Tooth & Law

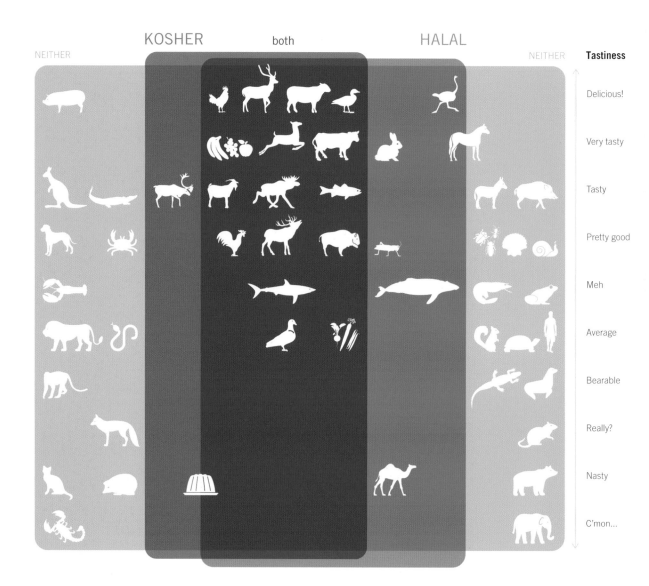

KOSHER both HALAL

NEITHER NEITHER **Tastiness**

Delicious!

Very tasty

Tasty

Pretty good

Meh

Average

Bearable

Really?

Nasty

C'mon…

PRINCIPLES

any animal not correctly, ritualistically slaughtered

no cloven hoofs

doesn't chew the cud

'every creeping thing that crawls'

every 'flying creeping thing'

seafood without scales & fins

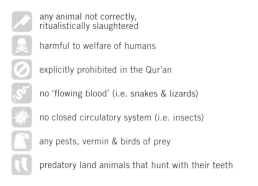

any animal not correctly, ritualistically slaughtered

harmful to welfare of humans

explicitly prohibited in the Qur'an

no 'flowing blood' (i.e. snakes & lizards)

no closed circulatory system (i.e. insects)

any pests, vermin & birds of prey

predatory land animals that hunt with their teeth

sources: BibleGateway.com, Jewfaq.org, Central-Mosque.com, personal communication
data: bit.ly/KIB_HalalKosher

Murder Stories

Story	Murders	Location

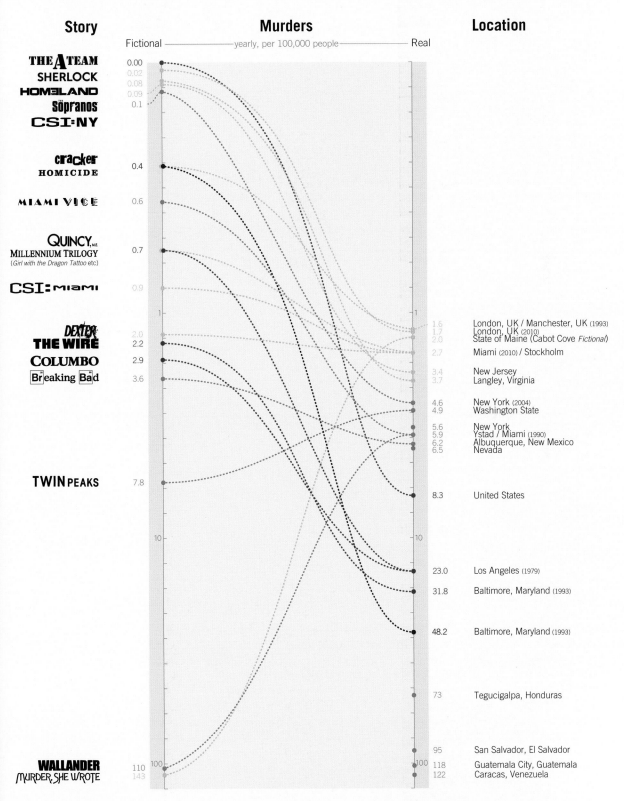

Story

THE A TEAM
SHERLOCK
HOMELAND
Sopranos
CSI:NY

cracker
HOMICIDE

MIAMI VICE

QUINCY, M.E.
MILLENNIUM TRILOGY
(Girl with the Dragon Tattoo etc)

CSI: MIAMI

DEXTER
THE WIRE
COLUMBO
Breaking Bad

TWIN PEAKS

WALLANDER
MURDER, SHE WROTE

Murders

Fictional —————— yearly, per 100,000 people —————— Real

0.00
0.02
0.08
0.09
0.1

0.4

0.6

0.7

0.9

1

2.0
2.2
2.9
3.6

7.8

10

100
110
143

Real side:

1.6   London, UK / Manchester, UK (1993)
1.7   London, UK (2010)
2.0   State of Maine (Cabot Cove *Fictional*)
2.7   Miami (2010) / Stockholm

3.4   New Jersey
3.7   Langley, Virginia

4.6   New York (2004)
4.9   Washington State

5.6   New York
5.9   Ystad / Miami (1990)
6.2   Albuquerque, New Mexico
6.5   Nevada

8.3   United States

10

23.0   Los Angeles (1979)

31.8   Baltimore, Maryland (1993)

48.2   Baltimore, Maryland (1993)

73   Tegucigalpa, Honduras

95   San Salvador, El Salvador

100
118   Guatemala City, Guatemala
122   Caracas, Venezuela

Location

sources: BBC, UNODC, British Medical Journal, UK Home Office, Guardian, US Census
data: bit.ly/KIB_MurderRates

In Good Company?

The US's top 500 corporations ethically rated

Overall ethical score

70

60

50

Ethical calculation = Charity donations · Ecological performance · Executive diversity · LGBT policy · Toxic waste · Best places to work index · Most-admired index · Subsidiaries in tax havens

Healthcare · Financial · Consumer · Tech & Telecoms · Industrial · Energy & utility

average % tax rate

Google

amazon.com

VISA

at&t

Sempra Energy

NetApp

Adobe

QUALCOMM

Coca-Cola Enterprises

intel

NIKE

STARBUCKS

WHOLE FOODS

Walt Disney

intuit

Kroger

charles SCHWAB

NORDSTROM

macy's

SOUTHWEST.COM

XL

AVON

Hospira

Cigna

SEARS HOLDINGS

Microsoft

Allstate

Coca-Cola

Agilent Technologies

MATTEL

Apple

Marriott

Texas Instruments Financial

Kimberly-Clark

Symantec

Medtronic

DARDEN

STAPLES

Limited brands

ESTÉE LAUDER

AMERICAN EXPRESS

US Bancorp

AON

YAHOO!

TARGET

Costco

McGraw-Hill

ADP

NORTHROP GRUMMAN

THE HOME DEPOT

GAP

Abercrombie & Fitch

CLOROX

CAREMARK

ConAgra Foods

CSX

Quest Diagnostics

CVS

Lincoln Financial Group

TJX

WYNDHAM

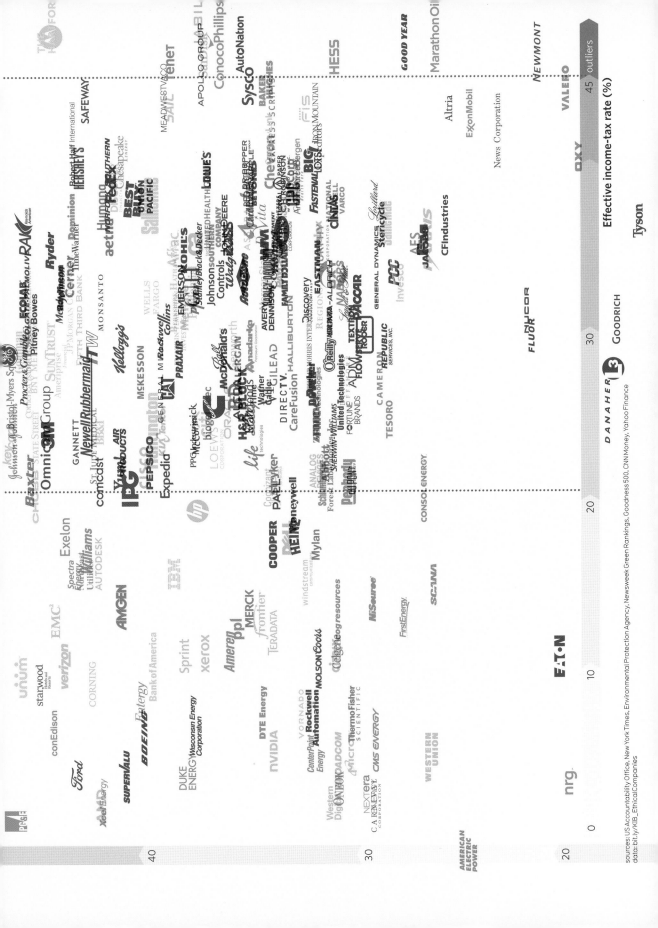

Effective income-tax rate (%)

sources: US Accountability Office, New York Times, Environmental Protection Agency, Newsweek Green Rankings, Goodness500, CNN Money, Yahoo Finance
data: bit.ly/KIB_EthicalCompanies

In Good Company?

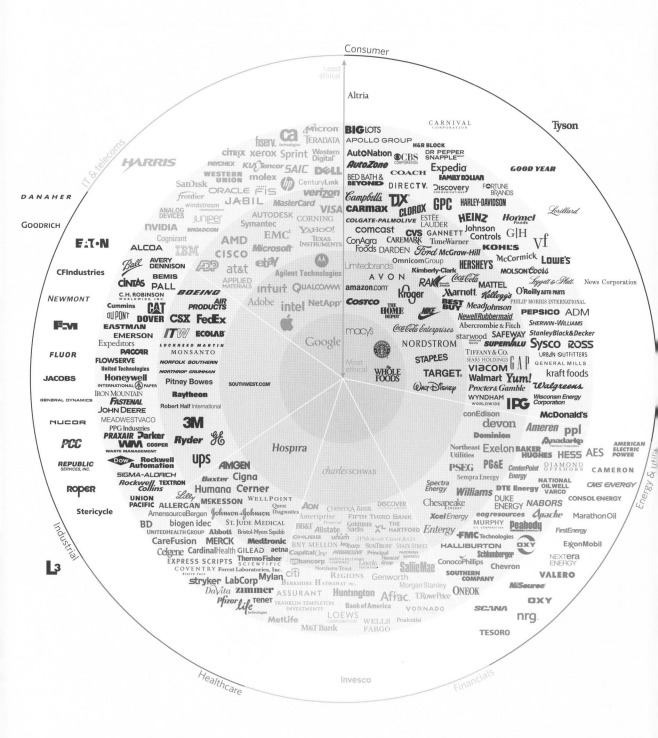

sources: US Accountability Office, NY Times, Environmental Protection Agency, Newsweek Green Rankings, Goodness 500, CNN Money, Yahoo Finance
data: bit.ly/KIB_EthicalCompanies

Meditation

The Gist

chill man
meditating is acknowledging and observing whatever happens – pleasant or unpleasant – in a relaxed way.

no 'no thoughts'
the goal of meditation is not to empty the mind, but to observe the present moment non-judgementally.

open
this gives insight into how the mind really works, reducing attachment, letting us relax more deeply...

microscope
...transforming the mind and using it as a device to explore itself and the nature of reality.

Good Posture

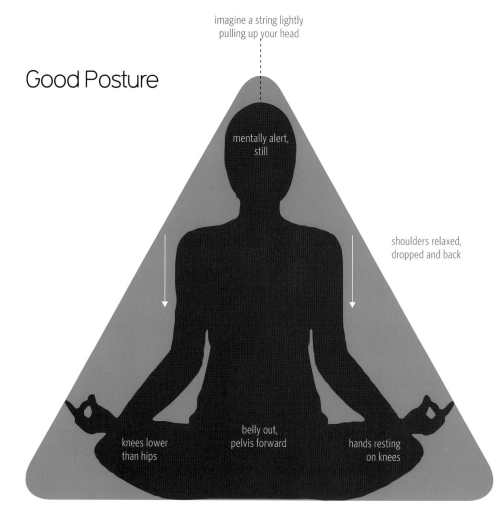

imagine a string lightly pulling up your head

mentally alert, still

shoulders relaxed, dropped and back

knees lower than hips

belly out, pelvis forward

hands resting on knees

SIT ——————————————

relaxed but erect

Common Hindrances

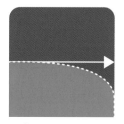

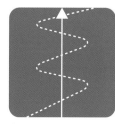

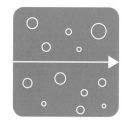

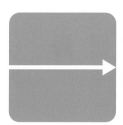

laziness
putting meditation off until later

sinking
fading of concentration, dullness, sleepiness

drifting
restless flightiness of mind, creating excitement or anxiety

stray thoughts
random mental phenomena like radio interference

trying too hard
over-focussing or trying to control restricts & tightens the mind

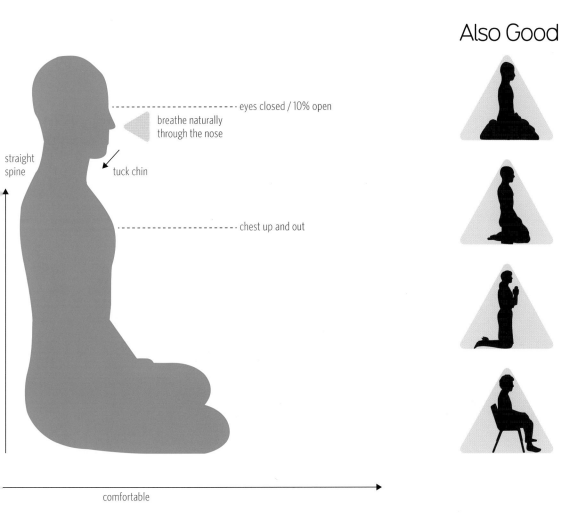

straight spine

eyes closed / 10% open

breathe naturally through the nose

tuck chin

chest up and out

comfortable

Also Good

Qualities of Mind Developed in elemental Eastern terms

open spacious, empty	**clear** sharp, perceptive	**warm** tolerant, positive	**pliant** receptive, flexible	**steady** concentrated, centred
space	air	fire	water	earth
tranquil calm, still	**agile** light, quick-witted	**confident** self-assured, proficient	**malleable** strong, workable	**upright** straightforward, direct

sources: Buddhist eLibrary, 'Meditation' (Wind Horse, 1999)

Types of Meditation

meditation name
alternative name

Simple, condensed instructions
on how to practise the technique

tradition of origin

concentration
focussed attention

Hold attention on a primary object,
usually your breath. Mentally note the
upward movement of your abdomen as
'rising', downward as 'falling'. That's it!

Many

mindfulness
open monitoring

Watch your thoughts, let them come
and go, without reacting, judging
or holding on.

Buddhism

attending
open monitoring

Concentrate while carefully naming
thoughts, sensations and other mental
processes and distractions.

Buddhism

belly
kath, hara, tan t'ien

Just focus on the sensation of the
breath in the belly as it rises and falls.

Many

three-part breath
long deep

First fill the abdomen with air, then
expand the chest, then lift ribs and collar
bone. Exhale in reverse.

Yoga

breath of fire
agni pran

Rapid rhythmic breaths through the nose.
Exhale explosively by contracting anus,
inhale by relaxing abdominal muscles.

Kundalini Yoga

circular breathing

Inhale from the base of your spine up
to the base of your neck. Exhale down
the back of your spine.

Yoga

alternate breath

Block right nostril with knuckle. Take 4
slow, even breaths through left nostril.
Repeat on other side.

Kundalini Yoga

zen
zazen, 'just sitting'

Counting your breaths (1 for inhalation,
2 for exhalation) up to 10. If your mind
wanders, gently go back to 1.
Just sit like this.

Zen Buddhism

microcosmic orbit

Use the breath to circulate energy
through an oval 'microcosmic' orbit.
Start at the throat, end at the forehead.

Taoism

transcendental
TM

Silently, repeat a given, single,
rhythmical sound-phrase (mantra)
over and over again.

Many

object of
concentration
BODY BREATH HEART MANTRA MIND

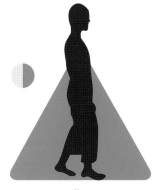

loving kindness for self
metta bhavana, cultivation of love

Acknowledge whatever you're feeling.
Playfully extend loving kindness to
yourself by silently expressing feelings
like: 'May I be happy / healthy / loved'
etc. Maintain this flow of intention.

Buddhism

silent gratitude
visualisation

Imagine the face of someone you feel
grateful to in great detail and silently
thank them. Repeat for 4–5 people.

Buddhism

loving kindness for others
metta bhavana

Picture someone you respect and love.
Send a stream of metta (loving kindness)
towards them using silent, suitable words.
If a feeling of happiness arises, absorb
yourself into it.

Buddhism

walking

Feel every sensation in your feet while slow
walking – contact, rolling, lifting etc.
Add attending and name every distraction.
Add 'loving kindness' and extend metta to
everyone who appears in your view.

Buddhism

segmented breathing 1

Mouth in an 'o' shape. Make 8 small
inhalations (sniffs) through the nose to
form one breath. Exhale powerfully and
deeply in one go. Repeat.

Kundalini Yoga

segmented breathing 2

Focus on your brow point.
Make 4 inhale sniffs, hold for a few
seconds, exhale in 4 sniffs. Repeat.

Kundalini Yoga

balancing

Inhale deeply through the nose.
Hold breath for 15 seconds.
Exhale completely through the nose.
Hold breath for 15 seconds. Repeat.

Kundalini Yoga

sensing loop
body scan, body contemplation

Feel into the sensations in your right foot
and then work up around each segment
of your body – lower leg, knee, thigh, hip,
hand, arm, shoulder – in a loop.

Sufism

mantra

Chant a single, rhythmical sound-phrase
(mantra) over and over again.
Examples: 'Haum Mani-Padme-Om',
'Sa-Ta-Na-Ma', 'Sabbe Satta Sukhi Hontu',
'So Hum' (I am), 'Sat Chit Ananda'.

Many

eating

Take twenty minutes to eat 3
raisins. Savour every detail: the look,
the anticipation, the chew, the taste,
the swallow.

---

analytical
rushen, self-inquiry

Sit with a deep question in your mind.
'Who am I?' is a good one. Explore who is
thinking, hearing, seeing, wondering.
What happens in the immediate moment
as you ask this question?

Dzogchen (Tibetan Buddhism)

sources: BuddhisteLibrary.org, BerzinArchives.com

Meditation: Evidence

strong
promising
inconclusive
slight / weak

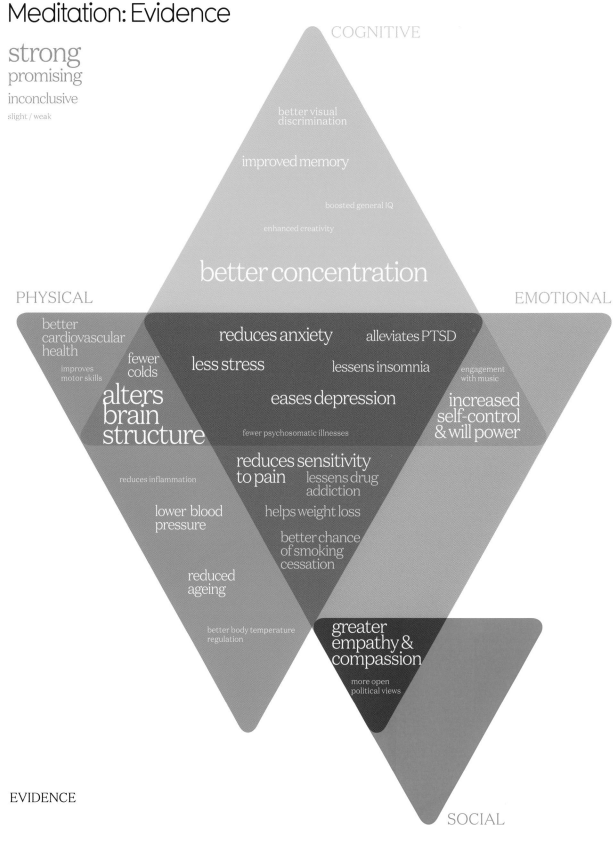

COGNITIVE

better visual discrimination

improved memory

boosted general IQ

enhanced creativity

better concentration

PHYSICAL

EMOTIONAL

better cardiovascular health

improves motor skills

fewer colds

reduces anxiety

alleviates PTSD

less stress

lessens insomnia

engagement with music

alters brain structure

eases depression

fewer psychosomatic illnesses

increased self-control & will power

reduces sensitivity to pain

lessens drug addiction

reduces inflammation

lower blood pressure

helps weight loss

better chance of smoking cessation

reduced ageing

better body temperature regulation

greater empathy & compassion

more open political views

EVIDENCE

SOCIAL

sources: Zanesco (2013), Hasenkamp & Barsalou (2012), Saggar (2012), Moore (2012), Menezes (2013), Chiesa (2011), Levy (2012), Chiesa & Serretti (2010), and many more
data: bit.ly/KIB_Meditation

Water World

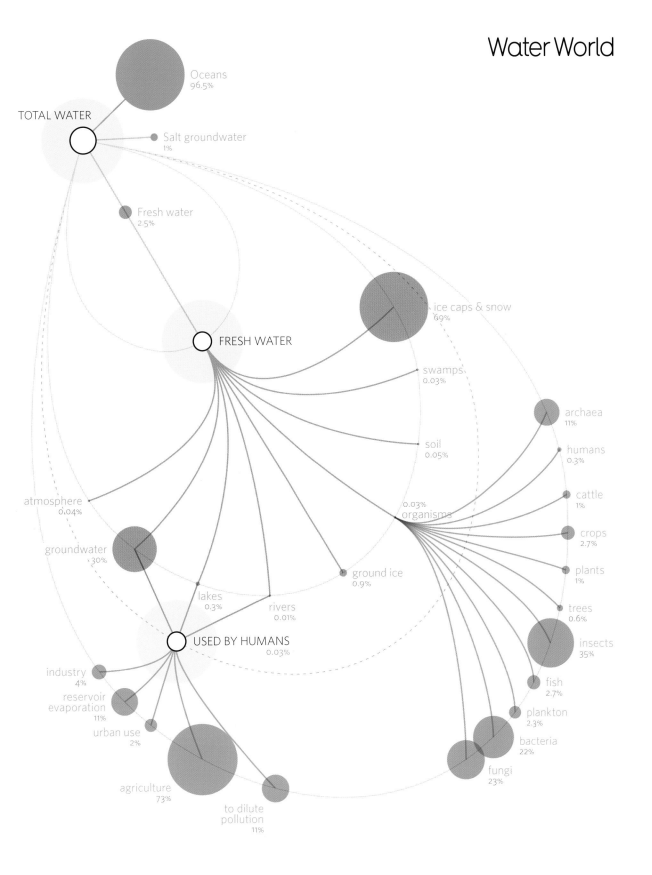

Oceans
96.5%

TOTAL WATER

Salt groundwater
1%

Fresh water
2.5%

ice caps & snow
69%

FRESH WATER

swamps
0.03%

soil
0.05%

archaea
11%

humans
0.3%

cattle
1%

atmosphere
0.04%

0.03%
organisms

crops
2.7%

groundwater
30%

plants
1%

ground ice
0.9%

trees
0.6%

lakes
0.3%

rivers
0.01%

insects
35%

USED BY HUMANS
0.03%

fish
2.7%

industry
4%

plankton
2.3%

reservoir
evaporation
11%

bacteria
22%

urban use
2%

agriculture
73%

fungi
23%

to dilute
pollution
11%

sources: Food and Agricultural Organisation, 'World Atlas of Biodiversity' (2012), Nature.com
data: bit.ly/KIB_WaterWorld

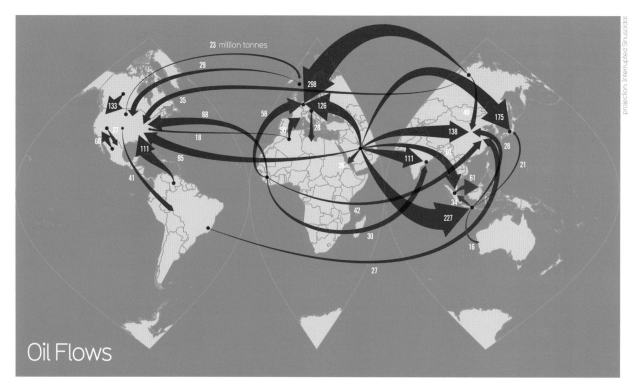

projection: Interrupted Sinusoidal

23 million tonnes

Oil Flows

projection: Briesemeister

Lactose Intolerance

tolerance level

100%

0%

no data

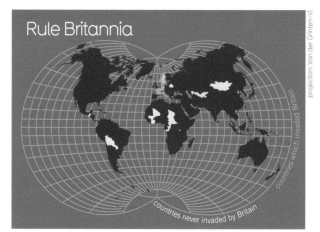

projection: Van der Grinten-VI

Rule Britannia

countries which invaded Britain

countries never invaded by Britain

projection: armadillo

with / without Google Street View

Lost Nations

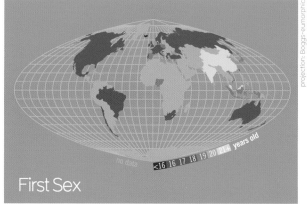

projection: Boggs-eumorphic

First Sex

no data

<16 16 17 18 19 20 21+ years old

sources: Telegraph.com, bost.ocks.org, Durex, Wikipedia
data: bit.ly/KIB_Maps

Superpower Showdown
Law & order

	China	EU	India	USA
PRISON POPULATION IN THOUSANDS	1,701	638	385	2,228
PRISON POPULATION PER 100,000 PEOPLE	125	125	30	700
DEATH SENTENCES PER YEAR	1,000	0	78	77
FREEDOM OF EXPRESSION INDEX	-1.6	1.1	0.4	1.1
POLITICAL STABILITY	-0.5	0.8	-1.2	0.6
GOVERNMENT EFFECTIVENESS	0.0	1.2	-0.2	1.5
REGULATORY QUALITY	-0.2	1.2	-0.5	1.3
RULE OF LAW	-0.5	1.2	-0.1	1.6
CONTROL OF CORRUPTION	-0.5	1.0	-0.6	1.4
No. OF FIREARMS AVERAGE PER 100 PEOPLE	5	15	4	89
HOMICIDE COUNT THOUSANDS PER YEAR	14	6	40	15
HOMICIDE COUNT PER YEAR / PER 100,000 PEOPLE	1	1.2	3.3	4.8
SEIZURES OF OPIATE DRUGS TONNES	5.4	5.8	0.8	3.5
SCORE	1	4	4	5

USA GETS JUSTICE!

sources: 'CIA World Factbook', World Bank, Eurostat
data: bit.ly/KIB_Superpowers

One in...

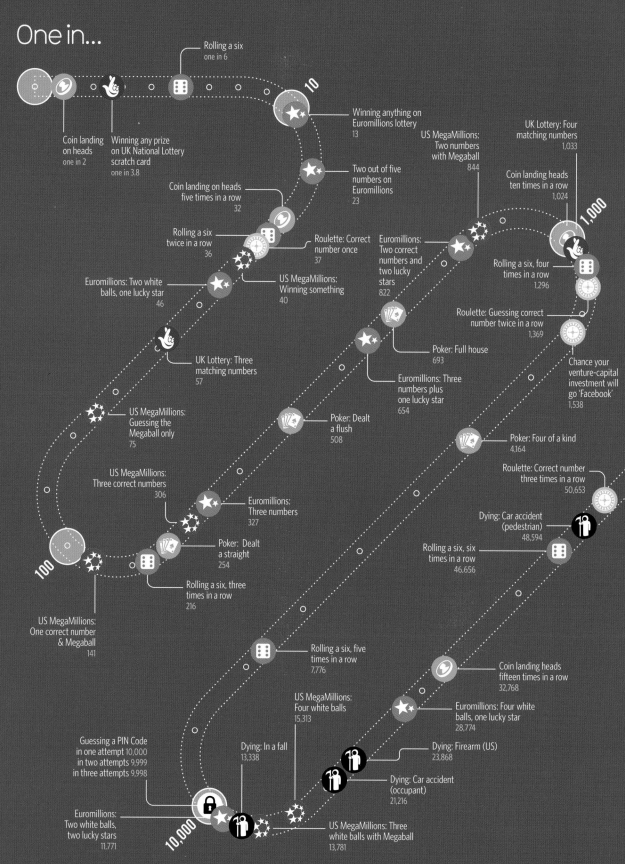

Rolling a six
one in 6

Coin landing
on heads
one in 2

Winning any prize
on UK National Lottery
scratch card
one in 3.8

Winning anything on
Euromillions lottery
13

Coin landing on heads
five times in a row
32

Two out of five
numbers on
Euromillions
23

US MegaMillions:
Two numbers
with Megaball
844

UK Lottery: Four
matching numbers
1,033

Coin landing heads
ten times in a row
1,024

Rolling a six
twice in a row
36

Roulette: Correct
number once
37

Euromillions:
Two correct
numbers and
two lucky
stars
822

Rolling a six, four
times in a row
1,296

Euromillions: Two white
balls, one lucky star
46

US MegaMillions:
Winning something
40

Poker: Full house
693

Roulette: Guessing correct
number twice in a row
1,369

UK Lottery: Three
matching numbers
57

Euromillions: Three
numbers plus
one lucky star
654

Chance your
venture-capital
investment will
go 'Facebook'
1,538

US MegaMillions:
Guessing the
Megaball only
75

Poker: Dealt
a flush
508

Poker: Four of a kind
4,164

Roulette: Correct number
three times in a row
50,653

US MegaMillions:
Three correct numbers
306

Euromillions:
Three numbers
327

Dying: Car accident
(pedestrian)
48,594

Poker: Dealt
a straight
254

Rolling a six, six
times in a row
46,656

Rolling a six, three
times in a row
216

US MegaMillions:
One correct number
& Megaball
141

Rolling a six, five
times in a row
7,776

Coin landing heads
fifteen times in a row
32,768

US MegaMillions:
Four white balls
15,313

Euromillions: Four white
balls, one lucky star
28,774

Guessing a PIN Code
in one attempt 10,000
in two attempts 9,999
in three attempts 9,998

Dying: In a fall
13,338

Dying: Firearm (US)
23,868

Dying: Car accident
(occupant)
21,216

Euromillions:
Two white balls,
two lucky stars
11,771

US MegaMillions: Three
white balls with Megaball
13,781

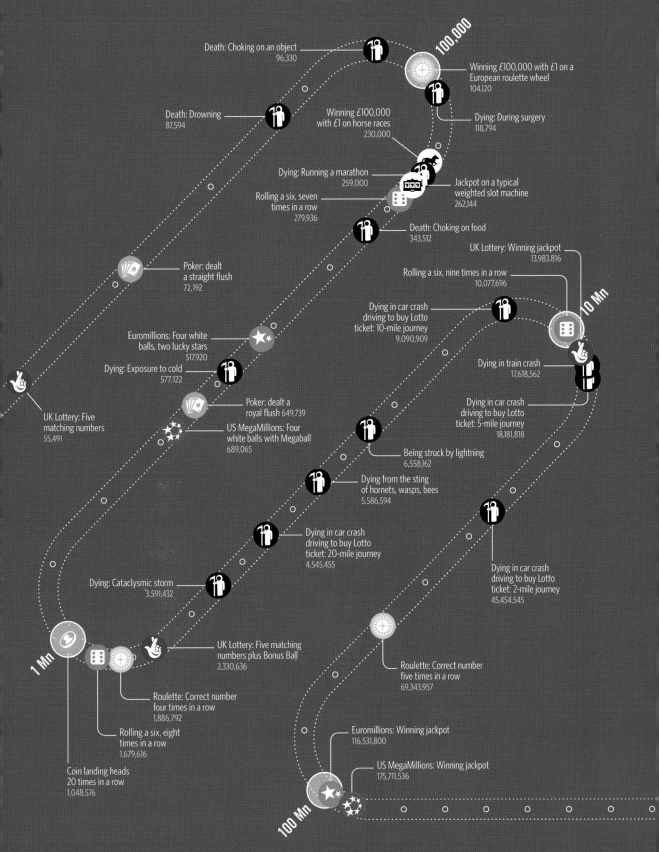

100,000

Death: Choking on an object
96,330

Winning £100,000 with £1 on a European roulette wheel
104,120

Death: Drowning
87,594

Dying: During surgery
118,794

Winning £100,000 with £1 on horse races
230,000

Dying: Running a marathon
259,000

Jackpot on a typical weighted slot machine
262,144

Rolling a six, seven times in a row
279,936

Death: Choking on food
343,512

UK Lottery: Winning jackpot
13,983,816

Rolling a six, nine times in a row
10,077,696

Poker: dealt a straight flush
72,192

Dying in car crash driving to buy Lotto ticket: 10-mile journey
9,090,909

Euromillions: Four white balls, two lucky stars
517,920

Dying in train crash
17,618,562

Dying: Exposure to cold
577,122

Dying in car crash driving to buy Lotto ticket: 5-mile journey
18,181,818

10 Mn

Poker: dealt a royal flush
649,739

UK Lottery: Five matching numbers
55,491

US MegaMillions: Four white balls with Megaball
689,065

Being struck by lightning
6,558,162

Dying from the sting of hornets, wasps, bees
5,586,594

Dying in car crash driving to buy Lotto ticket: 2-mile journey
45,454,545

Dying in car crash driving to buy Lotto ticket: 20-mile journey
4,545,455

Dying: Cataclysmic storm
3,591,432

UK Lottery: Five matching numbers plus Bonus Ball
2,330,636

Roulette: Correct number five times in a row
69,343,957

1 Mn

Roulette: Correct number four times in a row
1,886,792

Rolling a six, eight times in a row
1,679,616

Coin landing heads 20 times in a row
1,048,576

Euromillions: Winning jackpot
116,531,800

US MegaMillions: Winning jackpot
175,711,536

100 Mn

sources: Georgiadis and Zeilberger (2011), National Safety Council, Euro Millions, WizardOfOdds.com
data: bit.ly/KIB_Gambling

True Genius
Really a-head of their time?

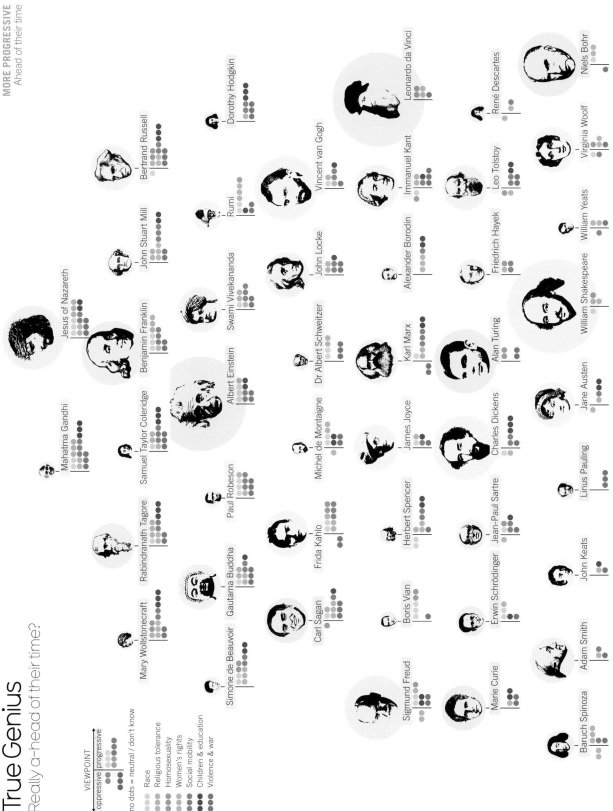

VIEWPOINT

oppressive | progressive

no dots = neutral / don't know

- Race
- Religious tolerance
- Homosexuality
- Women's rights
- Social mobility
- Children & education
- Violence & war

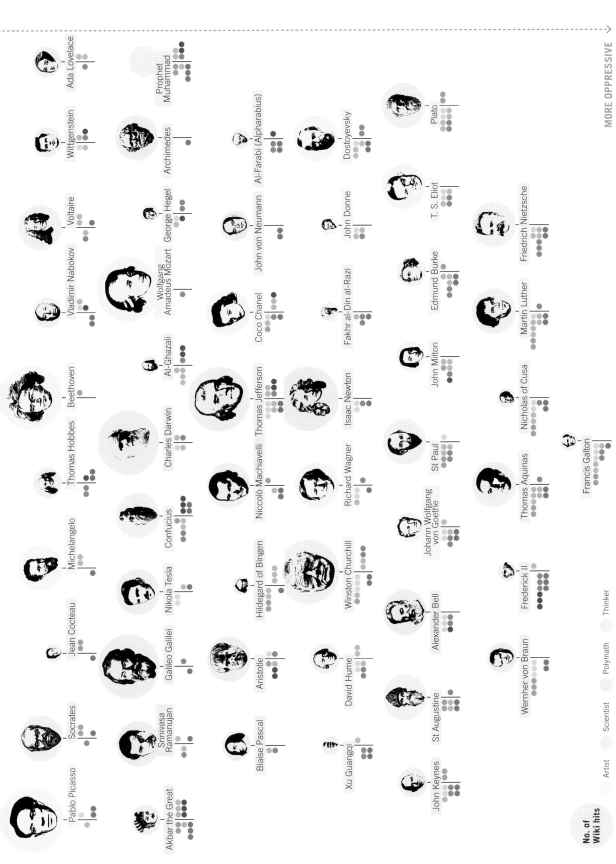

MORE OPPRESSIVE

Ada Lovelace

Prophet Muhammad

Wittgenstein

Archimedes

Al-Farabi (Alpharabius)

Dostoyevsky

Plato

Voltaire

George Hegel

John von Neumann

John Donne

T. S. Eliot

Vladimir Nabokov

Wolfgang Amadeus Mozart

Coco Chanel

Fakhr al-Din al-Razi

Edmund Burke

Friedrich Nietzsche

Beethoven

Al-Ghazali

John Milton

Martin Luther

Thomas Hobbes

Charles Darwin

Niccolò Machiavelli

Thomas Jefferson

Isaac Newton

St Paul

Nicholas of Cusa

Michelangelo

Confucius

Richard Wagner

Johann Wolfgang von Goethe

Thomas Aquinas

Francis Galton

Jean Cocteau

Nikola Tesla

Hildegard of Bingen

Winston Churchill

Alexander Bell

Frederick II

Galileo Galilei

Aristotle

David Hume

Wernher von Braun

Socrates

Srinivasa Ramanujan

Blaise Pascal

Xu Guangqi

St Augustine

John Keynes

Pablo Picasso

Akbar the Great

No. of Wiki hits

Artist   Scientist   Polymath   Thinker

sources: OxfordDNB.com, Britannica.com, NY Times, NobelPrize.org, UNESCO, Wikipedia
data: bit.ly/KIB_TrueGenius

True Genius: Details

MORE PROGRESSIVE
Ahead of their time

year of
mid life

1908 Mahatma Gandhi

12 Jesus of Nazareth

1485 Leonardo da Vinci
Polymath & creative genius. Gay. Veggie.

1923 Niels Bohr
Nobel physicist rescued German-Jewish scientists.

1623 René Descartes
French philosopher. 'I think, therefore I am.'

1921 Bertrand Russell
Nobel Peace Prize-winning philosopher & social activist. Life-long commitment to peace.

1952 Dorothy Hodgkin
Nobel chemist. Selfless humanitarian. Supported students & the downtrodden.

1871 Vincent van Gogh
Dutch humanistic painter, devoted Christian & man of the people.

1240 Rumi
Islamic mystic & poet. Wrote of love, charity & goodness.

1764 Immanuel Kant
Philosopher on peace, education. Anti gay, alas.

1869 Leo Tolstoy
Novelist. Anti power. Closet homosexual.

1911 Virginia Woolf
Writer & women's rights campaigner.

1839 John Stuart Mill
British philosopher. Believed in happiness as a political goal. Pro human & women's rights.

1748 Benjamin Franklin
Thinker & scientist. Face of the US $100 bill. Pro abolition of slavery & religious tolerance.

1803 Samuel Taylor Coleridge
Romantic poet. Advocate of democracy, child-protection & women's rights.

1882 Swami Vivekananda
Hindu monk. Critical of caste system. Pro women, positive education & the poor.

1668 John Locke
English philosopher, anti patriarchy, strong influence on US politics.

1860 Alexander Borodin
Composer & chemist, pro women's rights.

1945 Friedrich Hayek
Political thinker. Pro democracy, free markets.

1902 William Yeats
Poet & mystic. Right wing. But feminist.

1917 Albert Einstein
Anti nuclear, pro civil rights, anti-capitalist, pro education – pretty enlightened.

1920 Dr Albert Schweitzer
German theologian. Humanitarian. Anti-nuclear peace advocate.

1950 Karl Marx
Anti capitalism & religion. Pro violence.

1933 Alan Turing
Maths genius, persecuted for being gay.

1590 William Shakespeare
Themes in his work suggestive of tolerance.

1562 Michel de Montaigne
French writer. Invented the essay & concept of 'cultural diversity'.

1911 James Joyce
Irish novelist & anti marriage.

1841 Charles Dickens
Writer of *Oliver Twist*. Supported the poor.

1796 Jane Austen
Novelist, shared the subtlety of women's lives.

1778 Mary Wollstonecraft
Writer & feminist. For equal schooling for women, non-violence & religious tolerance.

1901 Rabindranath Tagore
Poet & thinker. For education for poor. Nobility of all cultures. Feminist leanings.

1937 Paul Robeson
African-American singer & civil rights activist. Stood for peace & against facism.

523 BCE Gautama Buddha
Indian prince. Rejected status for pursuit of enlightenment. Founded Buddhism.

1930 Frida Kahlo
Openly bisexual Spanish artist & defender of Jews. But loved Stalin, alas.

1861 Herbert Spencer
Sociologist. Coined 'survival of the fittest'.

1942 Jean-Paul Sartre
Writer & existentialist, highly socially active.

1947 Linus Pauling
Nobel chemist, refused to work on atom bomb.

1947 Simone de Beauvoir
Philosopher, writer & feminist. Believed women should not try to be like men.

1965 Carl Sagan
Freethinking astrophysicist & prof. Leftish.

1939 Boris Vian
Musician & author, fierce critic of racism.

1924 Erwin Schrödinger
Quantum scientist. Defended Jews from abuse.

1808 John Keats
Chauvinistic English Romantic poet.

1897 Sigmund Freud
Psychologist, strongly defended homosexuality.

1900 Marie Curie
Discovered radioactivity. First woman Nobel laureate.

1756 Adam Smith
Philosopher. Free markets create peace & growth.

1654 Baruch Spinoza
Rationalist. Early denier of Bible as literal truth.

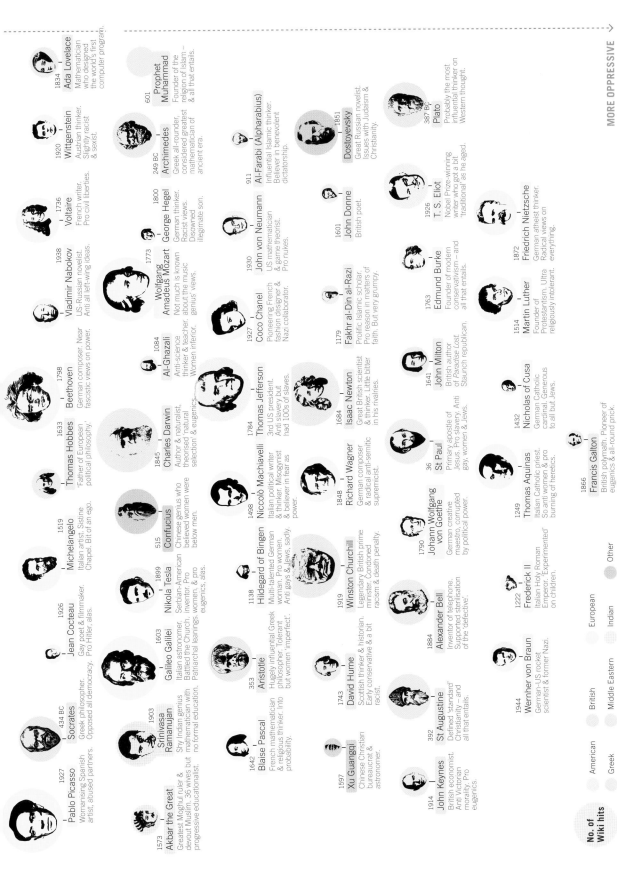

1834 **Ada Lovelace** — Mathematician who designed the world's first computer program.

601 **Prophet Muhammad** — Founder of the religion of Islam – & all that entails.

1920 **Wittgenstein** — Austrian thinker. Slightly racist & sexist.

249 BC **Archimedes** — Greek all-rounder, considered greatest mathematician of ancient era.

1851 **Dostoyevsky** — Great Russian novelist. Issues with Judaism & Christianity.

1736 **Voltaire** — French writer. Pro civil liberties.

1800 **George Hegel** — German thinker. Racist views. Disowned illegitimate son.

911 **Al-Farabi (Alpharabius)** — Influential Islamic thinker. Believer in benevolent dictatorship.

387 BC **Plato** — Probably the most influential thinker on Western thought.

1938 **Vladimir Nabokov** — US-Russian novelist. Anti all left-wing ideas.

1773 **Wolfgang Amadeus Mozart** — Not much is known about the music genius' views.

1930 **John von Neumann** — US mathematician & game theorist. Pro nukes.

1601 **John Donne** — British poet.

1926 **T. S. Eliot** — Nobel Prize-winning writer who got a bit traditional as he aged.

1872 **Friedrich Nietzsche** — German atheist thinker. Radical views on everything.

1798 **Beethoven** — German composer. Near fascistic views on power.

1084 **Al-Ghazali** — Anti-science thinker & teacher. Women inferior.

1927 **Coco Chanel** — Pioneering French fashion designer & Nazi collaborator.

1179 **Fakhr al-Din al-Razi** — Prolific Islamic scholar. Pro reason in matters of faith. But very grumpy.

1763 **Edmund Burke** — Founder of modern conservativism – and all that entails.

1514 **Martin Luther** — Founder of Protestantism. Ultra religiously intolerant.

1633 **Thomas Hobbes** — 'Father' of European political philosophy.

1845 **Charles Darwin** — Author & naturalist, theorised 'natural selection' & eugenics.

1784 **Thomas Jefferson** — 3rd US president. Anti slavery but had 100s of slaves.

1684 **Isaac Newton** — Great British scientist & thinker. Little bitter in his rivalries.

1641 **John Milton** — British author of *Paradise Lost*. Staunch republican.

1432 **Nicholas of Cusa** — German Catholic cardinal. Generous to all but Jews.

1519 **Michelangelo** — Italian artist. Sistine Chapel. Bit of an ego.

515 **Confucius** — Chinese genius who believed women were below men.

1498 **Niccolò Machiavelli** — Italian political writer & thinker. Misogynist & believer in fear as power.

1848 **Richard Wagner** — German composer & radical anti-semitic supremacist.

36 **St Paul** — Primary apostle of Jesus. Pro slavery. Anti gay, women & Jews.

1249 **Thomas Aquinas** — Italian Catholic priest. So anti women & pro burning of heretics.

1866 **Francis Galton** — British polymath. Pioneer of eugenics & all-round prick.

1899 **Nikola Tesla** — Serbian-American inventor. Pro eugenics, alas.

1138 **Hildegard of Bingen** — Multi-talented German woman. Pro women. Anti gays & Jews, sadly.

1919 **Winston Churchill** — Legendary British prime minister. Condoned racism & death penalty.

1790 **Johann Wolfgang von Goethe** — German creative maestro, corrupted by political power.

1222 **Frederick II** — Italian Holy Roman Emperor. 'Experimented' on children.

434 BC **Socrates** — Greek philosopher. Opposed all democracy.

1926 **Jean Cocteau** — Gay poet & filmmaker. Pro Hitler, alas.

1603 **Galileo Galilei** — Italian astronomer. Battled the Church. Patriarchal leanings.

353 **Aristotle** — Hugely influential Greek philosopher. Tolerant but women 'imperfect'.

1884 **Alexander Bell** — Inventor of telephone. Supported sterilisation of the 'defective'.

1903 **Srinivasa Ramanujan** — Shy Indian genius mathematician with no formal education.

1642 **Blaise Pascal** — French mathematician & religious thinker. Into probability.

1743 **David Hume** — Scottish thinker & historian. Early conservative & a bit racist.

392 **St Augustine** — Defined 'standard' Christianity – and all that entails.

1927 **Pablo Picasso** — Womanising Spanish artist, abused partners.

1573 **Akbar the Great** — Greatest Moghul ruler & devout Muslim. 36 wives but progressive educationalist.

1597 **Xu Guangqi** — Chinese bureaucrat & astronomer.

1914 **John Keynes** — British economist. Anti Victorian morality. Pro eugenics.

1944 **Wernher von Braun** — German–US rocket scientist & former Nazi.

No. of Wiki hits

American — British — European — Indian

Greek — Middle Eastern — Other

MORE OPPRESSIVE →

sources: OxfordDNB.com, Britannica.com, NY Times, NobelPrize.org, UNESCO, Wikipedia
data: bit.ly/KIB_TrueGenius

Simple II

Made, not Born
Average peak age of genius

Scientists

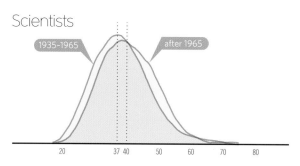

1935-1965   after 1965

20   37 40   50   60   70   80

Jazz musicians

female   male

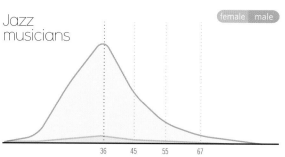

36   45   55   67

Painters

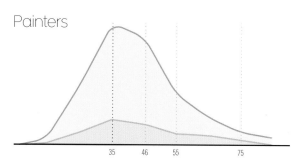

35   46   55   75

Authors

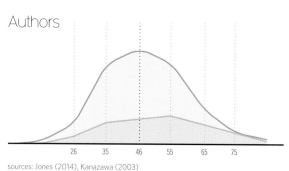

26   35   46   55   65   75

sources: Jones (2014), Kanazawa (2003)

Gut Feeling
Average % positive parole verdicts given by judges

after breakfast   before lunch

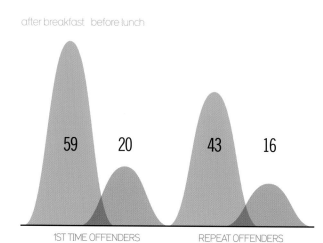

| 59 | 20 | 43 | 16 |

1ST TIME OFFENDERS   REPEAT OFFENDERS

source: Danziger et al (2011), average of 4 sentence lengths

DNA Databases
Total DNA records stored as % of population

S. Africa   Hong Kong   Lithuania   Canada   Slovenia   France

0.40%   0.42%

0.29%   0.78%

0.24%   1.29%

0.09%

0.26%   0.87%

0.37%   0.70%

0.41%

0.50%

China   Belgium   Israel   Cyprus   Croatia   Hungary   Germany

Big Oil
Highest mark-up

sources: Alibaba, Indexmundi.com

2,000%+ | 1,000%+ | 500%+ | 100%+ | <100%+

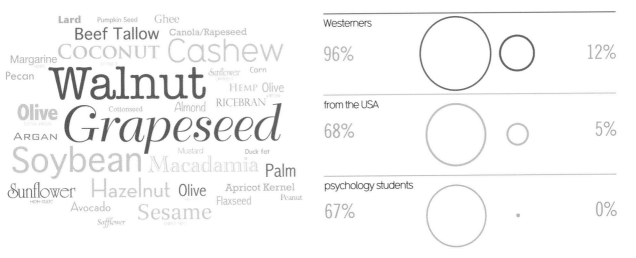

Lard Pumpkin Seed Ghee
Beef Tallow Canola/Rapeseed
Margarine COCONUT Cashew
Pecan Walnut Sunflower Corn
Olive HEMP Olive
Cottonseed Almond RICEBRAN
Olive Grapeseed
ARGAN
Soybean Mustard Duck fat
Macadamia Palm
Sunflower Hazelnut Olive Apricot Kernel
HIGH-OLEIC Flaxseed Peanut
Avocado Sesame
Safflower

Biased Reporting
% of subjects in psychology studies   % of world

Westerners
96%   12%

from the USA
68%   5%

psychology students
67%   0%

source: Arnett et al (2008)

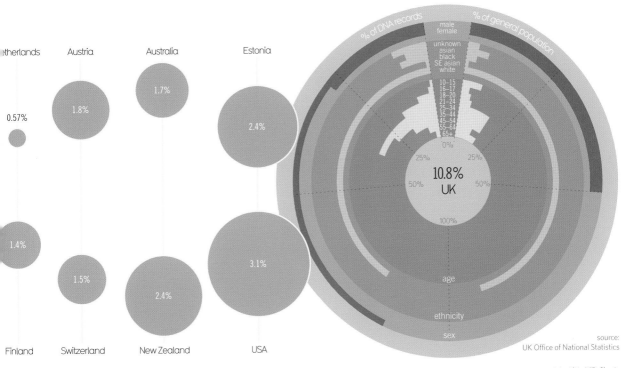

...etherlands Austria Australia Estonia
0.57% 1.8% 1.7% 2.4%

% of DNA records   % of general population
male
female
unknown
asian
black
SE asian
white
10–15
16–17
18–20
21–24
25–34
35–44
45–54
55–64
65+
0%
25%   25%
10.8%
UK
50%   50%
100%

age
ethnicity
sex

1.4%
1.5% 3.1%
2.4%

Finland Switzerland New Zealand USA

source:
UK Office of National Statistics

data: bit.ly/KIB_Simple

Non-Fiction Books Everyone Should Read

ECONOMY

The Art of War

The Second World War Guns,

CHILDREN OF CRISIS The Double H

SURELY YOU'RE JOKING, MR. FEYNMAN! THE S

The Diary of Anne Frank Zer

THE CRITIQUE OF PURE REASON Walder

THE CONSTITUTION OF LIBERTY A Brief History o

An American Dilemma

The Communist Manifesto TH

The Selfish Gene The Structu

The Prince In Cold

The Open Society

Dreams from My Father

A Room of One's Own

Gödel, Escher, Bach A SH

On the Origin of Species Homage

The Death and Life of Great American Ci

CAPITALISM, SOCIALISM and DEMOCRACY BURY M

Up from Slavery THE AUTOB

Eminent Victorians

LET US NOW PRAISE FAMOUS MEN

The Interpretation of Dreams

GOODBYE

The Go

HISTORY PHILOSOPHY SCIENCE BIOGR

NG

IETY ESSAYS

s of Totalitarianism

and Steel THE CIVIL WAR

Black Lamb and Grey Falcon

THE LIBERAL IMAGINATION   BLACK BOY

OF BLACK FOLK   THE GUNS OF AUGUST

Art of Motorcycle Maintenance Nickel and Dimed

Gulag Archipelago The Lives of a Cell

A THEORY OF JUSTICE

ime THE VARIETIES OF RELIGIOUS EXPERIENCE

eral Theory of Employment, Interest and Money

KING OF THE ATOMIC BOMB   OUT OF AFRICA

of Scientific Revolutions

lood THE AUTOBIOGRAPHY OF MALCOLM X

MERE CHRISTIANITY

Confessions FAST FOOD NATION

nt Spring Speak, Memory

TORY OF NEARLY EVERYTHING A Walk in the Woods

The Power Broker

atalonia Capitalism and Freedom

he Making of the English Working Class

WOUNDED KNEE The Omnivore's Dilemma

PHY OF ALICE B TOKLAS

Elements of Style

mation is Beautiful

LL THAT

ough

SOCIAL POLITICAL GUIDEBOOK

sources: Guardian, Times Literary Supplement, NYTimes.com, AskMetafilter.com, Pulitzer.org, ModernLibrary.com, National Review, Time, GoodReads.com
data: bit.ly/KIB_BestNonFiction

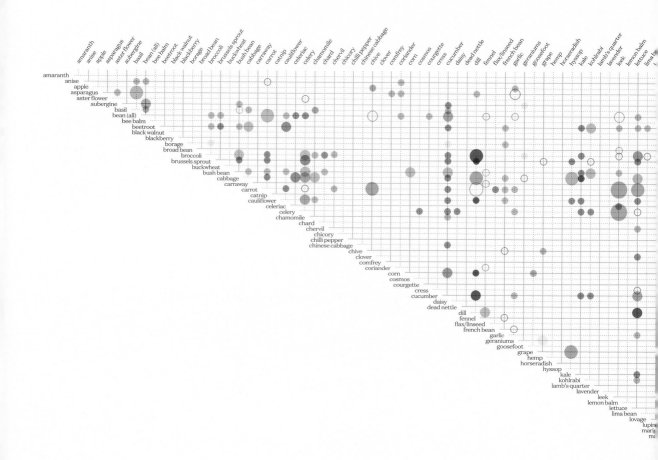

PESTS   attracts ○◑ deters
SOIL   bad for ○◑ good for
HEALTH & GROWTH   stunts ○◑ improves
FLAVOUR   inhibits ○◑ improves
GENERALLY   not good ○● good

◑ shares space well
● good decoy (distracts pests)
○ conflicting evidence
○ mysteriously great companion!

CERTAINTY   (no. of sources that agree)   ① ② ③ ④

Veg Table Bedfellows
Which plants pair well?

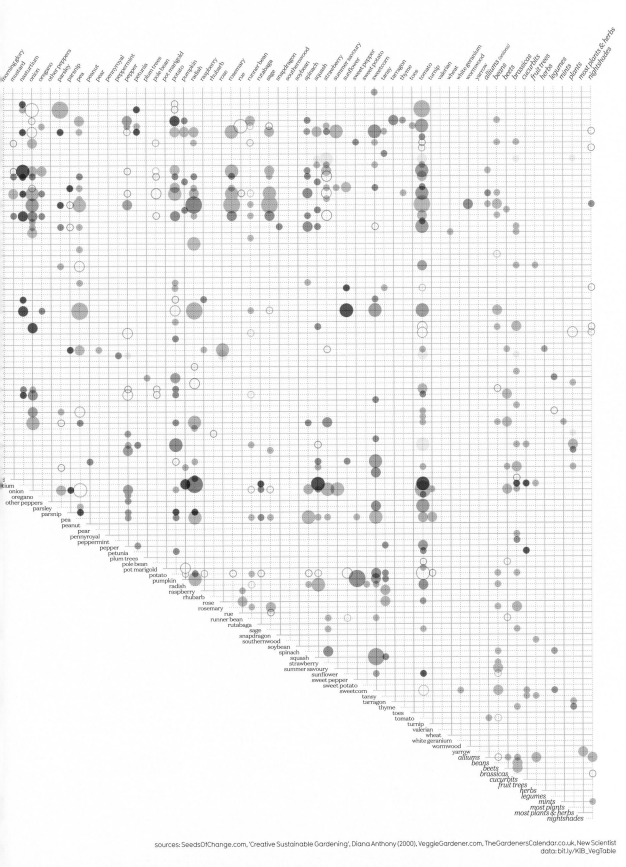

sources: SeedsOfChange.com, 'Creative Sustainable Gardening', Diana Anthony (2000), VeggieGardener.com, TheGardenersCalendar.co.uk, New Scientist
data: bit.ly/KIB_VegTable

Are We Alone in the Galaxy?

The Drake Equation estimates the number of intelligent civilisations in our galaxy

$$N = R* \times f_p \times n_e \times f_l \times f_i \times f_c \times L$$

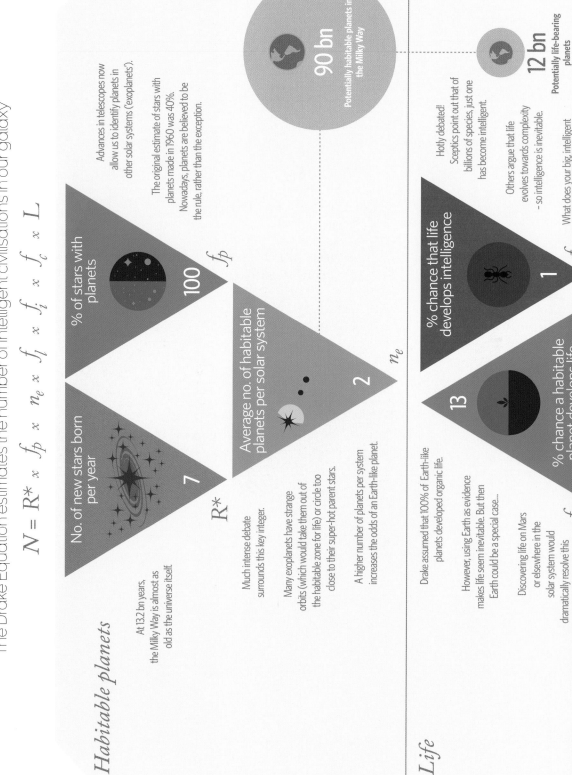

Habitable planets

$R*$

No. of new stars born per year

7

At 13.2 bn years, the Milky Way is almost as old as the universe itself.

Much intense debate surrounds this key integer.

f_p

% of stars with planets

100

Advances in telescopes now allow us to identify planets in other solar systems (exoplanets).

The original estimate of stars with planets made in 1960 was 40%. Nowadays, planets are believed to be the rule, rather than the exception.

n_e

Average no. of habitable planets per solar system

2

Many exoplanets have strange orbits (which would take them out of the habitable zone for life) or circle too close to their super-hot parent stars.

A higher number of planets per system increases the odds of an Earth-like planet.

90 bn

Potentially habitable planets in the Milky Way

Life

% chance that life develops intelligence

1

Hotly debated! Sceptics point out that of billions of species, just one has become intelligent.

Others argue that life evolves towards complexity - so intelligence is inevitable.

What does your big, intelligent

f

% chance a habitable planet develops life

13

Drake assumed that 100% of Earth-like planets developed organic life.

However, using Earth as evidence makes life seem inevitable. But then Earth could be a special case...

Discovering life on Mars or elsewhere in the solar system would dramatically resolve this

f

12 bn

Potentially life-bearing planets

Civilisation

% chance life can communicate across
space

5

f_c

---

optional addition

No. of times civilisation
could re-develop

5

e

This extra allows for the
chance of new civilisations
evolving, after a previous
civilisation has appeared
and ended.

An intuitive addition, if you consider
the billion-year lifespans of planets.

Length of time a civilisation
sends signals into space

10,000
years

L

How long does
a civilisation last?
Could a society overcome
all threats to its survival
and then endure
for millions of years?

Chances

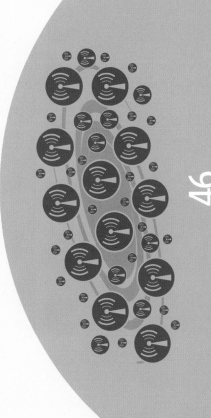

46

communicating civilisations in the galaxy

sources: Mayor et al. (2011), Wolfram Alpha, DiscoverMagazine.com, Wikipedia
data: bit.ly/KIB_AlienLife

6,900,000,000,000,000

(6.9 trillion)

communicating civilisations in the universe

This total is the estimated number of civilisations in our galaxy multiplied by the estimated number of galaxies in the visible universe (at least 150 bn).

sources: Mayor et al. (2011), WolframAlpha, DiscoverMagazine.com, Wikipedia

Astro Killers
Qu'est que c'est?

Comet
'Dirty ice ball' from
the outer solar system.
Can form glowing tail

Asteroid
Inactive, rocky body
originating from the
asteroid belt

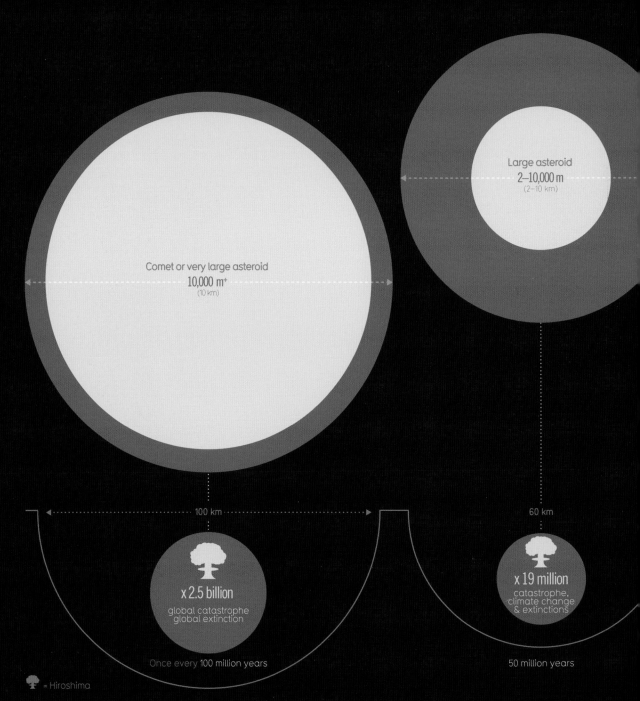

Large asteroid
2–10,000 m
(2–10 km)

Comet or very large asteroid
10,000 m+
(10 km)

100 km

60 km

x 2.5 billion
global catastrophe
global extinction

x 19 million
catastrophe,
climate change
& extinctions

Once every 100 million years

50 million years

= Hiroshima

Meteoroid	**Meteor**	**Meteorite**
Boulder- to bus-sized space debris	'Shooting star' when meteoroid vapourises in the atmosphere	Rock that survives the atmosphere & hits the surface

Small

Very small

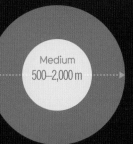

Medium
500–2,000 m

100–499 m

50–99 m

25–49 m

24–1 m

<1 m

12.5 km

 x 282,000+

huge tsunamis

small country-sized
area destroyed

1.2 million years

 x 2,300+

tsunamis

city-sized
area destroyed

75,000 years

x 3

explosion

severe
local damage

3,400 years

sources: NASA, Imperial College / Purdue, B612 Foundation, Space.com
data: bit.ly/KIB_Astrokillers

Astro Attempted Killers
Recent near misses

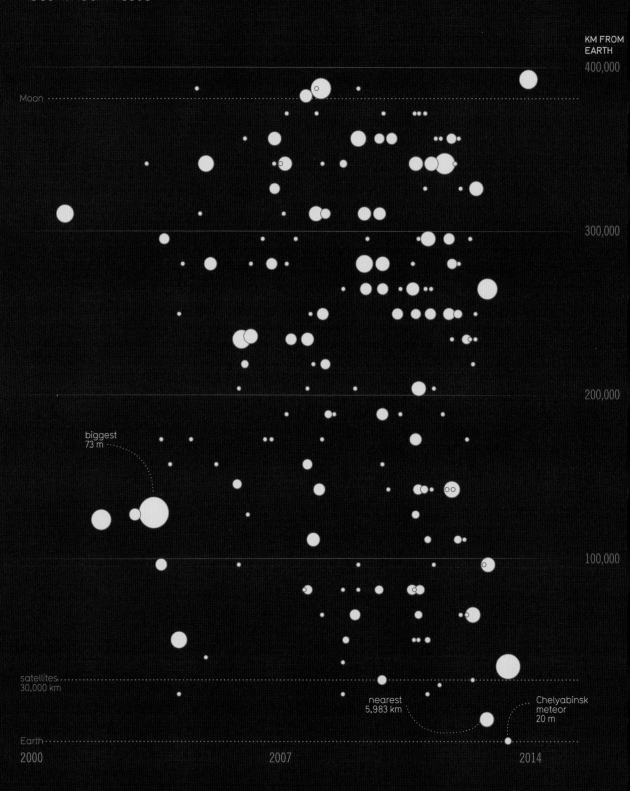

KM FROM
EARTH

400,000

Moon

300,000

biggest
73 m

200,000

satellites
30,000 km

nearest
5,983 km

Chelyabinsk
meteor
20 m

100,000

Earth

2000

2007

2014

Astro-Killer Killers
How could we stop one?

COST

ASTRONOMICAL

STRATOSPHERIC

SKY HIGH

ROCKETING

DOWN TO EARTH

tow it away
dock with a robotic tug-boat & use gravitational forces to shift it off course

attach giant sails & make them adjustable so we can waft the rock off its trajectory

strap-on
land & plant some ol' fashioned rockets on that bad boy & blow it clean away

feed it to nuclear robots who 'chew' through the surface & eject the fragments at high speed into space

armageddon
land Bruce Willis on that mofo & get the job D.O.N.E. Hell yeah!

laser it with a high-powered beam in order to vapourise part of the asteroid & deflect the rest

paint it white
so it feels more 'push' from solar radiation, nudging it gradually off course

use mirrors
to concentrate solar rays & heat the surface. The resultant vapours thrust it off target

nuke it
to deflect it. Not to destroy it, silly (that would create megatonnes of cosmic buckshot)

shoot it
with a 'kinetic interceptor' (i.e. large bullet). Could work if hit 20 years before impact

net it with a carbon-fibre mesh to create additional drag. 18 years of drag would do the job

REALISTIC   IMAGINABLE   FICTIONAL   SCIENCE-FICTIONAL   HOLLYWOOD

TECHNOLOGICAL FEASIBILITY

sources: NASA, Imperial College / Purdue, Discovery.com
data: bit.ly/KIB_Astrokillers

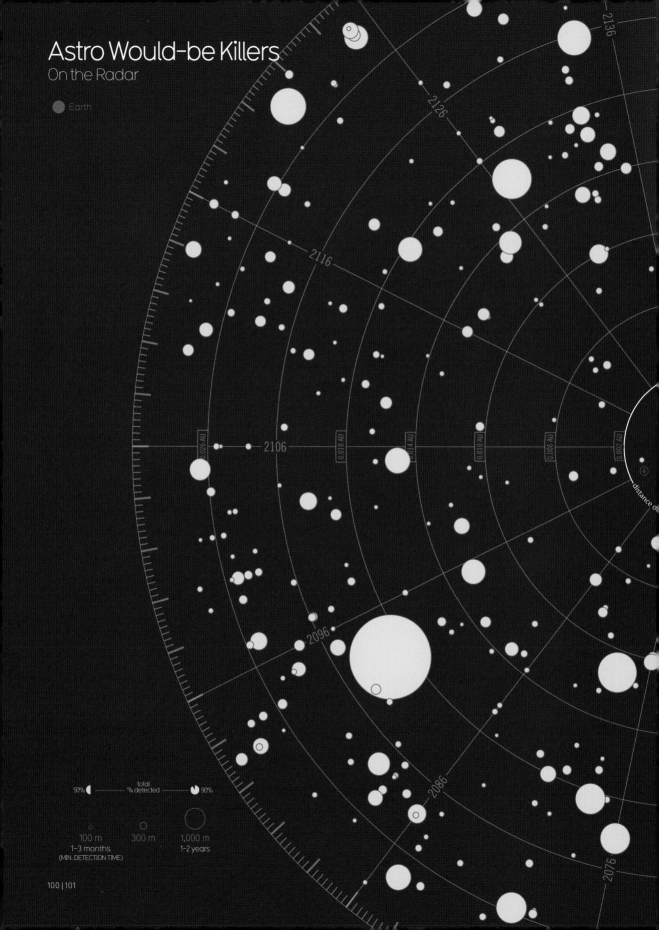

Astro Would-be Killers
On the Radar

● Earth

2136

2126

2116

2106

2096

2086

2076

0.026 AU 0.018 AU 0.014 AU 0.010 AU 0.006 AU 0.002 AU

④

distance o

total
50% ◖ ········· **% detected** ········· ◗ 90%

○ 100 m   ○ 300 m   ○ 1,000 m
1–3 months   **300 m**   **1–2 years**
(MIN. DETECTION TIME)

object name		date		size
①	2001 WN5	JUN	2028	1,100 m
②	Apropis	APR	2029	325 m
③	2005 WY55	MAY	2065	220 m
④	2007 WV56	JAN	2101	unknown

2025

2035

2046

2055

2065

2075

0.002 AU   0.006 AU   0.010 AU   0.014 AU   0.018 AU   0.026 AU

2,500m   5,000m
8 years+

sources: NASA, Earth Impact Effects Program, Asterank.com, minorplanetcenter.net
data: bit.ly/KIB_Astrokillers

(Un) Surprising Studies
Science of the (un)obvious

Cat Owners & Suicide
Women infected by the cat-borne parasite, *T. gondii*, are more likely to hurt & kill themselves.

- 35% self-harm
- 45% violent suicide attempt
- 51% any suicide attempt

source: Archives of General Psychiatry

€273 bn
€68 bn

Kidney Stones
If French sufferers drank 2+ litres of water a day it would save French health-care €68–273bn a year.

British Medical Journal

Never Bee Forgetful
Bees can recognise individual human faces with greater than 80% accuracy.

Experimental Biology

reading speed
20% speed increase
normal   wide
word spacing

Spacing Improves Dyslexia
Extra-wide spacing between letters increases accuracy & reading speed for most sufferers.

National Academy of Sciences

Toilet Training
Dogs urinate & defecate with their bodies aligned to the Earth's north-south magnetic field.

Frontiers in Zoology

Painkiller Kills Vultures
Anti-inflammatory Diclofenac has killed over 95% of India's white-backed vultures.

Nature

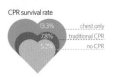

CPR survival rate
13.3% chest only
7.8% traditional CPR
5.2% no CPR

Chest CPR Is Better
Bystanders who perform chest-only CPR, rather than mouth-to-mouth, save 60% more lives.

American Medical Association

No Good Cholesterol?
Contrary to wisdom, high blood levels of 'good' cholesterol do not lower risk of heart attack.

The Lancet

psychosis
depression
eating disorders
bipolar disorder
times more likely

Born to Be Wild
Those born prematurely have a significant risk of later psychiatric problems such as depression.

British Medical Journal

11% transportation
83% growing & production

Eating Local Not Eco
Bulk of the carbon food footprint from growing & producing. Eat less meat if you want to help the planet.

Environmental Science & Tech.

chance of hearing loss
6% drop
13% drop

Deafness Declining
Despite headphones & iPods, hearing loss is decreasing across the generations.

Psychological Science

No Solar Phones
At best, solar power can maintain standby, but cannot supply enough energy for talk time.

Nokia

Plane Tasting
High altitudes impair your taste buds, decrease sensitivity to salty & sour, but increase sweetness.

Aviation, Space, & Env. Medicine

Nonsense for Minds
Absurd, unsettling or uncanny experiences prime the brain to sense unusual patterns.

Psychological Science

Born in Winter Thickie?
Those born in Dec–Feb are on average less intelligent, less educated, less healthy & lower paid.

Nat. Bureau of Economic Research

Lightning x Shrooms
A bolt of lightning-strength electricity doubles yields of 8 mushrooms, particularly nameko & shiitake.

Japan Society of Plasma Science

69% increased mortality
28%
4%
4-8 8-11 11+
hours sitting daily

Desk Jobs Kill
No matter how much you exercise, sitting too much raises your risk of death.

Archives of Internal Medicine

You're Not Tired!
The feeling of exhaustion is not determined by muscle failure but by belief that you're 'at your limit'.

European Journal of Applied Physiology

School Womb
Unborn babies learn speech in the womb. Newborn cries already carry the tonal lilt of their mother's language.

Current Biology

⟵ Most Surprising

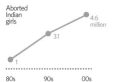

Aborting Girls in India
The selective abortion of female babies is increasing, becoming commonplace in India.

The Lancet

US Quickest Drugs
Nearly 60% of new drugs were approved by US regulators before any other nation.

New England Journal of Medicine

Gay Soldiers OK
Openly gay service members did not lower morale, cause resignations or mass 'comings out'

University of Santa Barbara

Cardio = Success
Physical fitness at age 18 predicts greater socio-economic & educational success.

National Academy of Sciences

Runny Mummies
Exercise prevents excessive weight gain for pregnant mums, both during & after pregnancy.

British Medical Journal

Signs of Lying Bosses
They're more likely to use extreme emotional words such as 'fantastic' rather than 'good' when lying.

The Lancet

Working Pregnancy Hurts
Average of 6% lower birth weight in babies whose mothers worked in the last month of pregnancy.

Journal of Labour Economics

Fat-Ass Neighbourhoods
Living in a less poor neighbourhood modestly but noticeably increases obesity & diabetes.

New England Journal of Medicine

Coral Reefs Are Dead
They will cease to exist within a generation, due to overfishing, pollution & acidification.

Science

Racists Are Stupid
Low childhood intelligence predicts greater racism in adulthood, usually via a right-wing ideology.

Psychological Science

45-m Nap Boosts Brain
Not only refreshes your mind, but makes you smarter & better able to absorb information.

Sleep Medicine

Love Costs Two Friends
A new partner pushes out two close friends on average for both men & women.

Personal Relationships

Nagging Wives Save Lives
Married men with heart disease sought hospital help earlier than single men.

British Medical Journal

Brainstorming No Good
'No criticism' policies during idea generation are less effective than debate scenarios.

University of California

Self-Control = Success
Childhood self-control predicts good health, financial success & low criminality.

National Academy of Sciences

Macho Men Most Wanted
By unhealthy women. Whereas women in the healthiest countries prefer men with feminine features.

Proceedings of the Royal Society

No Cell Phone Cancer
Study followed 16 million people for 29 years. Found no increased incidence of brain cancer.

National Cancer Institute

Northerners Cleverer?
Those at high latitudes have bigger eyes & brains to cope with poorer light. But they are not smarter.

Royal Society: Biology

Teenage Drinkers Happier
Suffer more family, psychological & school problems. But have better, higher-quality friends.

Scandinavian Public Health

Least Surprising

data: bit.ly/KIB_NoWay

Who Old Are You?
Average ages

5 10 15 20 25 30 35 40 45 50

First marriage (India) — (UK) — (US)
Peak cognitive / brain function — (US)
Leave parental home (UK) — Become a father (UK)
Buy first house (1960, UK) — (2011, UK)
Mozart: Symphony No. 1 in E flat — Become a mother (UK)
Young carer (UK) — Develop OCD (US) — Have second child (UK)
Schizophrenia (US) — Depression (US)
Begin puberty
Undergo IVF (UK)
Football club manager (UK)
First try smoking (US) — Diabetes, type I (US) — Martin Scorsese: Taxi Driver — Van Gogh: Sunflowers
First drink (UK) — (US) — Go to prison (UK) — File for bankruptcy (US) — (UK) — Monaco resident
Lose homosexual virginity (UK) — Hair starts to turn grey — Historian — Breast cancer (black women, UK)
Lose heterosexual virginity (UK) — Dickens: Oliver Twist — UK public think middle age begins — Nurse
(US) — Quit smoking — US public think middle age begins — Darwin: The Origin of Species
Bipolar disorder (Europe & US) — City trader — Barrister (freelance, UK) — Barrister (employed, UK)
Soldier (UK) — Mathematician — Veterinary nurse — Doctor (UK)
First smoke cannabis (UK) — (US) — (US) — Pepys wrote his diary — (US) — First grandchild
Gain wisdom teeth (UK)
Supermodel — Maths teacher (UK) — Vet (UK)
Steven Spielberg's first film — Chess player — Design & technology teacher (UK)
Picasso: Les Demoiselles d'Avignon — History teacher (UK) — Academic (UK) — (US)
Tenzin Gyatso becomes current Dalai Lama — Major League baseball player — Golfer — French / German teachers (UK) — Vicar (UK)
Gymnast — Teacher (average age, secondary, UK) — Headteacher / Principal (US)
(UK)
Einstein formulates E = mc² — Michelangelo: Sistine Chapel
George III becomes King of England — Advertising exec (US) — (UK) — TV presenter (UK)
Footballer (UK) — Pulitzer Prize-winning authors
Cleopatra ascends to throne of Egypt — Oscar-winning actors
NBA basketball player
Youngest Olympic gold medallist — Win the Tour de France — Shakespeare: The Tempest
Marie Antoinette becomes Queen of France — Tennis player — McCandless: Information is Beautiful
Alexander the Great ascends to throne of Macedonia — Primary-school headteacher
Poet — Chris Hoy becomes Britain's most successful Olympian — Secondary-school headteacher
NFL American football player
Ice hockey player (US & Canada)
London Marathon winners — Physics teacher (UK)
Swimmer
Average London 2012 Olympics competitor
Usain Bolt's first Olympic gold medal
Jessica Ennis wins Olympic heptathlon (2012)
Nadia Comaneci's perfect 10 — Shakespeare: Romeo and Juliet — John F. Kennedy becomes POTUS
Michael Phelps's first and last Olympic medals
Mo Farah wins Olympic 5,000 m and 10,000 m (2012)
Elizabeth II becomes Queen of England — Marcus Aurelius becomes Roman Emperor
Popstar (UK)
Member of Parliament (UK)
J. D. Salinger: Catcher in the Rye
Tutankhamen ascends to throne of Egypt

Divorce (UK) — Stanley Kubrick: The Shining
Remarry after divorce (UK) — Woody Allen: Annie Hall
Peak dexterity — Creative / intellectual peak
Charlie Chaplin: City Lights — Buy second home
Found tech startup (US) — Oil-rig worker (UK) — (Asia) — Menopause (UK)

5 10 15 20 25 30 35 40 45 50

Life moments   Career high   Creative zenith   Wordly success   Health issues

youngest — average age — oldest

55 60 65 70 75 80 85 90 95 100

Mortgage paid!
Retirement
Supreme Court judge (US)
High Court judge (UK)
public think old age begins   Cataract surgery   (UK)
US public think old age begins
Parkinson's onset (US)   Alzheimer's onset (US)   (diagnosis, US)
First heart attack (US)

Da Vinci: Mona Lisa   First stroke (US)   (UK)
(US)   Lung cancer (UK)
(white / all women, UK)   (US)
Skin cancer (US)   Prostate cancer (US)
Diabetes, type II (US)   Die   Die (UK)
Retire (UK)   Stomach cancer (US)
Picasso: Guernica   Cancer diagnosis (US)   Retirement home resident age (US)   Old peoples' home resident age (UK)
Hitchcock: Vertigo   Leukaemia (US)
Nobel Prize Medicine
David Lynch: Mulholland Drive   Richard Strauss: Four Last Songs
Farmer (US)   (China)
Clint Eastwood wins Oscar for Best Director
Bishop (UK)
Nobel Prize winner   Nelson Mandela becomes president of SA
Farmer (UK)
Senator (US)
Be a millionaire (UK)

Oldest Olympic gold medallist
Oldest competitor at London 2012 Olympics
CEO, large company   Chairman, large company
Director, large company   Age of death: athletes (average, US)
Serving leader (EU)   Performers
(Central America)   Authors, composers, artists
(S. America / N. America)   Politicians
(Africa)   Business people
Military people
Nobel Prize Physics
Member on Board of Directors committee
Nobel Prize Economics
Nobel Prize Chemistry
Nobel Prize Peace
Nobel Prize Literature
Chinese politburo committee member
Tolkien: The Lord of the Rings   Richest man in the world   Oldest Pulitzer Prize winner   Oldest marathon runner (100y, 6m)
Member of House of Lords
Member of House of Representatives (US)

55 60 65 70 75 80 85 90 95 100

sources: Jones & Weinberg (2011), Guardian, Office for National Statistics, Forbes, CIA World Factbook, 'Guinness World Records', Wikipedia
data: bit.ly/KIB_WhoOldAreYou

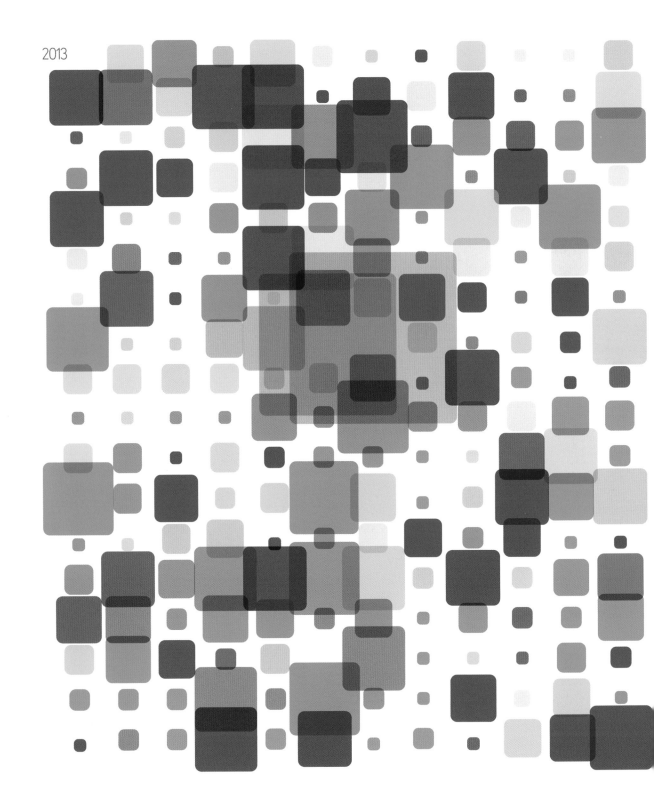

2013

Plane Truth

Fatal commercial passenger-plane crashes of the last 20 years

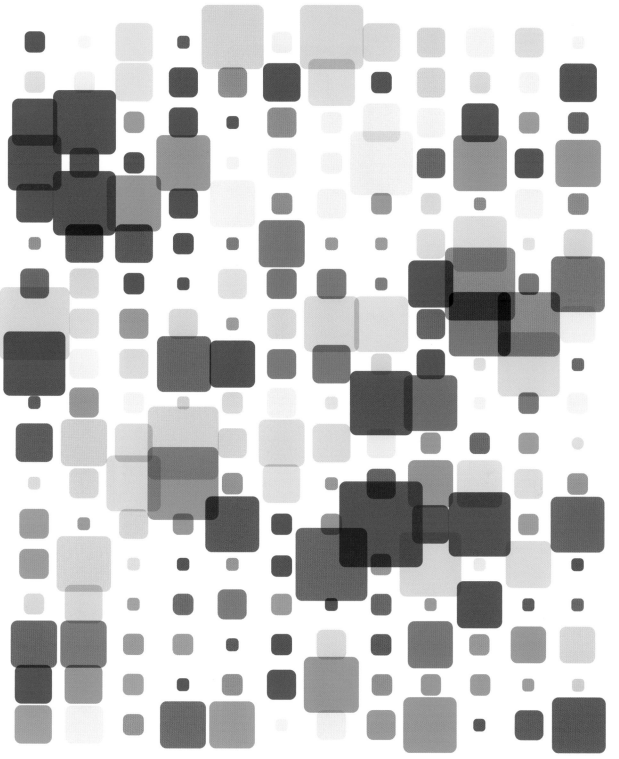

1993

Human Error | Weather | Mechanical | Unknown | Criminal | 9 / 11

lighter = less certain

1–5
6–15
31–50
fatalities 81–125

source: Aviation Safety Network, news reports
data: bit.ly/KIB_PlaneCrashes

Crash Cause

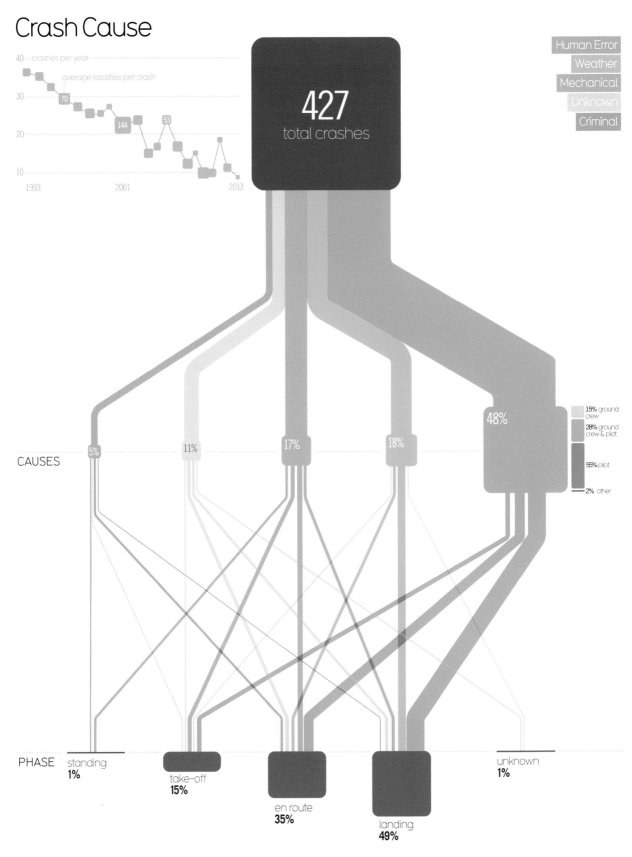

40 · crashes per year

average fatalities per crash

70

30

144

53

20

10

1993   2001   2013

427
total crashes

Human Error
Weather
Mechanical
Unknown
Criminal

15% ground crew
28% ground crew & pilot
56% pilot
2% other

CAUSES

5%   11%   17%   18%   48%

PHASE   standing
1%

take-off
15%

en route
35%

landing
49%

unknown
1%

Worst Planes

MODEL	SIZE	PROPORTION OF CRASH CAUSES	NO. OF INCIDENTS	ENTERED SERVICE
DHC-3 Otter				1952
Fokker F27 Friendship 200				
Hawker Siddeley HS 748-216 Srs				
Antonov 24				
Boeing 727				
Douglas DC-9				
DHC-6 Twin Otter				
Tupolev 134A				
Boeing 737				
Yakovlev 40				
Boeing 747				
Let L-410UVP				
Airbus A300				
Swearingen SA226 TC Metro II				
Tupolev 154B				
Tupolev 154M				
Embraer 110P1 Bandeirante				
Beechcraft 200 Super King Air				
McDonnell Douglas MD-82				
Boeing 767				
Dornier 228				
Harbin Yunshuji Y-12 II				
Airbus A310				
Beechcraft 1900D				
Boeing 757				
Saab 340B				
ATR-42				
Antonov 28				
Airbus A320				
Fokker 100				
ATR-72				
Canadair CL 600-2B19				1992

source: Aviation Safety Network, news reports
data: bit.ly/KIB_PlaneCrashes

Table Sugar

sugars

smaller is better

◯ = bad

name	what is it?	where found?	detail
Sucrose	table sugar		
Lactose	milk sugar	dairy products	up to 75% of adults have some lactose intolerance
Fructose	fruit sugar	dates, apples, oranges, etc	skips metabolic control so easily transformed into fat
Glucose	body sugar	sugar beet	
Honey	mix of fructose & glucose	bees	antiseptic & antibacterial
Molasses	dark treacle made from refined sugar cane	sugar cane	unsulphured version is high in minerals & B vitamins
Maple Syrup	mostly sucrose (> 60%)	maple-tree sap	like wine, varies widely in taste & quality
Galactose	plant sugar	dairy & beets	absorbed directly into blood, less harmful than fructose
Dextrose	plant sugar	honey, grapes	excellent for physical & mental exercise, kills hunger
Corn Syrup	processed starch, with short glucose chains	corn	easily dissolved in water so heavily used in soft drinks
High-Fructose Corn Syrup	fructose & glucose combined	corn	bypasses insulin response so may lead to over-eating
Maltodextrin	processed starch in long glucose chains	corn, wheat	often used as a 'hidden' sugar in ingredients
Maltose	plant sugar	barley, wheat, beer, malt shakes	very bad for diabetics
Inulin	plant-root sugar	chicory	often used in junk foods, can causes gas & bloating
Golden Syrup	pale treacle	sugar cane	excellent for cooking
Trehalose	insect sugar		natural preservative with unusual properies
Barley Malt Syrup	mostly maltose	barley, beer, bagels	good source of fibre
Coconut Sugar	mostly sucrose	flower buds of coconut palm	high levels of potassium, iron, magnesium, zinc & B vitamins
Sorghum Syrup	plant sugar	sweet sorghum	good for cooking, decent

Column headers (graphical circle data): sweetness vs. sucrose (0, 10x, 100x, 1000x) · glycaemic index (GI) blood sugar effects · calories per tsp · diabetics · bad for? (sports, diets, teeth, health, cooking)

alcohols

sweeteners

	(55%–90%)	mostly maltose	rice
Brown Rice Syrup			agave cactus — as pure fructose
Oligofructose	fructose extract	Jerusalem artichokes, bananas	health food in Japan, improves gut absorption
Inverted Sugar	modified sugar, glucose & fructose	jam, some alcoholic drinks	
Erythritol	sugar alcohol	fermented glucose	lowest laxative effect of all sweeteners
Hydrogenated Starch Hydrolysate	mix of several sugar alcohols		
Isomalt	sugar alcohol	chewing gum, cough drops, chocolate	good source of fibre
Lactitol	processed lactose	sugar-free candy, biscuits & ice cream	strong laxative effect
Maltitol	hydrogenated maltose	hard sweets, chewing gum, ice cream	
Mannitol	ash-tree sugar	chewing gum, dried fruits, tablets	some people allergic; mixer agent for cocaine
Sorbitol	processed fructose from corn syrup	apples, pears, peaches, prunes	laxative, don't give to dogs
Tagatose	processed galactose		tooth friendly, flavour enhancer, beneficial for gut
Xylitol	natural sugar alcohol	oats, berries & mushrooms	occurs naturally in fruit & veg fibre, antibacterial, good for teeth
Acesulfame-K	a potassium salt		paired with aspartame to cancel bitter aftertaste
Aspartame	processed version of natural amino-acids		most thoroughly tested, deemed safe in 90 countries
Cyclamate	a calcium salt	dates, apples, oranges, etc	
Neotame	chemical cousin of aspartame		more stable & sweeter than aspartame
Saccharin	aka 'Sweet'N Low' a calcium salt		probably safest sweetener (120+ years of use), can't cook it
Sucralose	aka 'Splenda'—chlorinated sucrose	processed food & drink	some people allergic, good for cooking
Glycyrrhizin	licorice sweetener	licorice root	host of health benefits, sweetness survives heat, so used to flavour cigarettes
Luo Han Guo	plant sweetener	monk fruit of SE Asia	treatment for sore throats, not yet approved in EU
Stevia	plant sweetener	Stevia plant of S. America	laxative effect, traditional use in Brazil & Paraguay

100x. 1000x.

sources: American Journal of Clinical Nutrition, American Diabetes Association
data: bit.ly/KIB_Sugar

How **much** your blood sugar rises (glycaemic load)

BAD

Vegetables
Pasta, rice & grains
Dairy & proteins
Snacks & fast food
Nuts & pulses
Bread & baked goods
Fruits & syrups

Short-grain white rice

Lucozade

Risotto rice

Combine carbs
with fats to
soften spikes

Macaroni & cheese

Oatmeal (instant)

Rice milk

Raisins   Basmati rice

Mars bar   Fruit Roll-Ups

Vanilla cake   Bagel   Boiled potatoes

Macaroni   Fanta   Baked potatoes   Cornflakes

White spaghetti   Cream of Wheat instant   Jelly beans

Chips   Sweet potato   Pizza (cheese & tomato)

McDonald's Fillet-O-Fish burger

Yam   Corn on the cob   Coco Pops
Dates   Snickers   Yoghurt (low-fat)   Potato (instant mashed)
Sponge cake   Ribena   Cream of Wheat   Puffed wheat   Rice cakes
Wholemeal spaghetti   Muesli   Grapenuts   Pretzels, oven-baked

OKAY

Brown Rice   Bananas   Coca-Cola   Doughnut
Fettucini   Cranberry juice   Special K   Graham crackers   Baguette
White rice (converted)   Banana cake, with sugar   Porridge (small oats)   Vanilla wafers
Apple juice   Quinoa   Oatmeal   Honey
Orange juice   Corn tortilla   All Bran   Raisin Bran   Soda crackers
Pearl barley   Crisps   Banana cake, no sugar   Kaiser roll   Gatorade
Bulgur wheat   Bread, 50% cracked wheat   Cream crackers
Whole wheat kernels   Corn chips   Grapes   Rye crisps
Prunes   Blackeye peas   Soy milk   Porridge (jumbo)   Hamburger bun   Waffles   Popcorn
Chickpeas (canned)   Barley bread   Chicken nuggets   Shortbread   Pitta bread   Whole wheat bread
Navy beans   Apples   Baked beans   Couscous   White bread
Wheat tortilla   M & M's   Peaches (canned)   Pumpernickel bread   Sunflower bread
Black beans   peanut   Peaches   Pears (canned)   Pineapple
Kidney beans   Pears   Full-fat milk   Ice cream (regular)
Lentils   Dried apricots   Oranges   Rye bread
Chickpeas   Custard (home-made)   Parsnips   Watermelon
Greek yoghurt   Cashew nuts   Tomato juice   Green peas
Agave syrup   Red lentils   Skimmed milk   Butternut squash
Peanuts   Ice cream (premium)
Hummus   Soy beans   Grapefruit   Carrot   Ice cream (premium)

GOOD   OKAY   BAD

How **quickly** your blood sugar goes up
(glycaemic index)

Glycaemix   Which foods spike your blood sugar

Teaspoons

ORANGE	LARGE CARTON
APPLE JUICE	LARGE CARTON
COCA-COLA	MEDIUM BOTTLE
MANGO JUICE	LARGE CARTON
FRUIT SMOOTHIE	LARGE CARTON
COCA-COLA	SMALL BOTTLE
LATTE	MEDIUM CUP
CAPPUCCINO	MEDIUM CUP
MOCHA	MEDIUM CUP
LUCOZADE	BOTTLE
BEER	SMALL BOTTLE
COCONUT WATER	SMALL CARTON
FANTA	CAN
GINGER BEER	CAN
SPRITE	CAN
DR PEPPER / 7-UP	CAN
COCA-COLA	CAN
MOUNTAIN DEW	LARGE CAN
FLAT WHITE	SHORT CUP
WHITE WINE	LARGE GLASS
RED WINE	LARGE GLASS
TOMATO JUICE	GLASS
MILK	GLASS
ORANGE JUICE	GLASS
APPLE JUICE	GLASS
FRUIT SMOOTHIE	GLASS
CRANBERRY JUICE	GLASS
GRAPEFRUIT JUICE	SMALL CARTON
APPLE JUICE	SMALL CARTON
FRUIT SHOOT	BOTTLE
MANGO JUICE	SMALL CARTON
CRANBERRY JUICE	SMALL CARTON
WHISKY	SINGLE

3g

recommended daily max

recommended daily max

average American
daily consumption

sources: Atkinson (2008), Holt (1997, 1995), our own calcs
data: bit.ly/KIB_Sugar

Superpower Showdown
Social economics

	China	EU	India	USA
PUBLIC HEALTH SPEND % OF GDP	8.5	17.9	3.9	5.2
DOCTORS PER 1,000 PEOPLE	1.4	3.3	0.6	2.4
HIV / AIDS DEATHS PER 100,000 PEOPLE	0.3	0.9	1.3	0.2
PEOPLE WITH HIV / AIDS PER 100,000 PEOPLE	8	22	21	12
ACCESS TO CLEAN DRINKING WATER % OF POPULATION	92%	99%	92%	99%
OBESE PEOPLE % OF POPULATION	5.7	17.0	1.9	33.0
UNDERWEIGHT CHILDREN % OF 0–5 YEARS OLD	3.4%	1.9%	43.5%	1.3%
OVERWEIGHT CHILDREN % OF 0–5 YEARS OLD	4.3%	21%	1.6%	4.5%
OVERWEIGHT CHILDREN % OF 5–17 YEARS OLD	5%	19%	19%	35%
WOMEN USING CONTRACEPTION % 15–49 YEARS OLD	84.6%	73.6%	54.8%	78.6%
UNEMPLOYMENT % LABOUR FORCE UNEMPLOYED	6%	10%	9%	7%
BELOW POVERTY LINE % OF POPULATION (SET BY COUNTRY)	13.4%	8.8%	29.8%	15.1%
INEQUALITY INDEX LOWER NUMBER = GREATER EQUALITY	48.0	30.7	36.8	45.3
GENDER INEQUALITY INDEX LOWER NUMBER = GREATER EQUALITY	0.2	0.1	0.6	0.3
SCORE	4	6	2	3

THE EU WINS THIS ROUND!

Superpower Showdown
Economics

	China	EU	India	USA
GDP PER CAPITA INTERNATIONAL DOLLARS	$9,800	$34,500	$4,000	$52,800
GDP GROWTH YEARLY %	7.6	0.0	3.8	1.6
CURRENT ACCOUNT $ BILLION GAIN / LOSS	+$176	-34	-75	-360
PUBLIC DEBT % GDP, ROUNDED	32	85	52	72
TAXES & OTHER REVENUES % GDP	23.1	40.6	10.3	17.0
VALUE OF EXPORTS % GDP	17	14	6	9
DIRECT FOREIGN INVESTMENT $ BILLION	253	295	24	204
INTEREST RATE LENDING %	6.0	0.75	10.6	3.3
BILLIONAIRES % OF WORLD'S	9	28	3	30
SCORE	5	2	0	2

CHINA EARNS THE MOST POINTS!

sources: 'CIA World Factbook', World Bank, Eurostat
data: bit.ly/KIB_Superpowers

Common Mythconceptions II
Most contagious falsehoods

Caffeine dehydrates you
Not really. The diuretic effect of caffeine is offset by the amount of water in a caffeinated drink.

Left & right brain areas
No solid division between brain hemispheres; left brain can learn 'right brain' functions & vice-versa.

Lightning never strikes...
No reason why it wouldn't; the Empire State Building gets hit about 100 times per year.

Sugar = hyperactivity
Studies have disproved this. ADHD still occurs in children with sugar-free diets.

Vaccines cause autism
Groundless fears based on fraudulent research that's been shown to have been manipulated.

Dropped pennies kill
Terminal velocity of a penny is 30–50 mph, which isn't fast enough. It would hurt, though.

Alcohol keeps you warm
Dilates warm blood vessels near the skin, creating the impression of warmth. It can drop core body temp.

Only 10% of our brains
Misunderstood metaphor. Only about 10% of neurons will be firing at one time. But all cells are important.

Why oceans are blue
Not because they reflect the sky. Absorption & scattering of light causes the blue colour.

Satan rules Hell
Doesn't say this anywhere in the Bible.

Milk increases mucous
Nope. It just straight doesn't. There's no need to avoid dairy if you have a cold.

Salty water boils quicker
Adding a sprinkle of salt to fresh water makes no difference. Sea-level amounts do.

Vegetarians & protein
Protein in eggs, beans, vegetables is easily enough for health. Vegans need B-12 supplements though.

Get warts from toads
Warts are a uniquely human phenomenon. Toads don't have them. And can't give them. Even if you kiss them.

Multiple personalities
Schizophrenia technically means 'split-mind', but it is different to multi-personality disorder.

7 years to digest
The chewy base of gum is indigestible, & passes straight through. The remainder is absorbed.

Washington & weed
He grew hemp to make rope & clothes, but there's no evidence he smoked a phat one most nights.

Black belts are masters
Only introduced in 1880, in Judo, to show competence in basic techniques. Not ninja-level mastery.

No sex before the game!
No evidence sex impairs athletic performance. Could even help males because of increased testosterone.

Flushed water rotation
Does not rotate the other way in the S. hemisphere. The Coriolis effect doesn't affect water in toilets.

Bubbles sized according to virulence of idea

 **Jesus born 25 Dec**
Christmas Day was made
official date in 350 CE.
Maybe based on winter
solstice. Or just made up.

 'Elementary, my dear Watson'
Never said in the original
stories. First used in the
1929 film.

 Banana-peel high
That you can get high
smoking banana skins
is a hoax, perpetuated
through the internet.

 The Three Wise Men
Nowhere in the New
Testament does it
specify there were three.

 Edison invented lightbulbs
Made the first practical
lightbulb, but was
obsolete within a year.
England's Joseph Swan
patented them.

 Photographic memories
No hard scientific
evidence, but camera-like
memory is unlikely. Some
people just have great
memories.

 Immaculate Conception
Does not refer to the
Virgin Birth. Instead it
means Mary was not
subject to original sin.

 Ford invented cars
Nah. He just improved
the design, mostly by
supporting the work
of his employees.

 LSD stays in spinal fluid
LSD is eliminated by the
body in under 10 hours.

 Alcohol kills brain cells
Only in heavy users &
alcoholics who rely on
alcohol to get most of
their calories.

 Macs can't get viruses
Yes they can – just less
frequently than Windows
computers.

 Shampoo 'repairs' hair
Nothing can fix split ends
or damaged hair. It can
prevent future damage
& make hair look better.

 Houseflies live 24 hours
Average lifespan is
about a month.
Maggots hatch within
24 hours, actually.

 Planes sky-dump waste
They're emptied on
ground. Blue ice is
accidental. Trains, though,
used to dump on the
tracks. Filthy trains.

 Fatwa = death sentence
It actually means 'non-
binding legal opinion'.

 Martyrs & 72 virgins
A matter of debate in
Islam. Nowhere in the
Qu'ran, but is reported in
other texts.

 Genes & personality
Oversimplification. Single
genes do not exist for
different personality
traits. There is no 'gay
gene', etc.

 Jihad is 'holy war'
It actually translates
as 'struggle'.

 Arts   Cooking   Language   Mind   Religion   Sport

Body & Drugs   History   Law   Nature   Science   Technology

sources: NASA, NYTimes.com, Snopes.com, Wikipedia
data: bit.ly/KIB_Mythconception

The Point

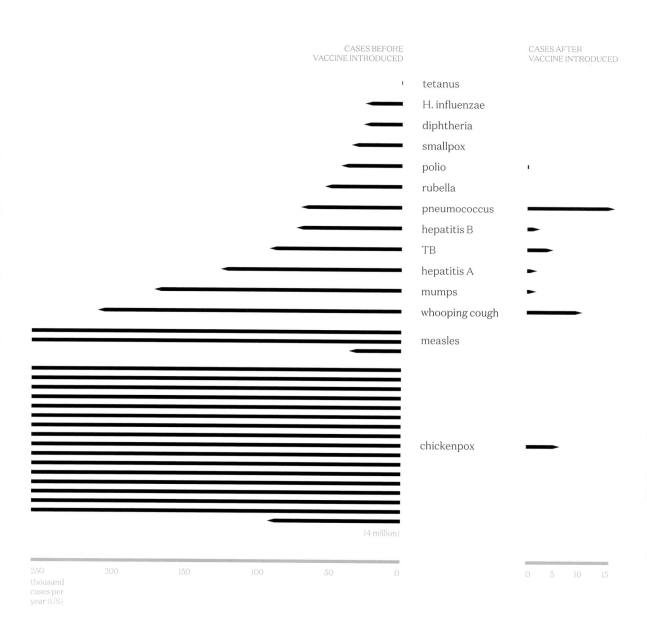

CASES BEFORE
VACCINE INTRODUCED

CASES AFTER
VACCINE INTRODUCED

tetanus
H. influenzae
diphtheria
smallpox
polio
rubella
pneumococcus
hepatitis B
TB
hepatitis A
mumps
whooping cough
measles

chickenpox

(4 million)

250
thousand
cases per
year (US)   200   150   100   50   0

0   5   10   15

sources: Centers for Disease Control & Prevention
data: bit.ly/KIB_Vaccines

which sandwich?

curveball

exciter / acidifier

herb / spice

green veg / herbs

fruit / veg 2

sauce

fruit / veg 1

secondary

primary ingredient

type of
sandwich

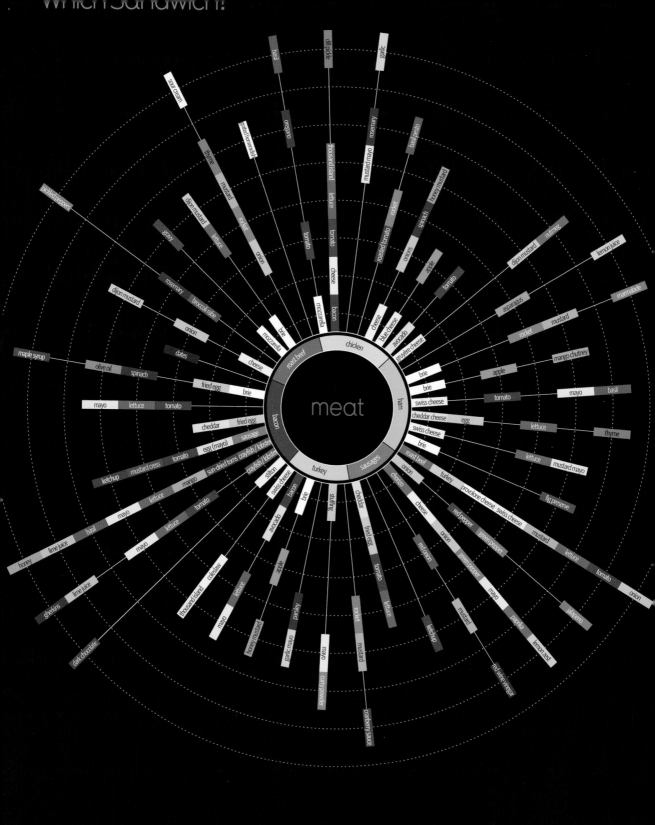

fish

tuna · anchovies · cod · crab · crayfish / lobster · mackerel · prawns · smoked salmon · sardine · trout

sources: Yummly.com, BBC Good Food, AllRecipes.com
data: bit.ly/KIB_Sandwiches

cheese
& egg

feta goat's swiss
egg (mayo) brie
cheddar
mozzarella
any cheese

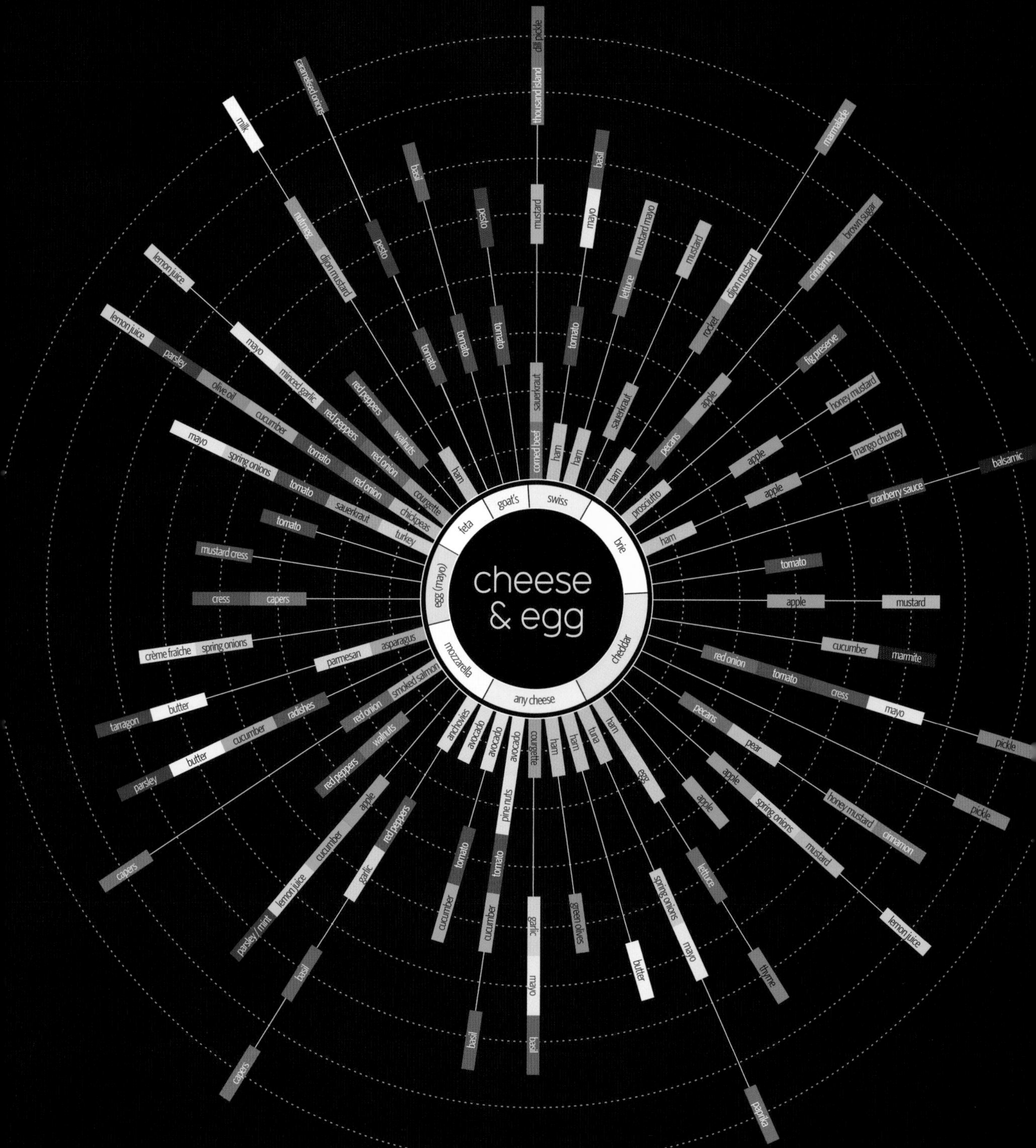

veg

sources: Yummly.com, BBC Good Food, AllRecipes.com
data: bit.ly/KIB_Sandwiches

Person Years

It would take one person...

ANCIENT

St Peter's
Basilica
300,000
person years

The Taj
Mahal
128,000

The
Colosseum
160,000

The Great
Pyramids
4,000,000

PRE-INDUSTRIAL

The Panama
Canal
387,000

INDUSTRIAL

The US Interstate
Highway
330,000

Person years

Number of workers ⟶

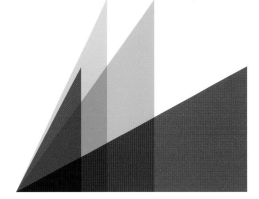

POST-INDUSTRIAL

| The First Atomic Bomb 330,000 | The Trans-Alaskan Pipeline 560,000 | The Apollo Moon Landing 3,268,000 | The Large Hadron Collider 140,000 | The Three Gorges Dam 340,000 | The 2012 Olympic Park 322,000 | Wikipedia .org 140,000 |

Personal Transport

Costs per hour of driving

VEHICLE	SMALL	ESTATE	SPORTS	MOTORHOME / RV	4x4 / SUV
Example model	Volkswagen Golf R	Subaru Outback	Mazda MX5	Chevrolet Express 2500	Chevrolet Suburban

COST PER HOUR

	SMALL	ESTATE	SPORTS	MOTORHOME / RV	4x4 / SUV
HEAVY USE 25,000 miles (~40,000 km) per year	$14	$12	$14	$21	$16
inc. depreciation (if new car)	$22	$17	$19	$41	$26
AVERAGE USE 12,500 m (~20,000 km)	$18	$16	$19	$28	$22
inc. depreciation	$35	$27	$30	$69	$42
LIGHT USE 5,000 m (~8000 km)	$30	$29	$32	$47	$37
inc. depreciation	$70	$55	$58	$147	$85

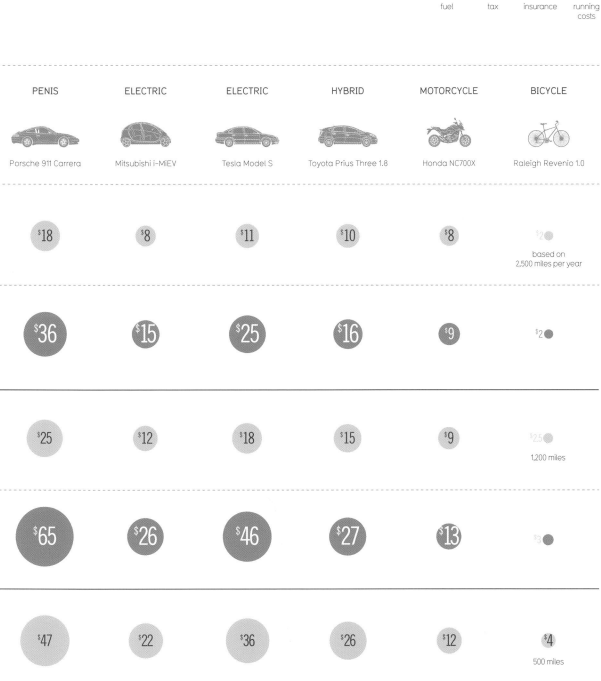

| fuel | tax | insurance | running costs |

	PENIS	ELECTRIC	ELECTRIC	HYBRID	MOTORCYCLE	BICYCLE
	Porsche 911 Carrera	Mitsubishi i-MiEV	Tesla Model S	Toyota Prius Three 1.8	Honda NC700X	Raleigh Revenio 1.0
fuel	$18	$8	$11	$10	$8	$2 based on 2,500 miles per year
tax	$36	$15	$25	$16	$9	$2
insurance	$25	$12	$18	$15	$9	$2.5 1,200 miles
running	$65	$26	$46	$27	$13	$3
	$47	$22	$36	$26	$12	$4 500 miles
	$141	$56	$105	$55	$21	$6

sources: US Energy Information Administration, The AA (UK), American Automobile Association
data: bit.ly/KIB_CarCosts

Snake Oil Baddies?

Solid scientific evidence for harmful foods and substances

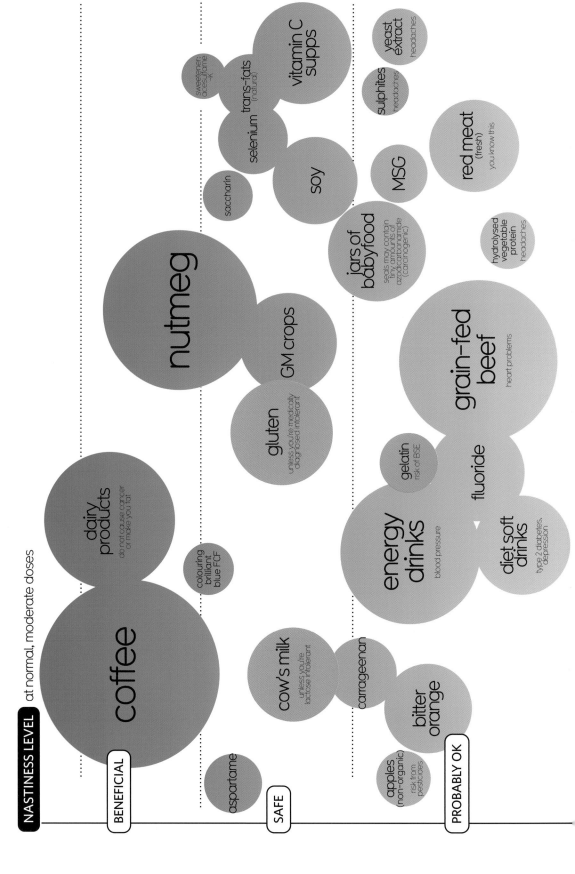

Popularity
(Google hits)

if allergic

NASTINESS LEVEL at normal, moderate doses

BENEFICIAL

coffee

dairy products
do not cause cancer
or make you fat

colouring
brilliant
blue FCF

nutmeg

gluten
unless you're medically
diagnosed intolerant

GM crops

jars of babyfood
seals may contain
tiny amounts of
azodicarbonamide
(carcinogenic)

saccharin

sweetener:
acesulfame
-K

selenium

trans-fats
(natural)

vitamin C supps

yeast extract
headaches

sulphites
headaches

soy

MSG

red meat
(fresh)
you know this

hydrolysed
vegetable
protein
headaches

SAFE

aspartame

cow's milk
unless you're
lactose intolerant

carrageenan

bitter orange

energy drinks
blood pressure

gelatin
risk of BSE

grain-fed beef
heart problems

fluoride

diet soft drinks
type 2 diabetes,
depression

PROBABLY OK

apples
(non-organic)
risk from
pesticides

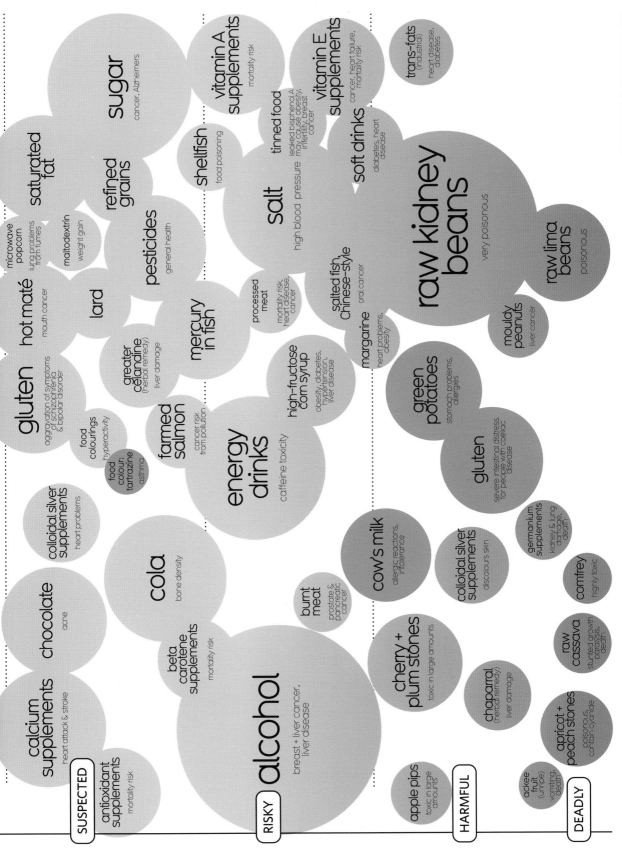

sources: PubMed, The Cochrane Library, JAMA
data: bit.ly/KIB_BadForYou

SUSPECTED

calcium supplements — heart attack & stroke

antioxidant supplements — mortality risk

chocolate — acne

colloidal silver supplements — heart problems

sugar — cancer, Alzheimers

saturated fat

refined grains

microwave popcorn — lung problems from fumes

maltodextrin — weight gain

hot maté — mouth cancer

lard

pesticides — general health

gluten — aggravation of symptoms of schizophrenia & bipolar disorder

greater celandine (herbal remedy) — liver damage

food colourings — hyperactivity

food colour: tartrazine — asthma

mercury in fish

farmed salmon — cancer risk from pollution

shellfish — food poisoning

vitamin A supplements — mortality risk

tinned food — leaked bisphenol A may cause obesity, infertility, breast cancer

vitamin E supplements — cancer, heart failure, mortality risk

salt — high blood pressure

processed meat — mortality risk, heart disease, cancer

salted fish, Chinese-style — oral cancer

soft drinks — diabetes, heart disease

trans-fats (industrial) — heart disease, diabetes

raw kidney beans — very poisonous

raw lima beans — poisonous

mouldy peanuts — liver cancer

margarine — heart problems, obesity

RISKY

beta carotene supplements — mortality risk

cola — bone density

alcohol — breast + liver cancer, liver disease

burnt meat — prostate & pancreatic cancer

high-fructose corn syrup — obesity, diabetes, hypertension, liver disease

energy drinks — caffeine toxicity

green potatoes — stomach problems, allergies

gluten — severe intestinal distress for people with coeliac disease

HARMFUL

apple pips — toxic in large amounts

chaparral (herbal remedy) — liver damage

cherry + plum stones — toxic in large amounts

cow's milk — allergic reactions, intolerance

colloidal silver supplements — discolours skin

germanium supplements — kidney & lung damage, death

comfrey — highly toxic

DEADLY

ackee fruit (unripe) — vomiting, death

apricot + peach stones — poisonous, contain cyanide

raw cassava — stunted growth, paralysis, death

Pole Position

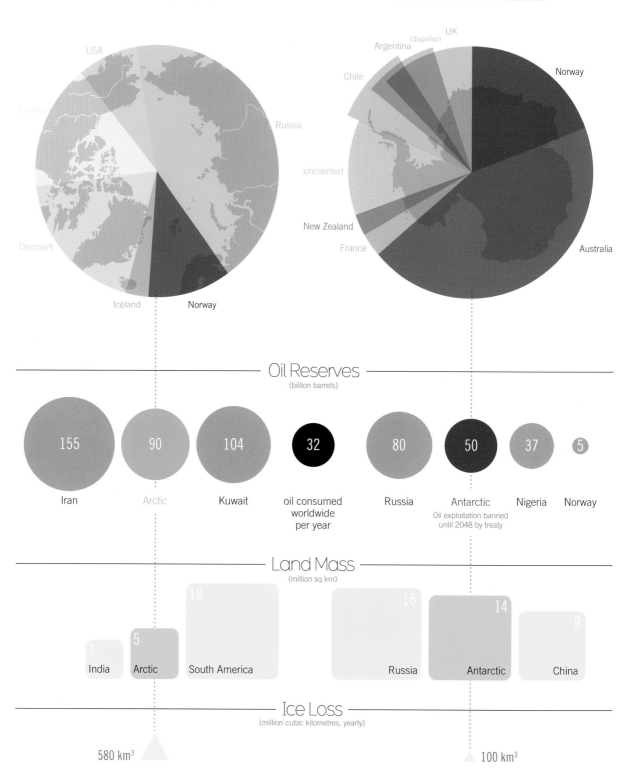

Who owns the Arctic?

USA
Canada
Denmark
Russia
Iceland
Norway

Who owns the Antarctic?

UK (disputed)
Argentina
Chile
Norway
unclaimed
New Zealand
France
Australia

Oil Reserves
(billion barrels)

155 — Iran
90 — Arctic
104 — Kuwait
32 — oil consumed worldwide per year
80 — Russia
50 — Antarctic — Oil exploitation banned until 2048 by treaty
37 — Nigeria
5 — Norway

Land Mass
(million sq km)

3 — India
5 — Arctic
18 — South America
16 — Russia
14 — Antarctic
9 — China

Ice Loss
(million cubic kilometres, yearly)

580 km³

100 km³

sources: World Bank, U.S. Energy Information Administration, International Energy Agency
data: bit.ly/KIB_PolePosition

Buddhism

The Gist

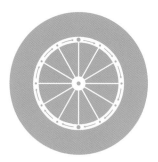

Craving pleasure & avoiding pain involuntarily perpetuates cycles of suffering (*samsara*) that extend over many lifetimes.

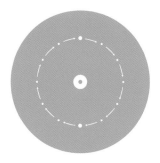

The impersonal, universal force of cause & effect (*karma*) generates consequences from 'good' (skilful) & 'bad' (unskilful) thoughts & deeds.

Liberation from suffering by directly experiencing & understanding the true nature of reality, via techniques, especially **meditation**.

Enlightenment

Not measured in terms of acquiring anything. Rather, of gaining freedom from fetters.

The Ten Fetters

		Practitioner	Stream-Enterer
lower fetters (material world)	01	belief in personality	
	02	sceptical doubt	
	03	clinging to rites & rituals	
	04	sensuous craving	
	05	ill will	
higher fetters (immaterial world)	06	craving for fine-material existence	
	07	craving for immaterial existence	
	08	conceit	
	09	restlessness	
	10	ignorance	

not knowing the real nature & significance of existence

Glimpse of the stream of true reality

Favourable rebirth guaranteed

Seven more lifetimes until enlightenment

Main Schools of Buddhism

Two types - concentration & mindfulness - produce the insight (*vipassana*) & calming (*samatha*) needed to dissolve ignorance & attain **enlightenment** (*nirvana*)

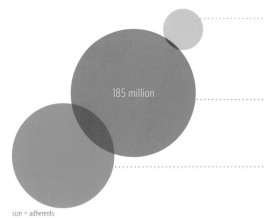

185 million

size = adherents

Vajrayana 'Diamond Vehicle'
Mystical form. Liberation in one lifetime via 'fast-track' practices in texts (*tantras*) & charts (*mandalas*).

Mahayana 'Great Vehicle'
Seek liberation for all living beings, not to just free yourself from pain of cyclical existence (*samsara*).

Theravada 'Ancient Doctrine'
Original simple conservative form. Pared down canon emphasising self-liberation (*nirvana*).

Once-Returner	Non-Returner	Worthy One	Bodhisattva
Weakening of the 4th & 5th fetters	Destruction of lower five fetters	Destruction of all fetters	Enlightened being
Will be reborn in the sensual realm	Rebirth in a celestial realm	Liberation from cycle of birth & death	Chooses to be reborn to free others
But just once more	Deepened realisation of nirvana	Attainment of nirvana (enlightenment)	

sources: 'The Experience of Samadhi', Richard Shankman (2008), Buddhanet, personal communication
data: bit.ly/KIB_Buddhism

Buddhism: States of Consciousness

State of Consciousness

Plane of

Embodied a

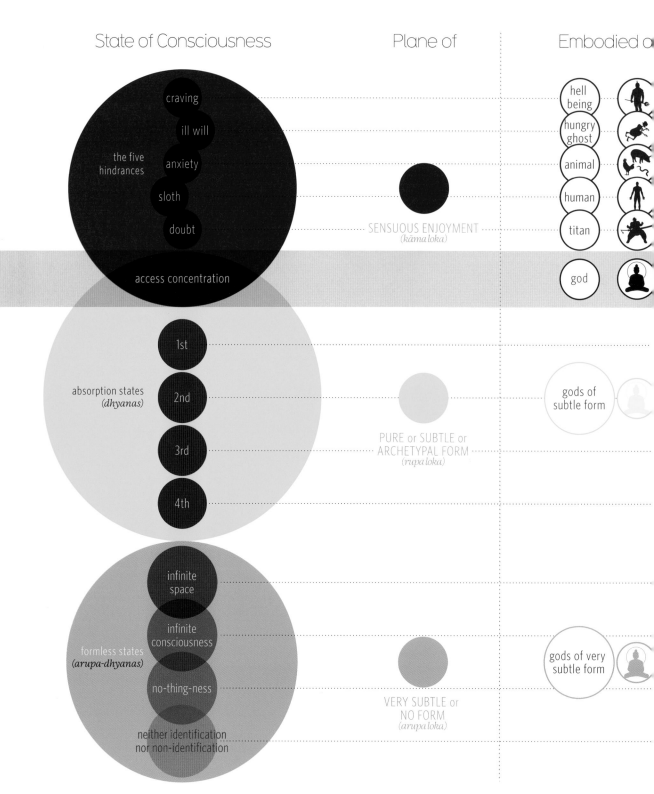

the five hindrances
- craving
- ill will
- anxiety
- sloth
- doubt

access concentration

SENSUOUS ENJOYMENT
(kāma loka)

- hell being
- hungry ghost
- animal
- human
- titan
- god

absorption states
(dhyanas)
- 1st
- 2nd
- 3rd
- 4th

PURE or SUBTLE or
ARCHETYPAL FORM
(rupa loka)

gods of subtle form

formless states
(arupa-dhyanas)
- infinite space
- infinite consciousness
- no-thing-ness
- neither identification nor non-identification

VERY SUBTLE or
NO FORM
(arupa loka)

gods of very subtle form

Felt as

Concentration Type

- paranoid hatred
- intense craving
- wilful stupidity   **MOMENTARY**   ordinary consciousness of everyday life
- passion, desire, doubt, pride
- angry competitive jealousy

- delight & bliss   **THRESHOLD**   effortless internal & external awareness with no distraction or agitation

- perfect mingling of opposites, happiness, profound calm

- lucid absorption with no thoughts, deep artistic state

- mystical state of one-ness

- happy, harmonious peace, neither pleasure nor pain

qualities that emerge in higher states (*dhyana* factors)

concentration	thought	concentration	bliss	rapture
unification of mind	calling to mind	sustained thought	intense satisfaction	ecstatic feeling

minor (goose bumps)
momentary (tremors)
showering (waves)
uplifting (floods)
pervading (high)

FULL   complete absorption

- awareness of body falls away, experience of limitless space with no object

- expanded experience becomes infinite space itself

- no individual things can be distinguished in infinite space

- no 'I', no sense of object or subject

 Meditative attainments & higher states of mind not valued for their own sake, but only in service of eradicating fetters.

sources: 'The Experience of Samadhi', Richard Shankman (2008), Buddhanet, personal communication
data: bit.ly/KIB_Buddhism

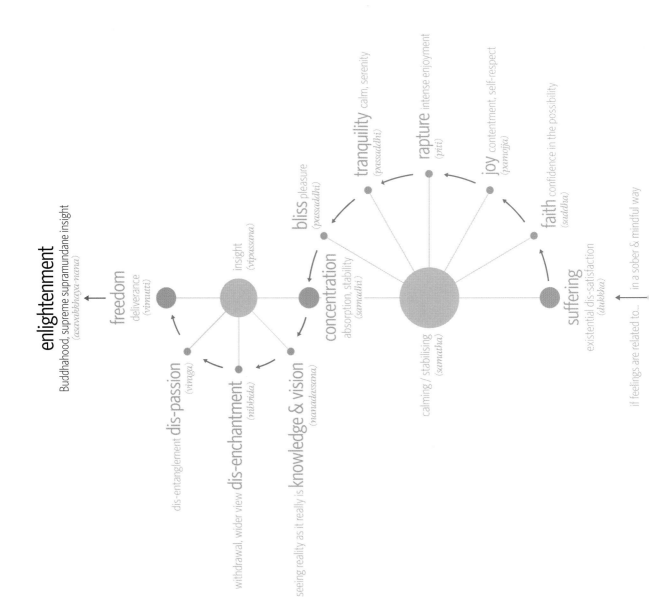

enlightenment
Buddhahood, supreme supramundane insight
(*asavakkhaya-ñana*)

freedom
deliverance
(*vimutti*)

insight
(*vipassana*)

dis-entanglement **dis-passion**
(*viraga*)

withdrawal, wider view **dis-enchantment**
(*nibbida*)

seeing reality as it really is **knowledge & vision**
(*nanadassana*)

bliss pleasure
(*passaddhi*)

concentration
absorption, stability
(*samadhi*)

tranquility calm, serenity
(*passaddhi*)

rapture intense enjoyment
(*piti*)

joy contentment, self-respect
(*pamojja*)

faith confidence in the possibility
(*saddha*)

suffering
existential dis-satisfaction
(*dukkha*)

calming / stabilising
(*samatha*)

if feelings are related to... | in a sober & mindful way

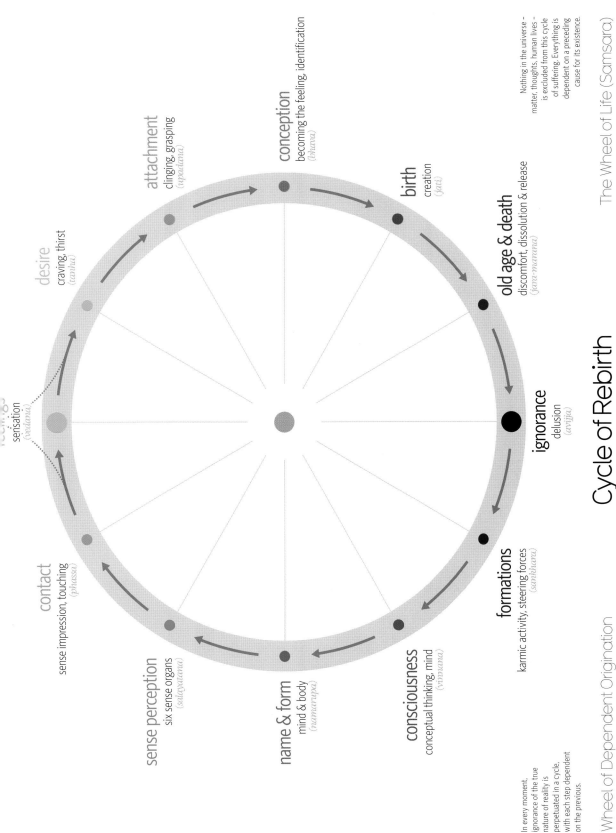

conception
becoming the feeling, identification
(bhava)

attachment
clinging, grasping
(upadana)

birth
creation
(jati)

desire
craving, thirst
(tanha)

old age & death
discomfort, dissolution & release
(jara-marana)

feeling
sensation
(vedana)

ignorance
delusion
(avijja)

contact
sense impression, touching
(phassa)

formations
karmic activity, steering forces
(sankhara)

sense perception
six sense organs
(salayatana)

consciousness
conceptual thinking, mind
(vinnana)

name & form
mind & body
(namarupa)

Nothing in the universe -
matter, thoughts, human lives -
is excluded from this cycle
of suffering. Everything is
dependent on a preceding
cause for its existence.

Cycle of Rebirth

The Wheel of Life (Samsara)

sources: Venerable P.A. Payyuto, sareoso.org.uk, personal communication
data: bit.ly/KIB_Buddhism

Wheel of Dependent Origination

In every moment,
ignorance of the true
nature of reality is
perpetuated in a cycle,
with each step dependent
on the previous.

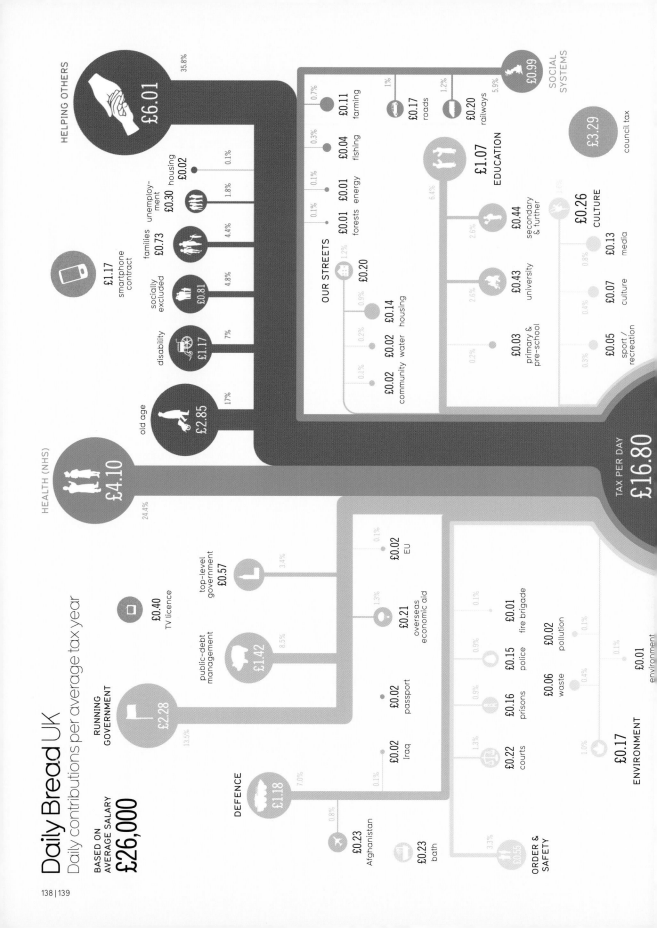

Daily Bread UK
Daily contributions per average tax year

BASED ON
AVERAGE SALARY
£26,000

138 | 139

HELPING OTHERS
£6.01   35.8%

smartphone contract
£1.17

old age
£2.85   17%

disability
£1.17   7%

socially excluded
£0.81   4.8%

families
£0.73   4.4%

unemployment
£0.30   1.8%

housing
£0.02   0.1%

HEALTH (NHS)
£4.10   24.4%

RUNNING GOVERNMENT

TV licence
£0.40

top-level government
£0.57   3.4%

public-debt management
£1.42   8.5%

£2.28   13.5%

DEFENCE
£1.18   7.0%

Iraq
£0.02   0.1%

Afghanistan
£0.23   0.8%

bath
£0.23

ORDER & SAFETY
£0.55   3.3%

courts
£0.22   1.3%

prisons
£0.16   0.9%

police
£0.15   0.9%

fire brigade
£0.01   0.1%

overseas economic aid
£0.21   1.3%

EU
£0.02   0.1%

passport
£0.02

waste
£0.06   0.4%

pollution
£0.02   0.1%

environment
£0.01   0.1%

ENVIRONMENT
£0.17   1.0%

OUR STREETS

forests
£0.01   0.1%

energy
£0.01   0.1%

fishing
£0.04   0.3%

farming
£0.11   0.7%

roads
£0.17   1%

railways
£0.20   1.2%

SOCIAL SYSTEMS
£0.99   5.9%

housing
£0.14   0.9%

£0.20   1.2%

water
£0.02   0.2%

community
£0.02   0.1%

EDUCATION
£1.07   6.4%

secondary & further
£0.44   2.6%

university
£0.43   2.6%

primary & pre-school
£0.03   0.2%

CULTURE
£0.26   1.6%

media
£0.13   0.8%

culture
£0.07   0.4%

sport / recreation
£0.05   0.3%

council tax
£3.29

TAX PER DAY
£16.80

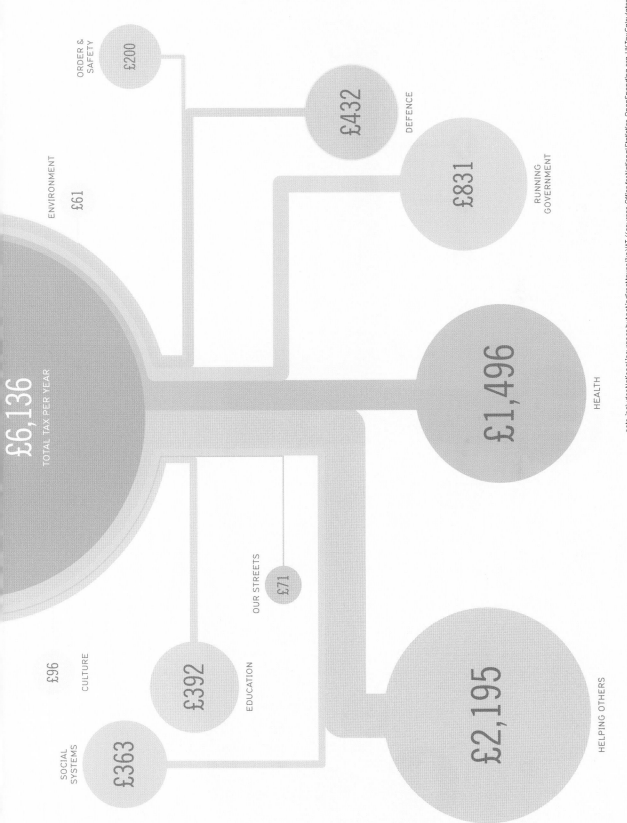

£6,136
TOTAL TAX PER YEAR

ORDER & SAFETY
£200

ENVIRONMENT
£61

DEFENCE
£432

RUNNING GOVERNMENT
£831

HEALTH
£1,496

SOCIAL SYSTEMS
£363

CULTURE
£96

EDUCATION
£392

OUR STREETS
£71

HELPING OTHERS
£2,195

note: includes National Insurance but not indirect taxes like VAT // sources: Office for National Statistics, OpenSpending.org, UK Tax Calculator
data: bit.ly/KIB_DailyTax

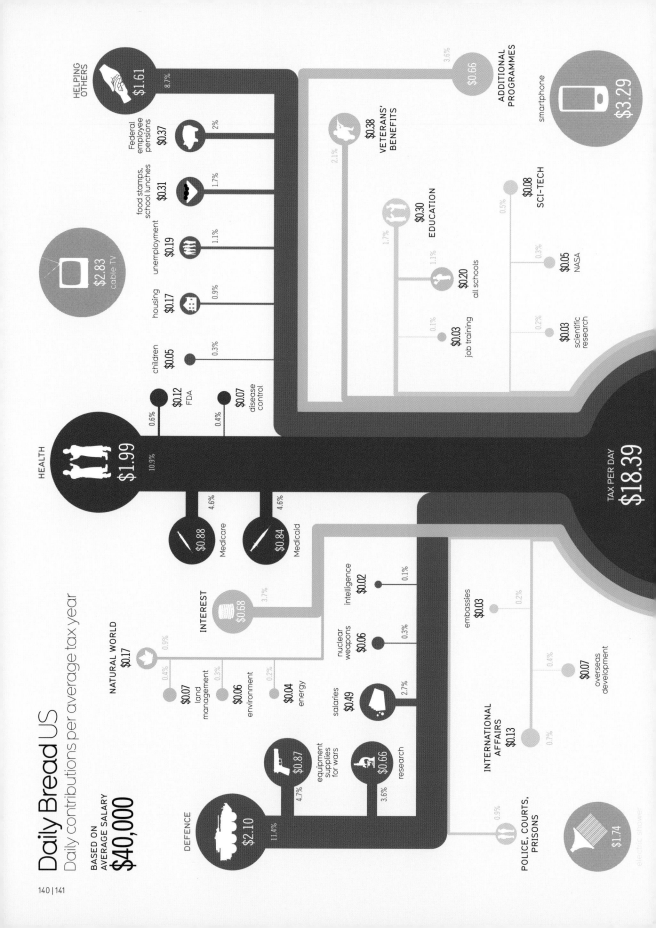

Daily Bread US

Daily contributions per average tax year

BASED ON
AVERAGE SALARY
$40,000

HELPING OTHERS $1.61 — 8.7%

$2.83 cable TV

Federal employee pensions $0.37 — 2%

food stamps, school lunches $0.31 — 1.7%

unemployment $0.19 — 1.1%

housing $0.17 — 0.9%

children $0.05 — 0.3%

$0.12 FDA — 0.6%

$0.07 disease control — 0.4%

HEALTH $1.99 — 10.9%

$0.88 Medicare — 4.6%

$0.84 Medicaid — 4.6%

ADDITIONAL PROGRAMMES $0.66 — 3.6%

smartphone $3.29

VETERANS' BENEFITS $0.38 — 2.1%

EDUCATION $0.30 — 1.7%

all schools $0.20 — 1.1%

job training $0.03 — 0.1%

SCI-TECH $0.08 — 0.5%

NASA $0.05 — 0.3%

scientific research $0.03 — 0.2%

NATURAL WORLD $0.17 — 0.9%

land management $0.07 — 0.4%

environment $0.06 — 0.3%

energy $0.04 — 0.2%

INTEREST $0.68 — 3.7%

intelligence $0.02 — 0.1%

nuclear weapons $0.06 — 0.3%

salaries $0.49 — 2.7%

embassies $0.03 — 0.2%

overseas development $0.07 — 0.4%

INTERNATIONAL AFFAIRS $0.13 — 0.7%

equipment supplies for wars $0.87 — 4.7%

research $0.66 — 3.6%

DEFENCE $2.10 — 11.4%

POLICE, COURTS, PRISONS — 0.9%

$1.74 electric shower

TAX PER DAY
$18.39

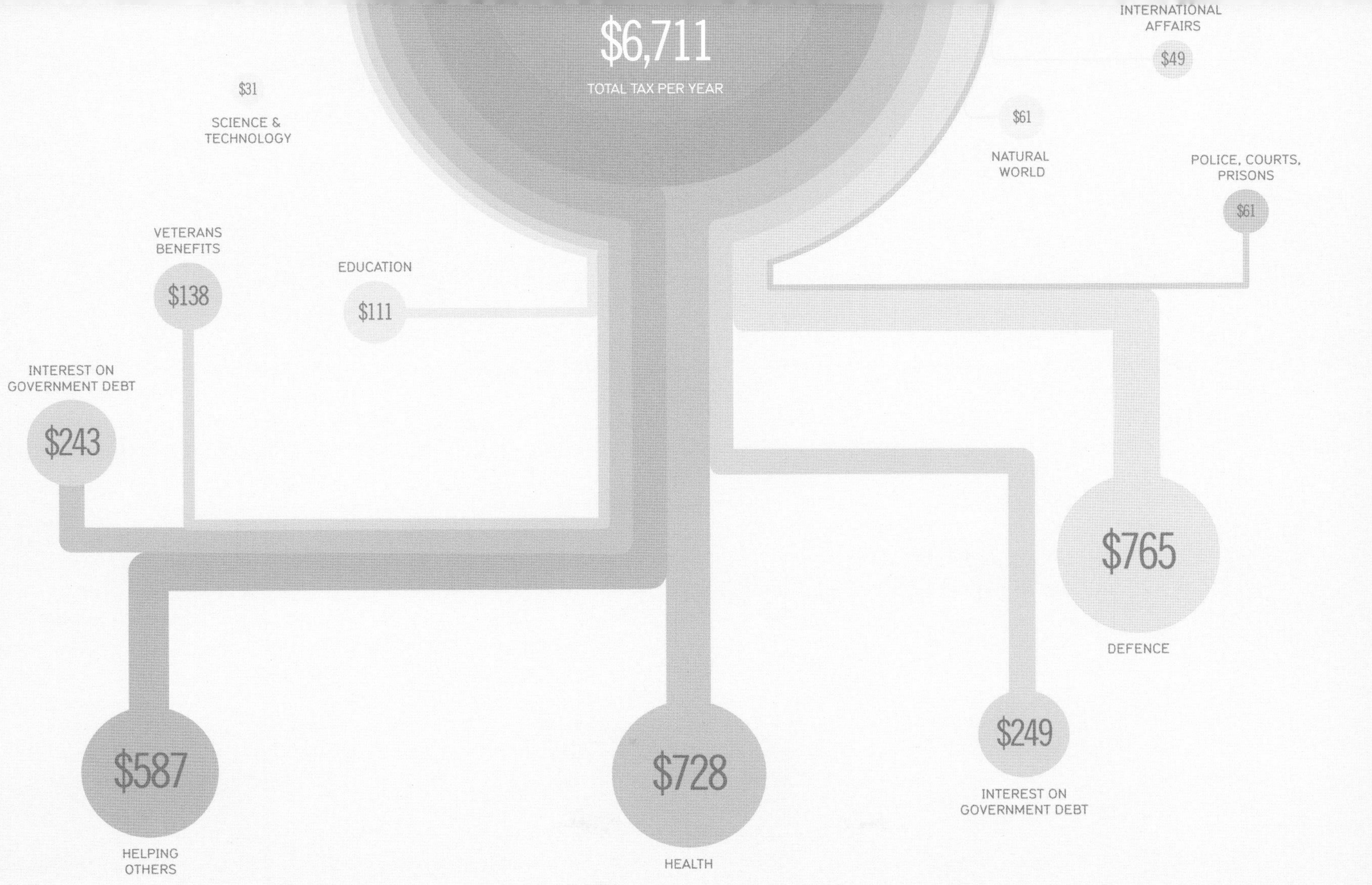

$6,711

TOTAL TAX PER YEAR

INTERNATIONAL
AFFAIRS

$49

POLICE, COURTS,
PRISONS

$61

NATURAL
WORLD

$61

$765

DEFENCE

$249

INTEREST ON
GOVERNMENT DEBT

$728

HEALTH

SCIENCE &
TECHNOLOGY

$31

EDUCATION

$111

VETERANS
BENEFITS

$138

INTEREST ON
GOVERNMENT DEBT

$243

$587

HELPING
OTHERS

sources: Census.gov, WhiteHouse.gov, US Tax Calculator
data: bit.ly/KIB_DailyTax

House Edges
Average % a player can expect to lose on each bet

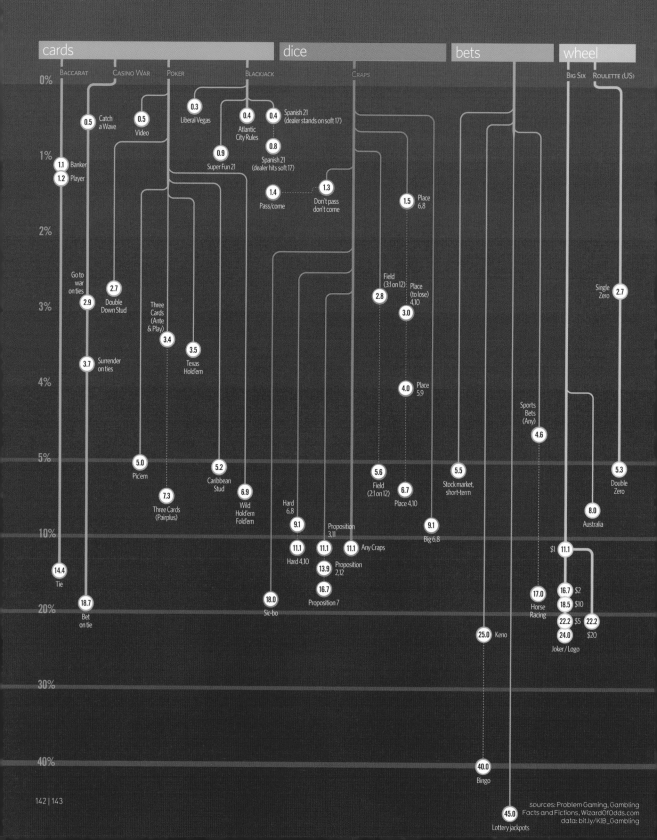

cards

Baccarat | Casino War | Poker | Blackjack

dice

Craps

bets

wheel

Big Six | Roulette (US)

0%

0.3 Liberal Vegas
0.5 Catch a Wave
0.5 Video
0.4 Atlantic City Rules
0.4 Spanish 21 (dealer stands on soft 17)

1%

1.1 Banker
1.2 Player
0.9 Super Fun 21
0.8 Spanish 21 (dealer hits soft 17)
1.4 Pass/come
1.3 Don't pass don't come
1.5 Place 6,8

2%

2.7 Double Down Stud
2.9 Go to war on ties
2.8 Field (3:1 on 12)
3.0 Place (to lose) 4,10
2.7 Single Zero

3%

3.4 Three Cards (Ante & Play)
3.5 Texas Hold'em
3.7 Surrender on ties

4%

4.0 Place 5,9

5%

5.0 Pic'em
5.2 Caribbean Stud
5.6 Field (2:1 on 12)
6.7 Place 4,10
5.5 Stock market, short-term
4.6 Sports Bets (Any)
5.3 Double Zero

7.3 Three Cards (Pairplus)
6.9 Wild Hold'em Fold'em
8.0 Australia

Hard 6,8
9.1

10%

9.1 Big 6,8
11.1 Hard 4,10
11.1 Proposition 3,11
11.1 Any Craps
$1 11.1

13.9 Proposition 2,12
16.7 Proposition 7
16.7 $2
18.5 $10
17.0 Horse Racing
14.4 Tie

20%

18.7 Bet on tie
18.0 Sic-bo
22.2 $5 22.2
24.0 Joker / Logo $20
25.0 Keno

30%

40%

40.0 Bingo

45.0 Lottery jackpots

sources: Problem Gaming, Gambling Facts and Fictions, WizardOfOdds.com
data: bit.ly/KIB_Gambling

Superpower Showdown
Education

	China	EU	India	USA
AVERAGE SCHOOL YEARS MEAN	7.5	10.8	4.4	13.3
BASIC LITERACY % MEN & WOMEN	98% 93%	99% 99%	75% 50%	99% 99%
YOUTH UNEMPLOYMENT % PEOPLE AGED 15–24	7.6%	22.6%	13.3%	16.3%
NO. OF UNIVERSITIES PER 100,000 PEOPLE	0.16	0.79	0.74	1.41
YOUNG GOING TO UNIVERSITY	17%	60%	10%	74%
25–64 WITH A DEGREE	4.6%	19%	10%	41%
% WORLD GRADUATES	12%	26%	12%	26%
% WORLD INT'L STUDENTS	16.5%	23%	6.2%	1.6%
BRAIN DRAIN 1 = WORST DRAIN 7 = BRIGHT PEOPLE STAY IN REGION	4.3	3.7	4.4	5.7
EDUCATION SPENDING % OF GDP / % OF GOVT SPENDING	13% 3.3%	11.5% 5.4%	10.5% 3.2%	13% 5.4%
EXPENDITURE PER STUDENT PRIMARY SCHOOL % GDP PER CAPITA	6%	22.2%	9%	22.6%
SECONDARY % GDP PER CAPITA	11%	29.5%	13.8%	25.3%
TERTIARY % GDP PER CAPITA	76%	28.5%	70%	64%
PUPILS TO TEACHER PRIMARY SCHOOL	17	15	40	14
SECONDARY SCHOOL	15	13	25	14
SCIENCE FUNDING % OF GDP	0.40	0.69	0.50	0.91
SCORE	3	7	0	13

USA SCORES TOP MARKS!

sources: CIA World Factbook, World Bank, Eurostat
data: bit.ly/KIB_Superpowers

The Antibiotic Abacus
Adding up drug resistance

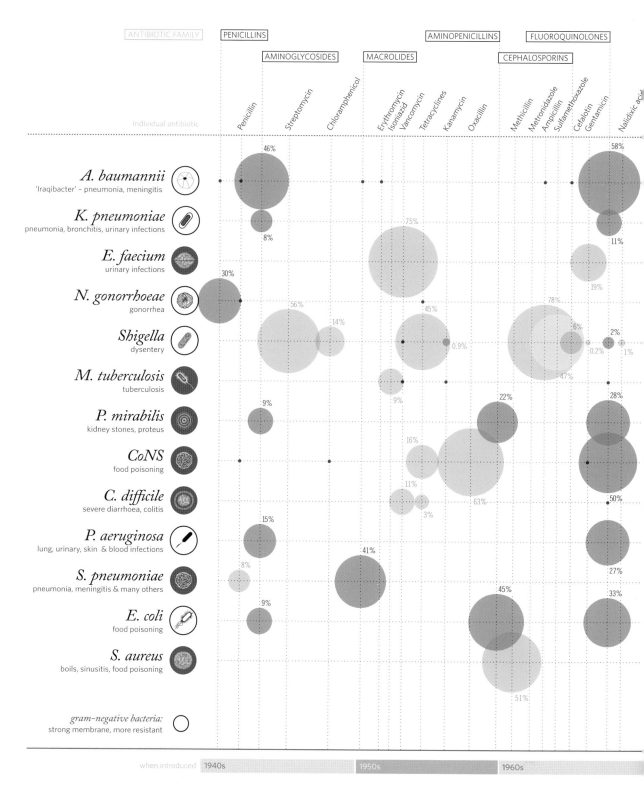

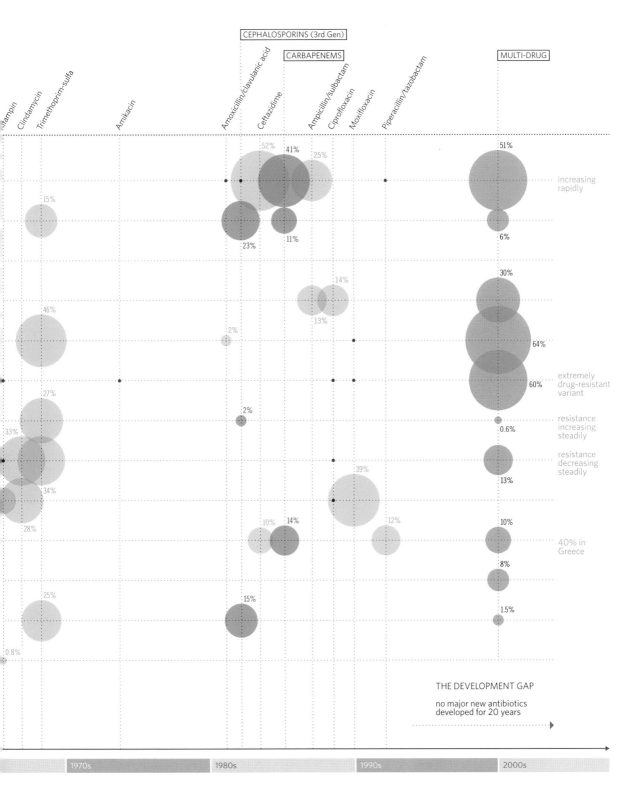

sources: Center for Disease Dynamics, Economics & Policy, World Health Organisation, Center for Disease Control, Guardian.com, US data
data: bit.ly/KIB_Antibiotics

The Etiquettrix

	USA	Canada	Brazil	China (Limao)	Japan	India	Thailand	Singapore
VISITING								
Greetings								
Caveat	firm	kiss French Canadians	men		limp	say 'Namaste'	slight, palms together	youths
Who first?				eldest / most senior	varies immensely	eldest / most senior	junior (in age/status)	in order of age/status
Introductions	Title / 1st / 2nd	Title / 1st / 2nd	Title / 1st / 2nd	Title / 1st / 2nd	Title / 1st / 2nd	Title / 2nd	Title / 1st / 2nd	Title / 1st / 2nd
Gifts for host(ess)								
Note				flowers for funerals		no white flowers	no marigolds, carnations	multi-cultural minefield!
Vino / Max lateness	10m	15m	30m	0m	5m be early	15-30m	0m	0m
MEAL TIMES								
Begin meal after...	host	host	host	host	honoured / eldest	oldest man	being invited	host
Ritual	saying grace			'Youyi' ('Here's to friendship')	'itadakimasu' (I humbly receive)			
Decline food				very rude			not to older people	
2nd portion?							as above	
leave food?	small	small			small		small	small
food note					clear plate = still hungry never leave rice	food on plate = full clear plate = still hungry	clear plate = still hungry never leave rice	
decline drinks?				unless drunk	must accept sake	empty glass = more plz		
Talking in-meal					subdued			
politics								
religion								
business								
money								
Licking fingers					slurp noodles and tea	yes, if eating with hands		
Yum-yum noises								
Burping							if honoured guest	
Toasting		host first		Gambai ('bottoms up')	'Kampai' ('Cheers!')			
Compliment food?				praise taste of host		praise = 'payment'		
Cutlery no no's			eat everything with knife & fork, even fruit	never tap chopsticks on table	never point with chopsticks, never lick them	serve yourself with spoons, never hands	spoon = fork fork = knife	may eat with a spoon & hands, but never use left hand
End of meal signal				leave food to signal fullness	replace lids, rest chopsticks	leave food to signal fullness	leave food to signal fullness	rest chopsticks
Absolute meal no no's	no elbows on the table	no elbows on the table	never use hands		don't mix food with rice, keep separate	never use left hand	never pass anything over someone's head	
PUBLIC CONDUCT								
Hand gestures								
Don't touch...								
Maximum rudeness...	the finger		'O.K.' gesture ('screw you!')			showing soles of feet	showing soles of feet	showing soles of feet, pounding fist on palm
Chat to strangers?						depending on status	depending on status	
Chat to women?								
Bartering								
Customer always	absolutely right			right				
Any bill paying etiquette	hand money bills unfolded	host usually pays	pretty flexible	an honour to pay a restaurant bill	not hand-to-hand exchange, use tray	host usually pays	host pays the bill, never offer to split	split the bill
Tipping culture?								
taxis %	15	10				15		
serving staff %	15-20	15-20	10	leave some coins		15		10% if foreigner
bar staff %	15-25+	15				15		
hotel staff %	15-20	10				15		
CULTURAL VALUES								
adored qualities	friendliness	politeness	family	'face' - honour & respect	harmony	family	harmony	harmony
	informality	tolerance	harmony	good reputation	politeness	politeness	courtesy, self-control	respect for seniority
	individualism		frankness	sincerity	responsibility	hospitality	family	family
abhorred qualities	lack of restraint	rowdiness	being unsociable	public disagreement	open criticism	saying no!	public criticism	showing anger
			boisterousness		insulting, putting on the spot	showing anger	losing face	

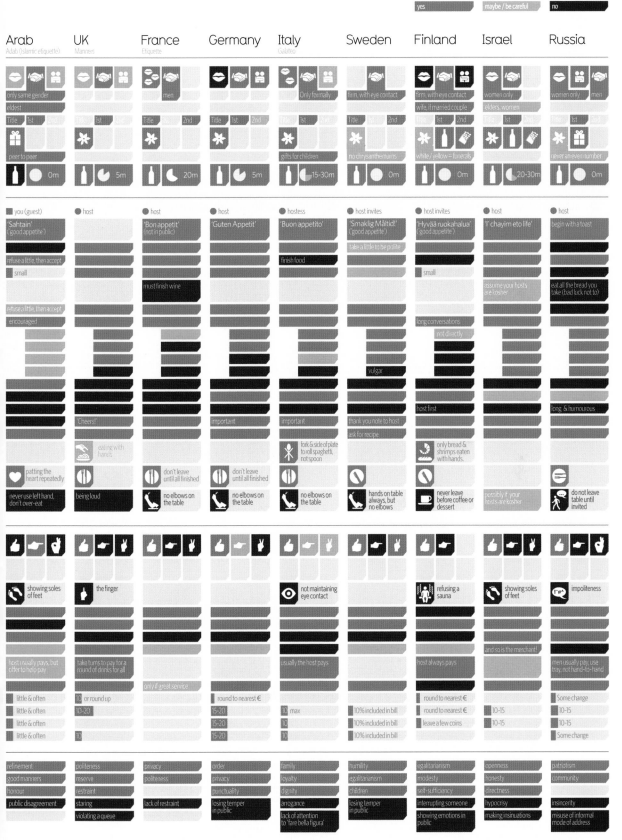

sources: Kwintessential.co.uk, eDiplomat.com, EtiquetteScholar.com, crowdsourcing
data: bit.ly/KIB_Etiquettrix

Simple III

Pluto Fail
The Dwarf planet in context

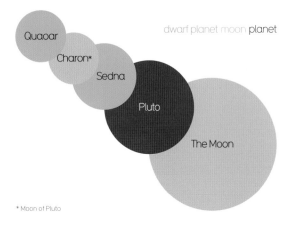

dwarf planet moon **planet**

Quaoar

Charon*

Sedna

Pluto

The Moon

* Moon of Pluto

source: NASA

Drop in the Ocean
The final frontier?

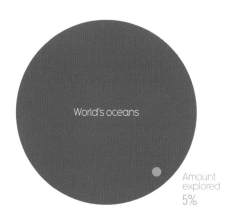

World's oceans

Amount
explored
5%

source: National Oceanic & Atmospheric Administration

It's the Jab, Silly!
Reported side-effects of the seasonal flu vaccine vs. placebo

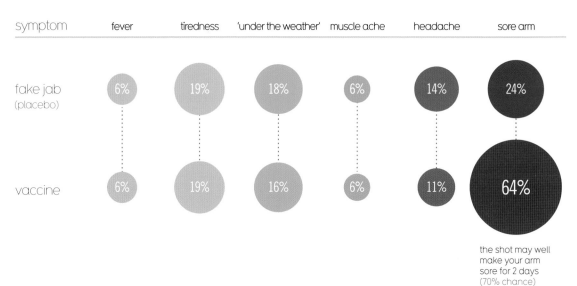

symptom	fever	tiredness	'under the weather'	muscle ache	headache	sore arm
fake jab (placebo)	6%	19%	18%	6%	14%	24%
vaccine	6%	19%	16%	6%	11%	64%

the shot may well
make your arm
sore for 2 days
(70% chance)

source: 'The Effectiveness of Vaccination Against Influenza In Healthy, Working Adults', Nichol et al (1995)

Drug Report
Deaths vs. media attention

Illicit substance	Deaths per 100,000 users	Press reports	Reports per death
Methadone	94.5	10	0.1
Heroin & morphine	44.9	83	1.8
Cocaine	2.3	157	68
Solvents	1.7	10	5.8
Anti-depressants	1.2	19	15
Alcohol	0.8	14	17.5
SSRI anti-depressants	0.7	16	22
Ecstacy	0.7	47	67
Aspirin	0.08	19	237
Cannabis*	0.07	92	1,314
Paracetamol	0.01	19	1,900

*Cannabis deaths questionable
sources: Guardian Datablog, UK Office of National Statistics, Google Insights, dailymail.co.uk

Sunken Measures
Drowned landmasses, km²

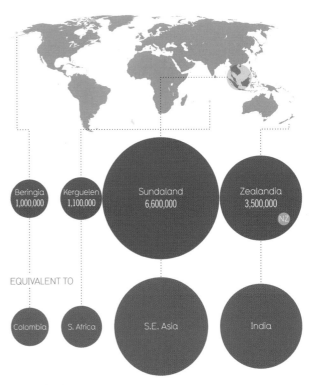

Beringia 1,000,000
Kerguelen 1,100,000
Sundaland 6,600,000
Zealandia 3,500,000
NZ

EQUIVALENT TO

Colombia
S. Africa
S.E. Asia
India

source: Wikipedia

Hot Spot
Accuracy of global temperature rise predictions

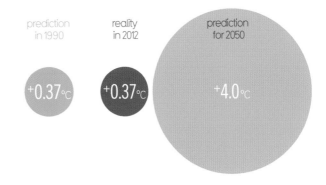

prediction in 1990
+0.37°C

reality in 2012
+0.37°C

prediction for 2050
+4.0°C

sources: International Panel of Climate Change (1990), Frame & Stone (2013)

data: bit.ly/KIB_Simple3

Average children per woman
1950-55

Niger

AFRICA

S Africa

Timor-Leste
Singapore

Chad
Brazil

DR Congo
India
LATAM

ASIA
China

WORLD

Hong Kong

Bosnia &
Herzegovina

OCEANIA

United States

France
EUROPE

UK

Japan

Natal Depression
The how & why of dropping fertility rates

Fewer infants dying
Less children needed
to ensure some make
it to adulthood.

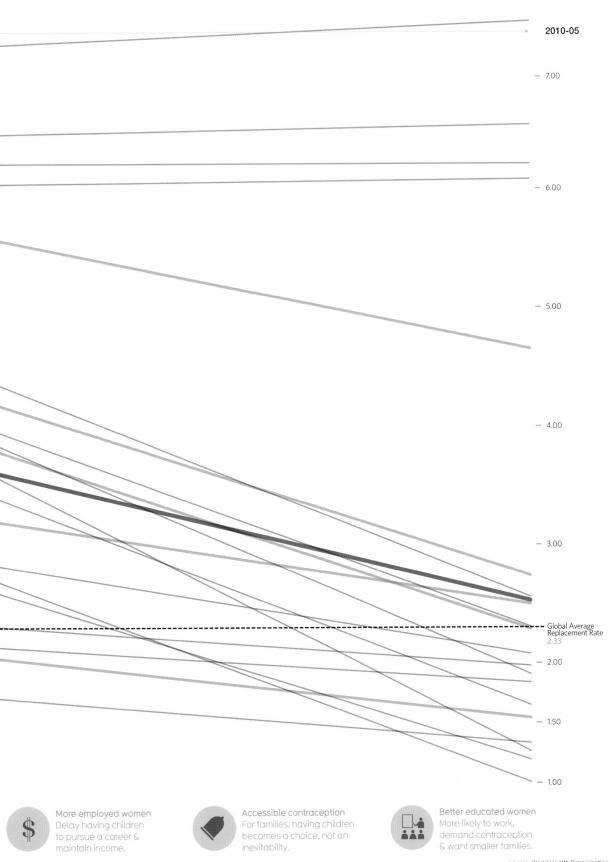

2010-05

— 7.00

— 6.00

— 5.00

— 4.00

— 3.00

Global Average
Replacement Rate
2.33

— 2.00

— 1.50

— 1.00

More employed women
Delay having children
to pursue a career &
maintain income.

Accessible contraception
For families, having children
becomes a choice, not an
inevitability.

Better educated women
More likely to work,
demand contraception
& want smaller families.

source: World Health Organisation

Timeline of the Far Future

- earth
- humanity
- heavens

---- size = magnitude of event

ONE THOUSAND YEARS FROM NOW

Most Words Extinct
Due to rapid evolution of languages, no single present-day word will have survived

Carbon Dioxide
29% of 20th-century CO_2 still here

1,000 **New North Star** Gamma Cephei replaces Polaris

3,200 **New North Star No.2** Iota Cephei wins the top spot

1,000 **Buildings Decayed**
If civilisation collapses, most buildings, bridges & dams around today will have fallen

2,000 **Greenland Ice Melted**
Ice sheet completely melted with extreme global warming (+8°C). Sea levels 6 m higher

2,372 **Hale-Bopp Returns**
Comet last seen 1997. Due around 4385 CE

5,125 **Mayan Calendar Ends (Again)**
3 May 7138 CE. You read it here first!

8,000 **Happy Birthday Humanity!**
Rough length of the period of human civilisation

TEN THOUSAND YEARS

Carbon Dioxide
14% of our CO_2 still here – assuming no solution has been found

10,000 **Earth's Axis Reversed**
Summer & winter months reversed. Northern hemisphere suffers more extreme weather (due to higher percentage of land)

18,860 **Calendars Concur**
The lunar Islamic calendar & the solar Gregorian calendar will share the same year: 20,860

25,000 **Arecibo Message Arrives**
The transmission radio data sent on 16 Nov 1974 is received by globular cluster Messier 13 on the far side of the galaxy...

Earliest a reply could arrive

50,000 **Niagara Falls Disappears**

20,000 **Chernobyl Finally Safe**

50,000 **KEO Time Capsule**
Launched in 2014, will re-enter the Earth's atmosphere. It has enough capacity to carry a 4-page message

50,000 **Greenland Ice Melted**
Completely melted with moderate global warming (+2°C)

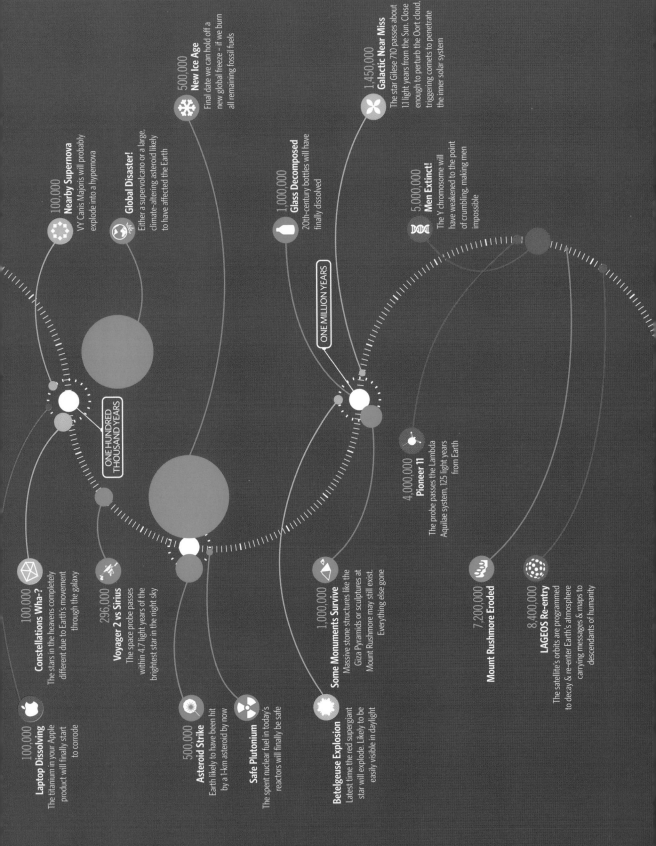

100,000

Nearby Supernova

VV Canis Majoris will probably explode into a hypernova

Global Disaster!

Either a supervolcano or a large, climate-altering asteroid likely to have affected the Earth

500,000

New Ice Age

Final date we can hold off a new global freeze – if we burn all remaining fossil fuels

1,450,000

Galactic Near Miss

The star Gliese 710 passes about 1.1 light years from the Sun. Close enough to perturb the Oort cloud, triggering comets to penetrate the inner solar system

1,000,000

Glass Decomposed

20th-century bottles will have finally dissolved

5,000,000

Men Extinct!

The Y chromosome will have weakened to the point of crumbling, making men impossible

ONE MILLION YEARS

ONE HUNDRED THOUSAND YEARS

4,000,000

Pioneer 11

The probe passes the Lambda Aquilae system, 125 light years from Earth

100,000

Laptop Dissolving

The titanium in your Apple product will finally start to corrode

100,000

Constellations Wha-?

The stars in the heavens completely different due to Earth's movement through the galaxy

296,000

Voyager 2 vs Sirius

The space probe passes within 4.7 light years of the brightest star in the night sky

500,000

Asteroid Strike

Earth likely to have been hit by a 1-km asteroid by now

Safe Plutonium

The spent nuclear fuel in today's reactors will finally be safe

1,000,000

Some Monuments Survive

Massive stone structures like the Giza Pyramids or sculptures at Mount Rushmore may still exist. Everything else gone

Betelgeuse Explosion

Latest time the red supergiant star will explode. Likely to be easily visible in daylight

7,200,000

Mount Rushmore Eroded

8,400,000

LAGEOS Re-entry

The satellite's orbits are programmed to decay & re-enter Earth's atmosphere carrying messages & maps to descendants of humanity

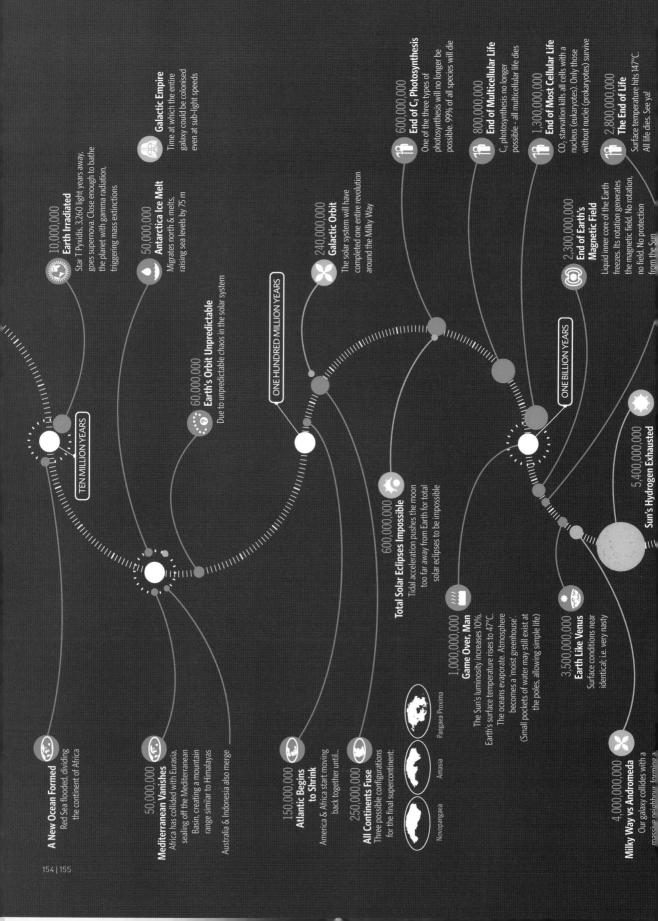

10,000,000
Earth Irradiated
Star T Pyxidis, 3,260 light years away, goes supernova. Close enough to bathe the planet with gamma radiation, triggering mass extinctions

Galactic Empire
Time at which the entire galaxy could be colonised even at sub-light speeds

50,000,000
Antarctica Ice Melt
Migrates north & melts, raising sea levels by 75 m

60,000,000
Earth's Orbit Unpredictable
Due to unpredictable chaos in the solar system

600,000,000
End of C₃ Photosynthesis
One of the three types of photosynthesis will no longer be possible. 99% of all species will die

800,000,000
End of Multicellular Life
C₄ photosynthesis no longer possible - all multicellular life dies

1,300,000,000
End of Most Cellular Life
CO₂ starvation kills all cells with a nucleus (eukaryotes). Only those without nuclei (prokaryotes) survive

240,000,000
Galactic Orbit
The solar system will have completed one entire revolution around the Milky Way

2,300,000,000
End of Earth's Magnetic Field
Liquid inner core of the Earth freezes. Its rotation generates the magnetic field. No rotation, no field. No protection from the Sun

2,800,000,000
The End of Life
Surface temperature hits 147°C. All life dies. See ya!

ONE HUNDRED MILLION YEARS

TEN MILLION YEARS

ONE BILLION YEARS

5,400,000,000
Sun's Hydrogen Exhausted

A New Ocean Formed
Red Sea flooded, dividing the continent of Africa

50,000,000
Mediterranean Vanishes
Africa has collided with Eurasia, sealing off the Mediterranean Basin, creating a mountain range similar to Himalayas

Australia & Indonesia also merge

600,000,000
Total Solar Eclipses Impossible
Tidal acceleration pushes the moon too far away from Earth for total solar eclipses to be impossible

1,000,000,000
Game Over, Man
The Sun's luminosity increases 10%. Earth's surface temperature rises to 47°C. The oceans evaporate. Atmosphere becomes a 'moist greenhouse'. (Small pockets of water may still exist at the poles, allowing simple life)

3,500,000,000
Earth Like Venus
Surface conditions near identical: i.e. very nasty

150,000,000
Atlantic Begins to Shrink
America & Africa start moving back together until...

250,000,000
All Continents Fuse
Three possible configurations for the final supercontinent:

Novopangaea   Amasia   Pangaea Proxima

4,000,000,000
Milky Way vs Andromeda
Our galaxy collides with a massive neighbour, forming a

154 | 155

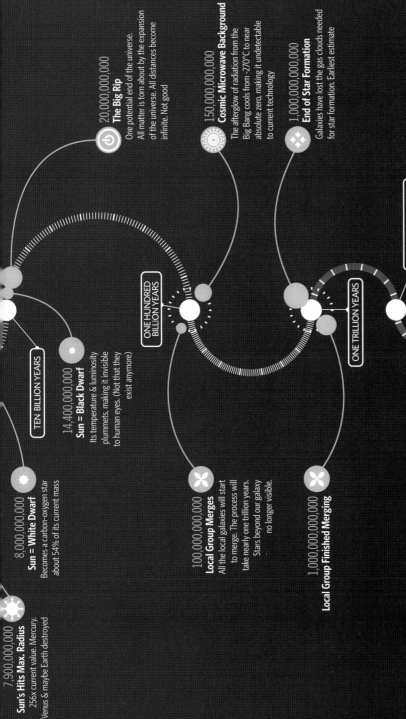

7,900,000,000
Sun's Hits Max. Radius
256x current value. Mercury, Venus & maybe Earth destroyed

8,000,000,000
Sun = White Dwarf
Becomes a carbon-oxygen star about 54% of its current mass

14,400,000,000
Sun = Black Dwarf
Its temperature & luminosity plummets, making it invisible to human eyes. (Not that they exist anymore)

TEN BILLION YEARS

20,000,000,000
The Big Rip
One potential end of the universe. All matter is torn about by the expansion of the universe. All distances become infinite. Not good

100,000,000,000
Local Group Merges
All the local galaxies will start to merge. The process will take nearly one trillion years. Stars beyond our galaxy no longer visible.

ONE HUNDRED BILLION YEARS

150,000,000,000
Cosmic Microwave Background
The afterglow of radiation from the Big Bang cools from −270°C to near absolute zero, making it undetectable to current technology

1,000,000,000,000
Local Group Finished Merging

1,000,000,000,000
End of Star Formation
Galaxies have lost the gas clouds needed for star formation. Earliest estimate

ONE TRILLION YEARS

TEN TRILLION YEARS

100,000,000,000,000
End of Star Formation
Lowest estimate for the end of stellar birth. Beginning of the 'Degenerate Era' of universe-wide star death

ONE HUNDRED TRILLION YEARS

110,000,000,000,000
Stars Fuel Exhausted
All stars will have died. The only objects left are leftovers: white dwarfs, neutron stars & black holes

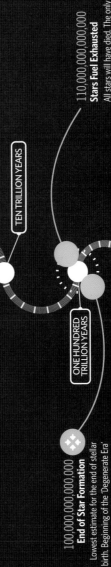

ONE QUADRILLION YEARS

100,000,000,000,000,000
Earth Dies
If not consumed by a swollen Sun at 5.4 bn years, the Earth's orbit will have finally decayed & it will plunge into the sun

TEN QUADRILLION YEARS

Superpower Showdown
Business

	China	EU	India	USA
WORKFORCE % OF POPULATION	59	46	40	49
% EMPLOYED IN AGRICULTURE	9.7	5.2	16.9	0.70
% EMPLOYED IN INDUSTRY	45.3	22.7	17.0	20.3
% EMPLOYED IN SERVICES	45.0	72.2	66.1	79.1
LARGEST MANUFACTURING ACTIVITY BASED ON VALUE ADDED	BASIC METALS	FOOD & DRINK	CHEMICALS	CHEMICALS
% OF MANUFACTURING	14.3	11.7	15.5	16.2
EASE OF DOING BUSINESS 1 = BEST	96	40	134	4
TIME TO DO TAXES HOURS PER YEAR	338	193	243	175
BUSINESS COMPETITIVENESS INDEX RANKING 1 = BEST	27TH	36TH	51ST	4TH
VALUE OF SHARES $ BILLIONS	5.7	9.3	1.0	15.6
INDUSTRIAL PRODUCTION GROWTH RATE %	7.7	-0.2	0.9	2.5
AVERAGE MONTHLY SALARY $ (IN PURCHASING POWER PARITY)	656	2,215	295	3,263
AVERAGE HOURS WORKED PER WEEK	45	42	41	34
FEMALE : MALE LABOUR FORCE % RATIO	85	65	36	82
WOMEN IN NATIONAL PARLIAMENTS % SEATS	21	26	11	17
LEGAL MATERNITY LEAVE WEEKS	14	18	12	0
MALE/FEMALE PAY GAP AVERAGE %	31	16	30	19
SCORE	4	3	1	7

USA CLINCHES THE DEAL!

source: CIA World Factbook, World Bank, Eurostat
data: bit.ly/KIB_Superpowers

Disappearing Varieties

Disappearing Varieties?

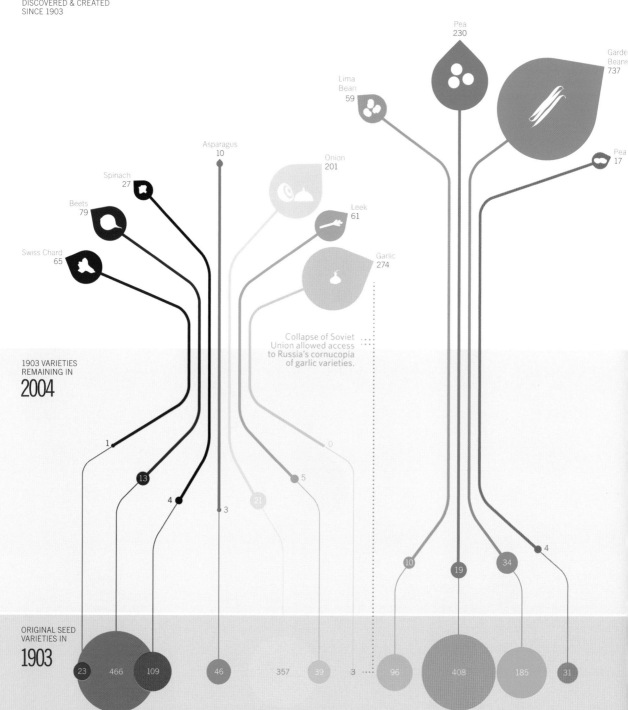

vegetable family

miscellaneus
(beetroot & asparagus)

fabaceae
(bean)

2004
NEW SEED VARIETIES
DISCOVERED & CREATED
SINCE 1903

Pea
230

Garden
Beans
737

Lima
Bean
59

Asparagus
10

Onion
201

Pea
17

Spinach
27

Leek
61

Beets
79

Garlic
274

Swiss Chard
65

Collapse of Soviet
Union allowed access
to Russia's cornucopia
of garlic varieties.

1903 VARIETIES
REMAINING IN
2004

1

13

4

3

0

5

21

10

19

34

4

ORIGINAL SEED
VARIETIES IN
1903

23

466

109

46

357

39

3

96

408

185

31

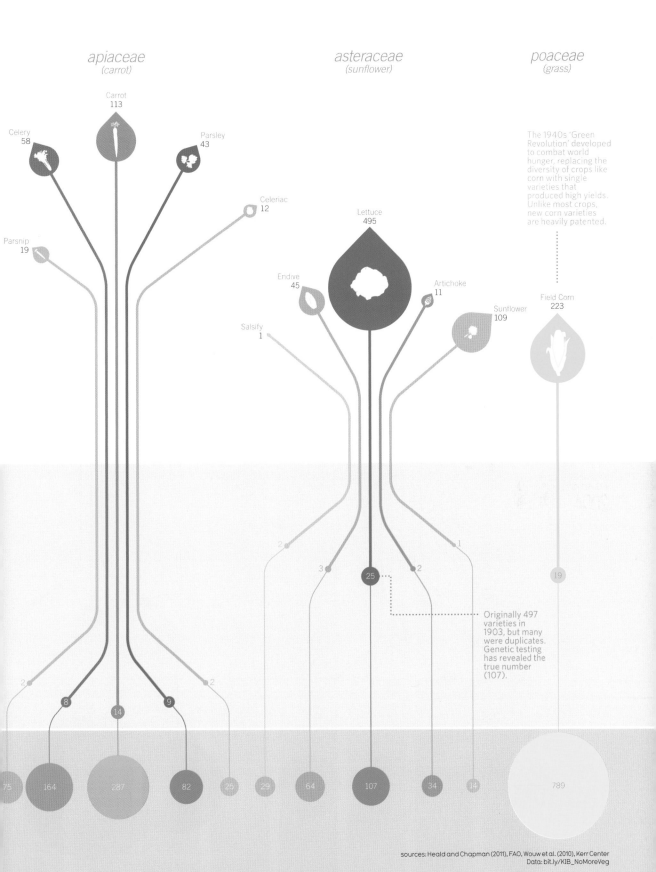

apiaceae
(carrot)

asteraceae
(sunflower)

poaceae
(grass)

Carrot
113

Celery
58

Parsley
43

Celeriac
12

Parsnip
19

Lettuce
495

Endive
45

Artichoke
11

Sunflower
109

Salsify
1

The 1940s 'Green Revolution' developed to combat world hunger, replacing the diversity of crops like corn with single varieties that produced high yields. Unlike most crops, new corn varieties are heavily patented.

Field Corn
223

2

3   25   2   1

19

Originally 497 varieties in 1903, but many were duplicates. Genetic testing has revealed the true number (107).

2   2

8   9

14

75   164   287   82   25   29   64   107   34   14   789

sources: Heald and Chapman (2011), FAO, Wouw et al. (2010), Kerr Center
Data: bit.ly/KIB_NoMoreVeg

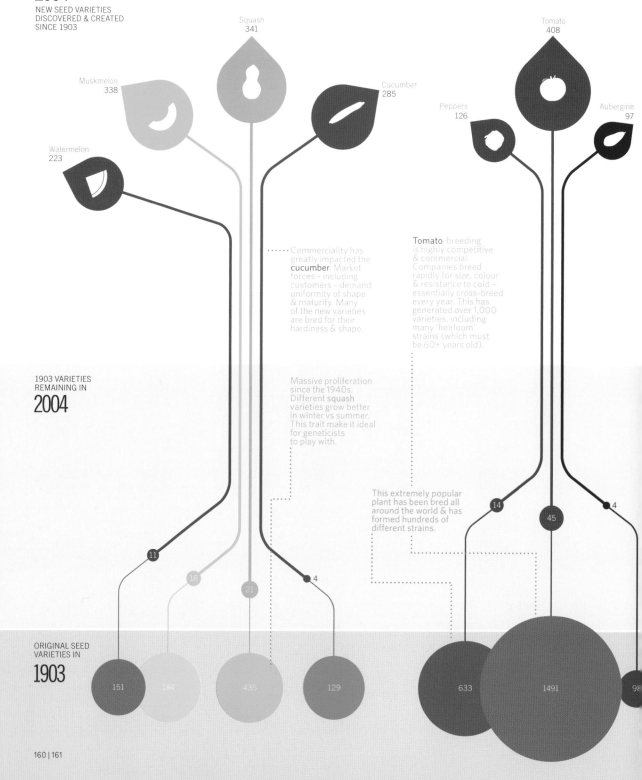

vegetable family   *cucurbitaceae*
(gourd)

solanaceae
(potato)

2004
NEW SEED VARIETIES
DISCOVERED & CREATED
SINCE 1903

Squash
341

Tomato
408

Muskmelon
338

Cucumber
285

Peppers
126

Aubergine
97

Watermelon
223

Commerciality has
greatly impacted the
cucumber. Market
forces – including
customers – demand
uniformity of shape
& maturity. Many
of the new varieties
are bred for their
hardiness & shape.

Tomato-breeding
is highly competitive
& commercial.
Companies breed
rapidly for size, colour
& resistance to cold –
essentially cross-breed
every year. This has
generated over 1,000
varieties, including
many 'heirloom'
strains (which must
be 60+ years old).

1903 VARIETIES
REMAINING IN
2004

Massive proliferation
since the 1940s.
Different **squash**
varieties grow better
in winter vs summer.
This trait make it ideal
for geneticists
to play with.

This extremely popular
plant has been bred all
around the world & has
formed hundreds of
different strains.

14

45

4

11

16

21

4

ORIGINAL SEED
VARIETIES IN
1903

151

184

435

129

633

1491

98

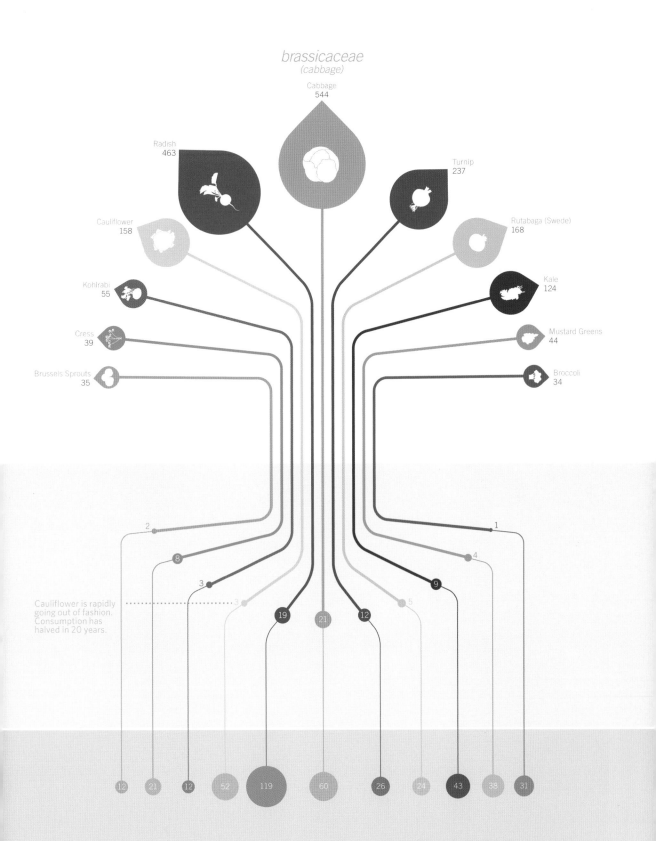

brassicaceae
(cabbage)

Cabbage
544

Radish
463

Turnip
237

Cauliflower
158

Rutabaga (Swede)
168

Kohlrabi
55

Kale
124

Cress
39

Mustard Greens
44

Brussels Sprouts
35

Broccoli
34

Cauliflower is rapidly
going out of fashion.
Consumption has
halved in 20 years.

sources: Heald and Chapman (2011), FAO, Wouw et al. (2010), Kerr Center
Data: bit.ly/KIB_NoMoreVeg

Total Varieties

Why
has diversity dropped?

2004
NEW SEED VARIETIES
DISCOVERED & CREATED
SINCE 1903

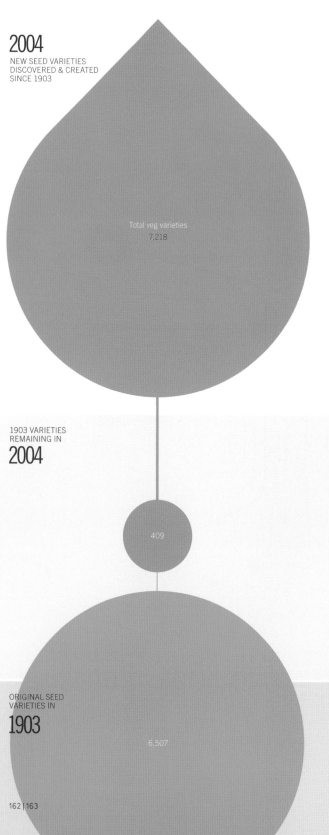

Total veg varieties
7,218

Copycats
The sheer number
of early-20th-century
varieties may have
been over-estimated

Lack of DNA testing
& global databases
may have created an
illusion of diversity.

One hundred years
ago, seeds were shared
between neighbours
& local farmers.

Today, farmers buy
their seeds from fewer
than 10 companies.

1903 VARIETIES
REMAINING IN
2004

409

Cash crops
Commercial plant
growers invest more
in plants that give
a higher return.

Mostly major crops
(corn, soy & wheat)
over minor crops
(oats & vegetables).

Economic forces also
affect public research.
Big university grants
for big cash crops.

ORIGINAL SEED
VARIETIES IN
1903

6,507

Number of varieties of
major crops is likely to
grow over time, while
minor crops steadily
dwindle.

Seed Money

Who owns the seed companies?

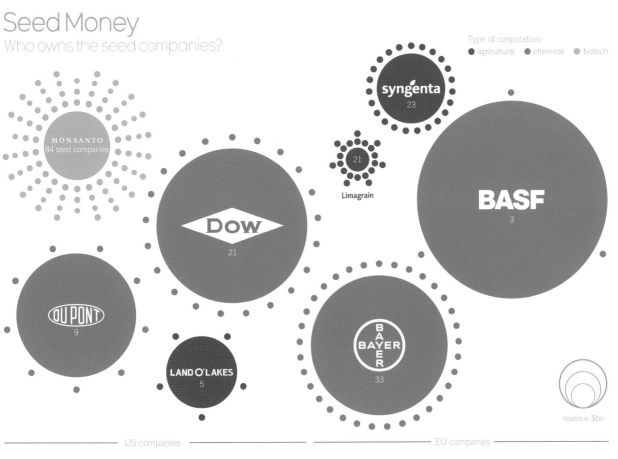

Type of corporation:
● agricultural   ● chemical   ● biotech

MONSANTO
84 seed companies

syngenta
23

Limagrain
21

Dow
21

BASF
3

DU PONT
9

BAYER
33

LAND O'LAKES
5

revenue $bn

———— US companies ————   ———— EU companies ————

Most Produced								
YEARLY GLOBAL PRODUCTION (million tonnes)	300	300	300	365	671	720	872	1,833
	Vegetables	Sugar Beet	Palm	Potatoes	Wheat	Rice	Maize	Sugar Cane

Most Productive								
YIELD PER KM² (tonnes)	963	1,288	1,424	1,740	1,900	3,368	5,507	7,024
	Grapes	Cassava	Vegetables	Palm	Potatoes	Tomatoes	Sugar Beet	Sugar Cane

Most Lucrative								
VALUE PER KM² ($ thousand)	153	177	262	269	304	364	625	1,415
	Cassava	Tea	Sugar Cane	Sugar Beet	Vegetables	Potatoes	Grapes	Tomatoes

sources: Heald and Chapman (2011), FAO, Wouw et al. (2010), Kerr Center
Data: bit.ly/KIB_NoMoreVeg

Cash Crops: Most Lucrative

$47,660,000
per km²

Cannabis

source: FAOSTAT
Data: bit.ly/KIB_NoMoreVeg

Human Cost
Inflation-adjusted

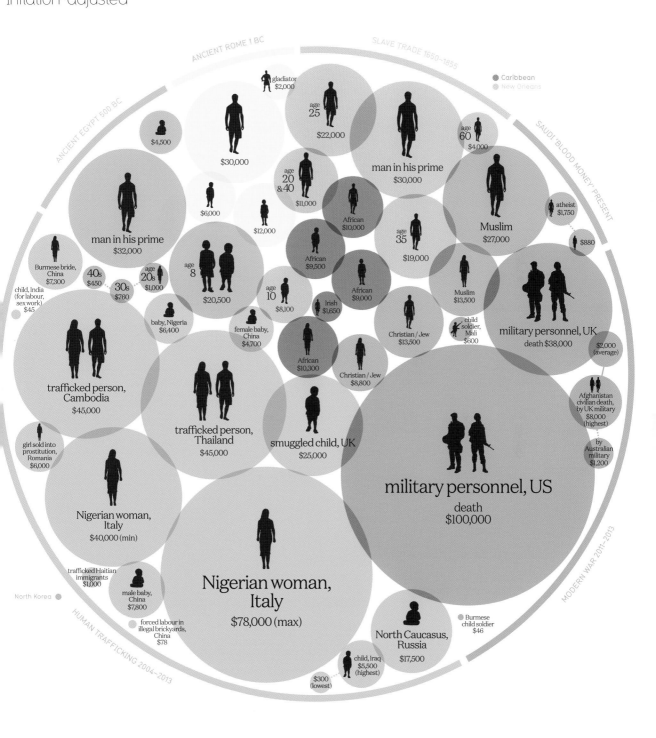

ANCIENT ROME 1 BC

ANCIENT EGYPT 500 BC

SLAVE TRADE 1650–1855

SAUDI 'BLOOD MONEY' PRESENT

MODERN WAR 2011–2013

HUMAN TRAFFICKING 2004–2013

● Caribbean
● New Orleans

gladiator
$2,000

$4,500

age 25
$22,000

age 60
$4,000

age 20 & 40
$11,000

man in his prime
$30,000

$30,000

$6,000

$12,000

man in his prime
$32,000

African
$10,000

Muslim
$27,000

atheist
$1,750

$880

Burmese bride, China
$7,300

40s
$450

20s
$1,000

age 8

30s
$760

African
$9,500

age 35
$19,000

child, India (for labour, sex work)
$45

baby, Nigeria
$6,400

age 10
$8,100

Irish
$1,650

African
$9,000

Muslim
$13,500

$20,500

female baby, China
$4,700

Christian / Jew
$13,500

child soldier, Mali
$600

military personnel, UK
death $38,000

$2,000
(average)

trafficked person,
Cambodia
$45,000

African
$10,300

Christian / Jew
$8,800

Afghanistan civilian death, by UK military
$8,000
(highest)

girl sold into prostitution, Romania
$6,000

trafficked person,
Thailand
$45,000

smuggled child, UK
$25,000

by Australian military
$1,200

Nigerian woman, Italy
$40,000 (min)

military personnel, US
death
$100,000

trafficked Haitian immigrants
$1,000

male baby, China
$7,800

North Korea ●

forced labour in illegal brickyards, China
$78

Nigerian woman,
Italy
$78,000 (max)

North Caucasus, Russia
$17,500

● Burmese child soldier
$46

child, Iraq
$5,500
(highest)

$300
(lowest)

sources: Havoscope.com, Guardian, BBC, 'The Slave Systems of Greek & Roman Antiquity', William Linn Westermann
data: bit.ly/KIB_HumanCost

Drug Deal

Potential tax revenue from legalising drugs worldwide

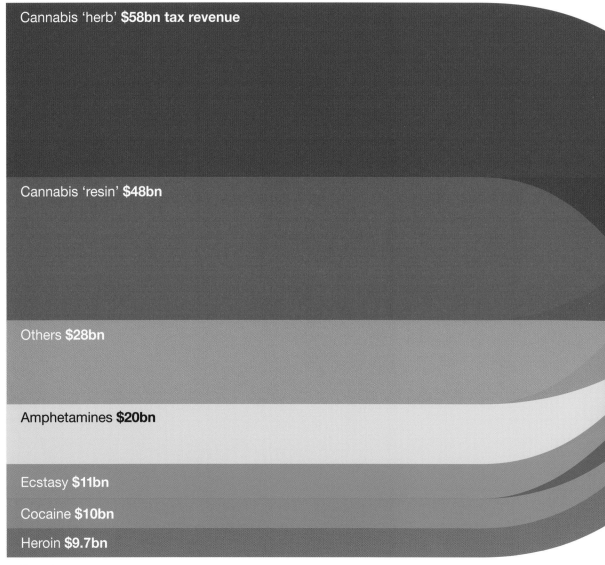

Most users

Cannabis 'herb' **$58bn tax revenue**

Cannabis 'resin' **$48bn**

Others **$28bn**

Amphetamines **$20bn**

Ecstasy **$11bn**

Cocaine **$10bn**

Heroin **$9.7bn**

Fewest users

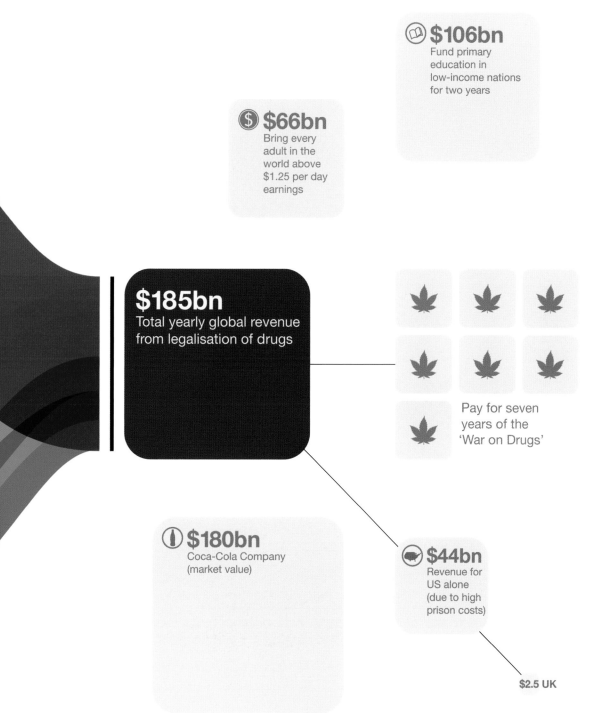

$106bn
Fund primary
education in
low-income nations
for two years

$66bn
Bring every
adult in the
world above
$1.25 per day
earnings

$185bn
Total yearly global revenue
from legalisation of drugs

Pay for seven
years of the
'War on Drugs'

$180bn
Coca-Cola Company
(market value)

$44bn
Revenue for
US alone
(due to high
prison costs)

$2.5 UK

sources: Independent Drug Monitoring Unit, CIA Factbook, UNODC.org, NASA
data: bit.ly/KIB_DrugsLegal

Age of Empires

If every dynasty lasted 100 years...

type of government
Autocracy
Bureaucracy
Monarchy
Stratocracy
Theocracy

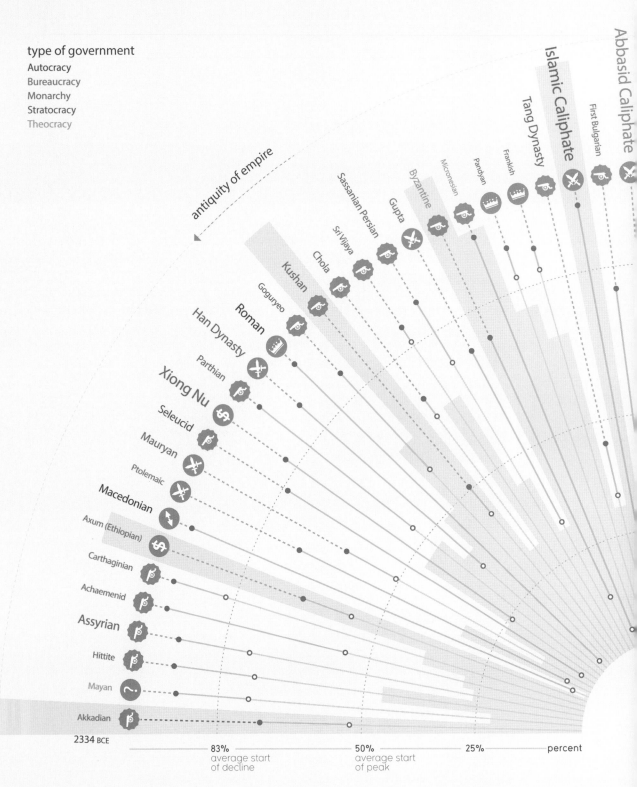

antiquity of empire

Abbasid Caliphate

Islamic Caliphate

Tang Dynasty

First Bulgarian

Frankish

Pandyan

Micronesian

Byzantine

Gupta

Sassanian Persian

Sri Vijaya

Chola

Kushan

Goguryeo

Roman

Han Dynasty

Parthian

Xiong Nu

Seleucid

Mauryan

Ptolemaic

Macedonian

Axum (Ethiopian)

Carthaginian

Achaemenid

Assyrian

Hittite

Mayan

Akkadian

2334 BCE

83%
average start
of decline

50%
average start
of peak

25%

percent

Size of Empire at **Peak**

actual duration (years)

start of peak ○——————— golden age ————————• •-- start of decline

reason for collapse

- economics
- external conflict
- internal conflict
- leadership issues
- $ overstretch
- ? unknown

Khmer
Klingon
Fatimid Caliphate
Song Dynasty
Holy Roman
Great Seljuk
Mameluk
Mongol
Chagatai
Mali
Golden Horde
Il Khan
Ottoman
Oyo
Vijayanagara
Ming Dynasty
Timurid
Portuguese
Spanish
British
Mughal
French
Danish Colonial
Qing Dynasty
Galactic Empire
Russian
Japanese
Third Reich
Soviet
1952 CE

actual duration   250 years   500   830   1,000

sources: Encyclopedia Britannica, Wikipedia
data: bit.ly/KIB_empires

HUMANITARIAN	41%	
		Children	16%
		Disaster relief	12.5%
		International poverty	7%
		International development	3%
		Human rights	2%
		Peace	0.5%
HEALTH	21%	Terminal illnesses	9.5%
		Medical research	7%
		Non-terminal illnesses	1%
		Hospitals	1%
		Mental health & addiction	0.5%
		Rescue services	2%
ARTS & CULTURE	13%	Arts	11.7%
		Culture and learning	1.5%
SOCIAL CARE	10%	Disability	5%
		Socio-economic disadvantage	2.5%
		Care and support	2.5%
ANIMALS	7%	Welfare	5.4%
		Conservation	1.4%
OCCUPATION SUPPORT GROUPS	3%	Armed forces	3%
ENVIRONMENT	3%	Conservation & public spaces	3%
SPORT & RECREATION	2%	Sport	2%

Welfare	6.5%
Health	4%
Poverty	2.5%
Abuse	1.5%
General	1.5%
General	12%
Medical	0.5%
General poverty	5.5%
Water	1%
Refugees	0.5%
General	3%
Women's rights	1.3%
General	0.7%
Landmine clearance	0.5%
Cancer	5.5%
Cardiovascular	1.5%
Neurodegenerative	1%
Other	1.5%
Cancer research	4.8%
Other	2.2%
Diabetes & arthritis	1%
Private	1%
All mental health & addiction	0.5%
All rescue services	2%
All arts	6.2%
Visual arts	2.4%
Music	1.8%
Dramatic arts	1.3%
Learned societies	0.8%
Heritage sites & museums	0.7%
Visual impairment	4%
Other	1%
Local community	1.5%
Homelessness	1%
For the elderly	1.25%
Palliative care	1.25%
All animals	3.9%
Dogs & cats	1.5%
Birds	1.4%
Veterans	3%
Parks & gardens	1.8%
Eco-systems	0.9%
Woodland & trees	0.3%
Football	1%
Cricket	1%

Orphans
0.08%

Missing children
0%

Basic healthcare
0.13%

Fairtrade
0.03%

LGBT rights
0.01%

Autism
0.11%

Asthma
0.10%

]— £70m

Schizophrenia / Depression & suicide / Eating disorders
0.01%

Landmarks & monuments
0.03%

Care for carers
0.05%

Victims of abuse
0.11%

Counting the Cause UK
What do we donate most to?   And what do we not?

sources: Charity Commission, UK Giving 2012, Guardian
data: bit.ly/KIB_GiveNotGive, errors due to rounding

Rainforest / Coastline & waterways
0.03%

HUMANITARIAN	40%	International poverty	25.1%
		Children	9.3%
		Disaster relief	4.9%
		International development	0.7%
SOCIAL CARE	26%	Care & support	16.6%
		Socio-economic disadvantage	7%
		Disability	2.4%
HEALTH	17%	Terminal illnesses	7%
		Hospitals	5.8%
		Medical research	2.5%
		Non-terminal illnesses	1.7%
ARTS & CULTURE	6%	Culture & learning	4.1%
		Arts	1.8%
SPORT & RECREATION	3.6%	Recreation	2.9%
		Sport	0.7%
ENVIRONMENT	2.5%	Conservation	0.9%
		Public spaces	1.6%
OTHER	2%	Associations	0.9%
		Encouraging enterprise	1%
ANIMALS	1.6%	Welfare	0.7%
		Conservation	0.9%
OCCUPATION SUPPORT GROUPS	1.5%	Armed forces	1.5%

Counting the Cause US
What do we donate most to?   And what do we not?

Category	%
Basic healthcare	5.8%
Hunger	2.8%
Refugees	2%
Other	14.5%
International	2%
Hunger	1.5%
Health: terminally ill	1%
Other	4.8%
Disaster relief	4.9%
Agricultural	0.7%
Those in need	12.4%
Young people	3.2%
Families	1%
Food banks	4.3%
Homelessness	1.8%
Other	0.9%
All disability	2.4%
Cancer	3.9%
Cardiovascular	1.3%
Neurodegenerative	1%
Other	0.8%
For children	3.4%
Other	2.4%
Cancer	1%
Other	1.5%
Diabetes	0.9%
Other	0.8%
Heritage sites & museums	0.7%
Public libraries	1%
Public broadcasting	1.2%
Education	1.2%
Performing arts	1%
Visual arts	0.8%
Youth clubs & other	1.8%
Boy scouts	1.1%
Athletics	0.7%
All eco-systems	0.9%
All public spaces	1.6%
Israeli	0.9%
All encouraging enterprise	1%
Welfare	0.7%
Wildlife	0.9%
Veterans	1.5%

$400m

Peace
0.13%

Health: Cleft palette
0.43%

Human Rights
0.12%

Local community
0.39%

Education
0.36%

Health
0.19%

Cystic Fibrosis
0.3%

Birth defects
0.5%

Parkinsons
0.14%

Autism
0.12%

Girl scouts
0.26%

Climate change
0.39%

sources: Giving USA 2012, Forbes.com
data: bit.ly/KIB_GiveNotGive, errors due to rounding

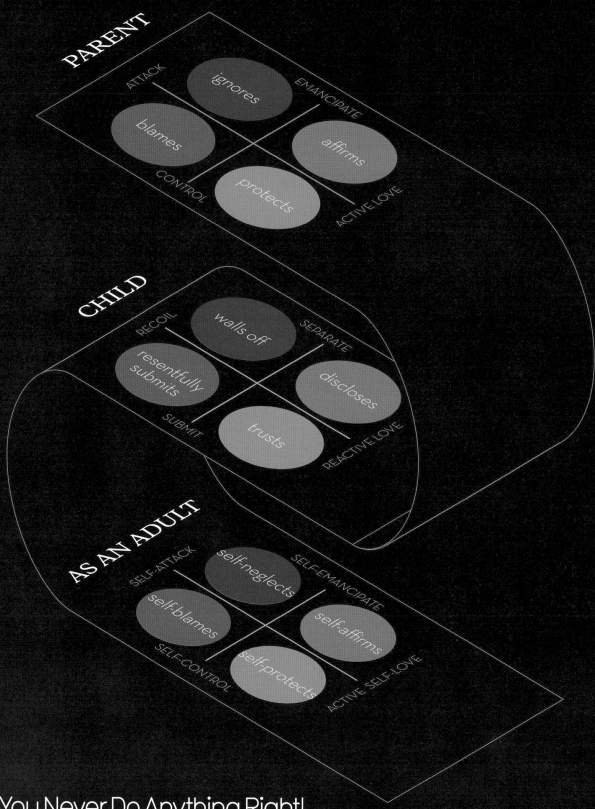

PARENT

ATTACK · EMANCIPATE · CONTROL · ACTIVE LOVE

ignores · blames · affirms · protects

CHILD

RECOIL · SEPARATE · SUBMIT · REACTIVE LOVE

walls off · resentfully submits · discloses · trusts

AS AN ADULT

SELF-ATTACK · SELF-EMANCIPATE · SELF-CONTROL · ACTIVE SELF-LOVE

self-neglects · self-blames · self-affirms · self-protects

You Never Do Anything Right!
Coding the interaction of parent with child

source: 'Interpersonal Diagnosis & Treatment of Personality Disorders', Lorna Smith Benjamin

Action Movie Badasses
Who's killed the most?

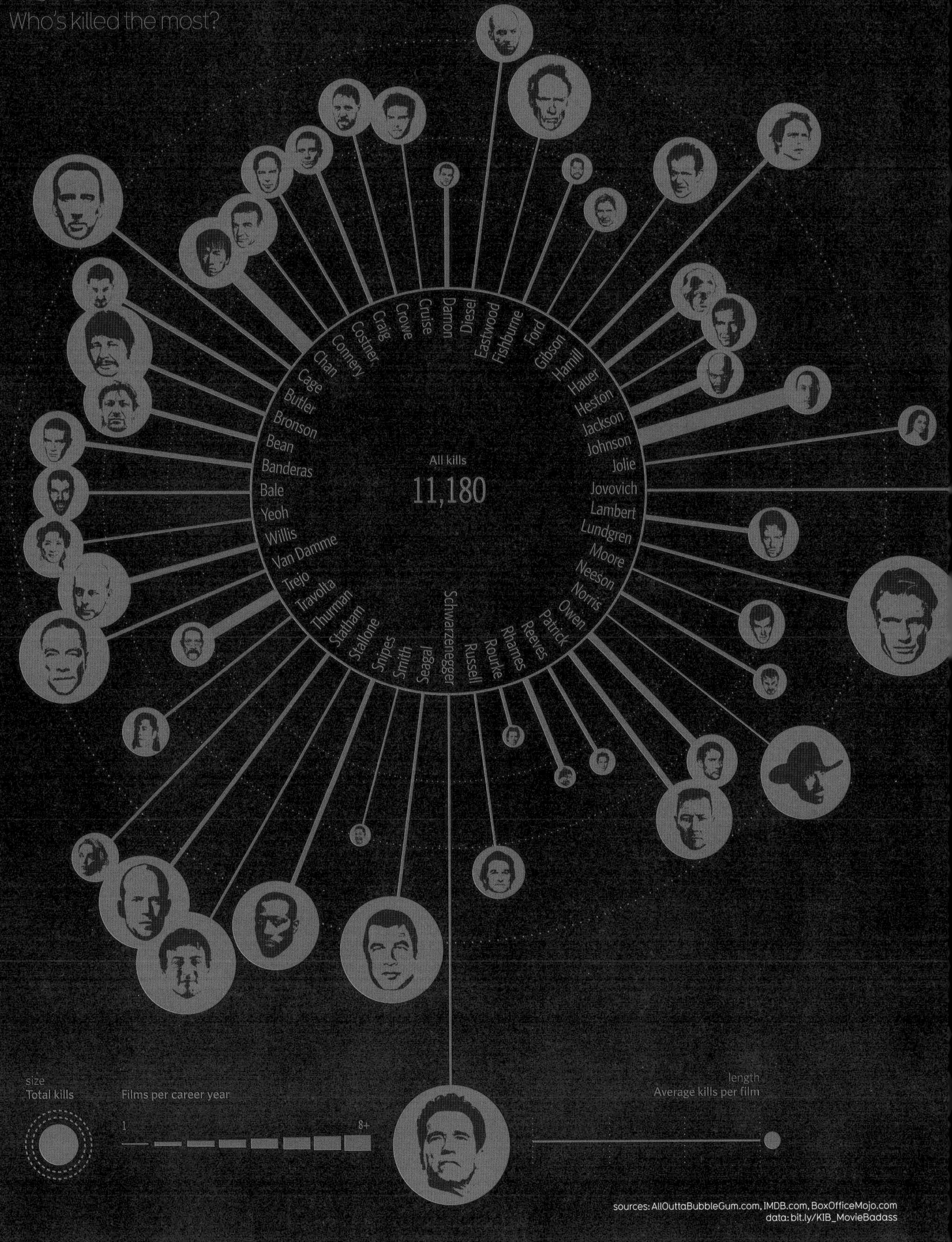

All kills
11,180

Cage
Chan
Connery
Costner
Craig
Crowe
Cruise
Damon
Diesel
Eastwood
Fishburne
Ford
Gibson
Hamill
Hauer
Heston
Jackson
Johnson
Jolie
Jovovich
Lambert
Lundgren
Moore
Neeson
Norris
Owen
Patrick
Reeves
Rhames
Rourke
Russell
Seagal
Schwarzenegger
Smith
Snipes
Stallone
Statham
Thurman
Travolta
Trejo
Van Damme
Willis
Yeoh
Bale
Banderas
Bean
Bronson
Butler

size
Total kills

Films per career year

1   8+

length
Average kills per film

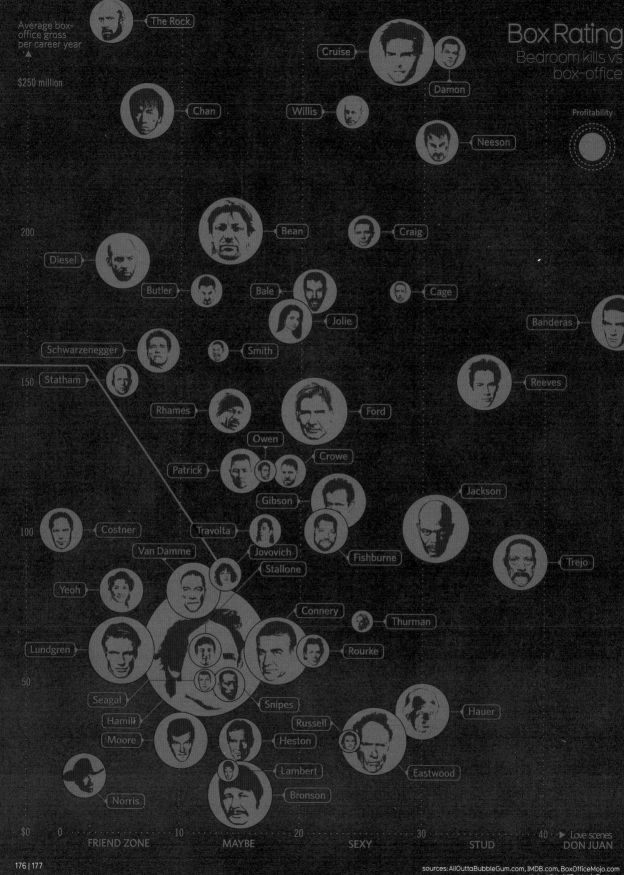

Box Rating
Bedroom kills vs
box-office

Average box-
office gross
per career year

$250 million

Profitability

The Rock

Cruise

Damon

Chan

Willis

Neeson

200

Diesel

Bean

Craig

Butler

Bale

Cage

Jolie

Banderas

Schwarzenegger

Smith

150

Statham

Reeves

Rhames

Ford

Owen

Crowe

Patrick

Gibson

Jackson

100

Costner

Travolta

Jovovich

Fishburne

Trejo

Van Damme

Stallone

Yeoh

Connery

Thurman

Lundgren

Rourke

50

Seagal

Snipes

Hauer

Hamill

Russell

Moore

Heston

Lambert

Eastwood

Norris

Bronson

$0   0   10   20   30   40   ▶ Love scenes
    FRIEND ZONE   MAYBE   SEXY   STUD   DON JUAN

sources: AllOuttaBubbleGum.com, IMDB.com, BoxOfficeMojo.com
data: bit.ly/KIB_MovieBadass

Influ-Venn-Za

Who can catch what?

LIGHT TEXT = rarely infects humans   text SIZE = human fatality rate

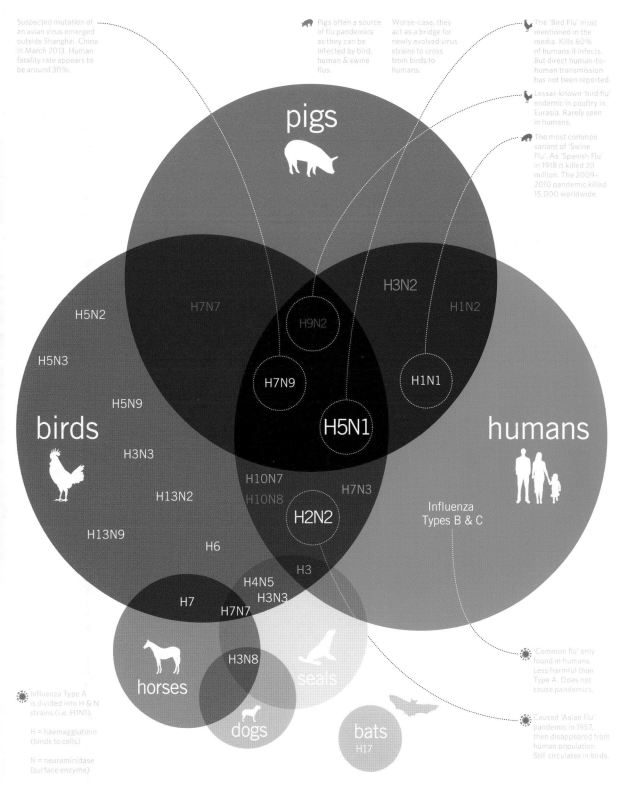

Suspected mutation of an avian virus emerged outside Shanghai, China in March 2013. Human fatality rate appears to be around 30%.

Pigs often a source of flu pandemics as they can be infected by bird, human & swine flus.

Worse-case, they act as a bridge for newly evolved virus strains to cross from birds to humans.

The 'Bird Flu' most mentioned in the media. Kills 60% of humans it infects. But direct human-to-human transmission has not been reported.

Lesser-known 'bird flu' endemic in poultry in Eurasia. Rarely seen in humans.

The most common variant of 'Swine Flu'. As 'Spanish Flu' in 1918 it killed 20 million. The 2009-2010 pandemic killed 15,000 worldwide.

pigs

birds

humans

H5N2

H5N3

H5N9

H3N3

H13N2

H13N9

H6

H7N7

H9N2

H7N9

H5N1

H3N2

H1N2

H1N1

H10N7
H10N8

H7N3

H2N2

Influenza Types B & C

H3

H4N5
H3N3

H7

H7N7

H3N8

horses

seals

dogs

bats

H17

Influenza Type A is divided into H & N strains (i.e. H1N1).

H = haemagglutinin (binds to cells)

N = neuraminidase (surface enzyme)

'Common flu' only found in humans. Less harmful than Type A. Does not cause pandemics.

Caused 'Asian flu' pandemic in 1957, then disappeared from human population. Still circulates in birds.

sources: World Health Organisation, Centers for Disease Control and Prevention
data: bit.ly/KIB_InfluVennZa

Prison Bars

MOST PRISONERS

total

USA	**2,267,000**
China	1,640,000
Russia	708,000
Brazil	515,000
India	372,000
Iran	250,000
Thailand	245,000
Mexico	238,000
South Africa	157,000
Ukraine	151,000
Indonesia	142,000
Turkey	125,000
Colombia	114,000

per 100,000 people

USA	**730**
Rwanda	527
Cuba	510
Russian Federation	495
Georgia	492
Belarus	438
El Salvador	425
Azerbaijan	407
Thailand	349
Ukraine	334
Iran	333
Kazakhstan	316
South Africa	307

per 100,000 people, OECD nations only

Country	Value		Decade increase
USA	730		0%
Chile	279		24%
Israel	236		38%
Poland	220		3%
Czech Rep.	219		15%
Mexico	206		26%
Slovakia	205		40%
New Zealand	194		31%
Hungary	173		2%
Turkey	165		121%
England & Wales	153		13%
Spain	149		18%
Australia	130		16%

sources: OECD, US Bureau of Justice Statistics, UK Ministry Of Justice, US Department of Justice
data: bit.ly/KIB_PrisonBars

Prison Bars: US Prison Population

	BY CRIME %	ETHNICITY % white	% black
violent crime	53	35	38
murder	13	28	40
manslaughter	1	39	35
robbery	14	21	55
assault	10	31	41
other violent	3	43	40
sex crime	12	48	24
rape	5	48	24
other sexual assault	7	59	23
property	19	44	32
burglary	10	42	36
larceny	4	47	30
motor-vehicle theft	1	45	23
fraud	2	49	27
other property	2	48	24
drugs	18	30	41
public order	9	39	36
driving under influence	no data	no data	
other / unspecified	1	31	25
prison population		35	38
US population		64	12

statistical significance: ▨ high ▨ very high

% hispanic	% other	REOFFENDING % re-convicted within 3 years	MEN VS WOMEN if gender balance were equal: ← % more men | % more women →
21	6		18.5
23	3.9	⎱ 27	2.4
16	2.4	⎰	1.2
20	2.1	47	5.4
28	3.7	45	1.5
25	4.1	34	0.3
22		no data	no data
10	2.8	28	4.5
15	3.2	23	6.2
16	2.7		11.2
17	2.4	55	3.2
14	2.4	⎱ 56	5.6
28	4.6	⎰	0.2
9	2.7	no data	8.2
13	2.9	47	0.6
21	2.0	47	8.4
23	3.5	no data	1.7
no data		32	no data
10	3.6	46	0.5
21	3		
16	8		

sources: US Bureau of Justice Statistics, US Department of Justice
data: bit.ly/KIB_PrisonBars

Superpower Showdown
War & peace

	China	EU	India	USA
MILITARY SPENDING $ BILLIONS	129	298	44	689
MILITARY SPENDING % OF GDP	2.0	1.9	2.4	4.2
ACTIVE TROOPS MILLIONS	2.2	1.6	1.3	1.4
ACTIVE TROOPS PER 100,000 PEOPLE	169	318	107	448
NUCLEAR WARHEADS	240	65	100	7,700
COST OF NUCLEAR WEAPONS PROGRAMME % OF WORLD TOTAL NUCLEAR-WEAPONS SPENDING	7	NO DATA	5	58
DONATIONS TO UN % OF TOTAL YEARLY UN CONTRIBUTIONS	3	43	1	24
AID DONATIONS % OF GDP	0.08	0.19	0.01	0.02
HUMANITARIAN AID DONATIONS % OF GDP	0.01	0.03	0	0
DONATIONS TO IMF % OF GDP	0.14	0.41	0.29	0.24
SCORE	1	4	0	5

USA IS VICTORIOUS!

sources: CIA World Factbook, World Bank, Eurostat
data: bit.ly/KIB_Superpowers

Walled World

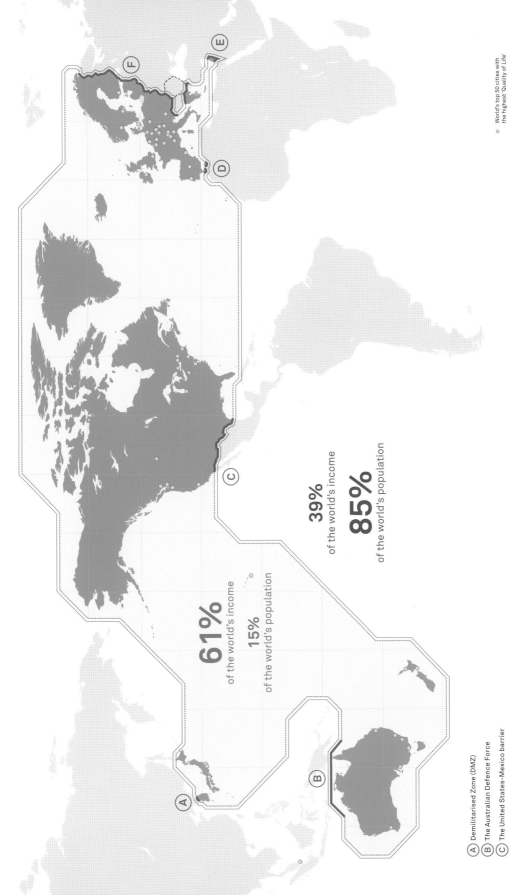

61%
of the world's income

15%
of the world's population

39%
of the world's income

85%
of the world's population

(A) Demilitarised Zone (DMZ)
(B) The Australian Defence Force
(C) The United States-Mexico barrier
(D) The Melilla & Cueta border fences
(E) The West Bank barrier
(F) Schengen Border

sources: Guardian, Wikipedia, BBC, EUobserver, Queens University Belfast, CNN
data: bit.ly/KIB_WalledWorld

○ World's top 50 cities with
  the highest 'Quality of Life'
━ High-security border zone
--- Future Schengen Border line

Be op
Don't have a script for
Give little gifts Stay 'in the roo

Do stuff that makes y

Before you pick a fight, think: is it worth it? Don't
Be romantic
Remember: your partner is not you Learn from arguments

Compliment & appreciate every day C

Shut the bathroom door! Stop trying

Keep it adventu

Outsource housework

Appreciate all their strengths & gifts When the going gets tough, the to

Touch a lot Own your emotions Have reg

Go to bed angry - don't argue all night Enjoy a steady diet of
Never go to bed angry
Cook together

Have a vision, find common goals Don't compare your relatio

Have quickies Always unite to battle outside forces Remember t

Master the art of compromise Learn how t
Ask the questions you're most afraid to ask

Be polite & conscientious

Accept that you will both have bratty mom

Say sorry,

Don't go ou

loving *mature* *playful* *prag*

nest

riage in your head

n't run away from conflict

Never stop dating

happy

Be fully present

Think of them first

re

Don't try to change or fix them

to your partner what you want from them

municate empathically

ments

us, playful, fun

Talk about the little things

Ask your partner what they need more of

g... to therapy

Eat & work out like you're single

ar bonding time

Get a prenup

Talk about money

Remember the positives about them

Don't try to make love happen

d sex

Boring is okay

others'

Don't blame

Share power

gh

Ask - don't make assumptions

Prioritise your relationship, not your children

eally listen

Never stop working on your relationship

Every morning ask, 'How can I make my partner happy today?'

nce dependence & independence

rn their love language so they feel cherished

e peace

tine's Day

rational   *respectful*   *sexy*   *wise*

sources: Harville Hendrix, Huff Post, Cosmo, ELLE, Psychcentral, Reader's Digest, Happy Wives Club and others
data: bit.ly/KIB_Relationtips

Pin Point
Patterns in PIN numbers

Most common ▬▬▬▬▬▬▬▬▬▬▬▬ Least common

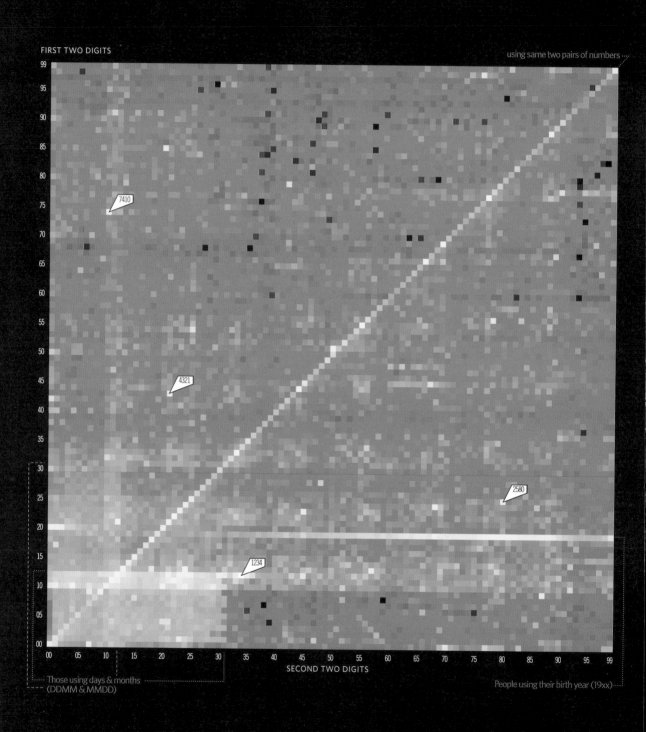

FIRST TWO DIGITS

using same two pairs of numbers

7410

4321

2580

1234

SECOND TWO DIGITS

Those using days & months
(DDMM & MMDD)

People using their birth year (19xx)

◣ Keypad numbers

| 1234 | 0000 | 7777 | 2000 | 2222 | 9999 | 5555 | 1122 | 8888 | 2001 |
| 1111 | 1212 | 1004 | 4444 | 6969 | 3333 | 6666 | 1313 | 4321 | 1010 |

27% of all
PIN numbers

image credit & sources: Nick Berry, DataGenetics.com
data & analysis: datagenetics.com/blog/september32012/

Ruling Casts
Types of Government

Power Structure

STATE

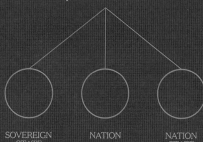

a political & territorial unit

SOVEREIGN STATE

not dependent on any other power or state

NATION

cultural (& sometimes ethnic) entity

NATION STATE

when cultural & political entities are one

MOST COUNTRIES

UNITARY STATE

union where sub-units only have as much power as central supreme power gives

UK, RUSSIAN FEDERATION

FEDERATION / FEDERAL STATE

union of partially self-governing units under a central (federal) power

USA, INDIA

FEDERACY

some units have more independence than others

USA & PUERTO RICO

DE-FACTO

central power could revoke power of units, but doesn't

CHINA

CONFEDERATION

permanent union of politically separate units for purposes of joint & communal action

EU, SPORTS LEAGUES

EMPIRE

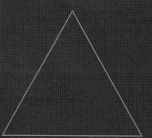

union of partially self-governing units directly ruled through coercion by central power

BRITISH EMPIRE, THIRD REICH, USA (arguably)

HEGEMONY

union of partially self-governing units indirectly ruled through coercion & cultural dominance of central power

ROMAN EMPIRE

Ideology / Intensity

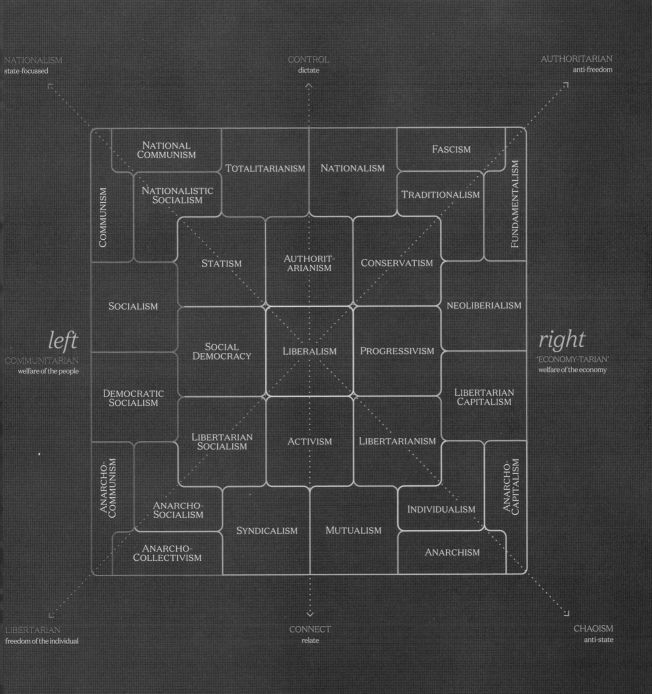

NATIONALISM
state-focussed

CONTROL
dictate

AUTHORITARIAN
anti-freedom

NATIONAL COMMUNISM

TOTALITARIANISM

NATIONALISM

FASCISM

COMMUNISM

NATIONALISTIC SOCIALISM

TRADITIONALISM

FUNDAMENTALISM

STATISM

AUTHORIT-ARIANISM

CONSERVATISM

SOCIALISM

NEOLIBERIALISM

left
COMMUNITARIAN
welfare of the people

SOCIAL DEMOCRACY

LIBERALISM

PROGRESSIVISM

right
'ECONOMY-TARIAN'
welfare of the economy

DEMOCRATIC SOCIALISM

LIBERTARIAN CAPITALISM

LIBERTARIAN SOCIALISM

ACTIVISM

LIBERTARIANISM

ANARCHO-COMMUNISM

ANARCHO-SOCIALISM

INDIVIDUALISM

ANARCHO-CAPITALISM

SYNDICALISM

MUTUALISM

ANARCHO-COLLECTIVISM

ANARCHISM

LIBERTARIAN
freedom of the individual

CONNECT
relate

CHAOISM
anti-state

sources: Wikipedia, BBC History, CIA World Factbook
data: bit.ly/KIB_RulingCasts

Power Source

DEMOCRACY
rule by the people

DIRECT
people vote & decide
on everything

REPRESENTATIVE
people elect representatives
who vote & decide on everything

EMERGENT
no central planning,
usually via technology

PARTICIPATORY
broader participation, such as
consensus decision-making

REPUBLIC
rule by elected president
via an elected executive

PARLIAMENTARY
ruler bound by constitution,
often just a figurehead

TECHNOCRACY
de-facto rule by technical
experts (usually scientists)

BUREAUCRACY
important decisions made
by (non-elected) technical officials

WIKICRACY
high-level bureaucracy
mediated by software

AUTOCRACY
absolute (usually abusive) rule
by a single person or party

ARISTOCRACY
rule by a small, unelected,
privileged ruling class

ANOCRACY
power between warring elites
(halfway autocracy & democracy)

STRATOCRACY
constitutional rule
by military power

THEOCRACY
rule by spiritual leader or
God-given spiritual system

MONARCHY

unquestioned rule by unelected,
power, unbound by constitution

SAUDI ARABIA

EMIRATE

rule by Emir
(a dynastic Muslim leader)

UNITED ARAB EMIRATES

SULTANATE

rule by Sultan
(an Arabian king)

BRUNEI

CALIPHATE

rule by Caliph (supreme Islamic
political & spiritual leader)

OTTOMAN EMPIRE

CONSTITUTIONAL

ruler bound by constitution,
often just a figurehead

UNITED KINGDOM

ANARCHY

no publicly enforced power

TWITTER,
FRENCH REVOLUTION

MATRIARCHY

rule by women

ELEPHANTS, BEES, ALIENS

SOCIOCRACY

rule by group reasoning

QUAKERS

ADHOCRACY

rule by disorganised
individuals

THE INTERNET

MERITOCRACY

power held according to
merit or ability

CONFUCIANISM

OLIGARCHY

rule by a small group
of elites

APARTHEID SOUTH AFRICA,
USA (arguably)

PLUTOCRACY

rule by a small minority
of rich citizens

CITY OF LONDON

KLEPTOCRACY

corrupt rule by 'thieves' for
personal power & wealth

RUSSIA (arguably)
USA (arguably)

NARCOCRACY

rule by powerful
drug lords

GUINEA-BISSAU,
MEXICO (arguably)

CORPORATOCRACY

rule by corporations
or corporate interests

EAST INDIA COMPANY,
USA (arguably)

sources: Wikipedia, BBC History
data: bit.ly/KIB_RulingCasts

Divas

4 octaves

3 octaves

5 octaves

SIZE OF EGO TO VOCAL PROWESS CORRELATION

Jennifer Hudson

Whitney Houston (pre-drugs)

Janet Jackson

Diana Ross

Barbra Streisand

Lana Del Rey

Cher

Madonna

Miley Cyrus

Beyoncé

Mary J. Blige

Jennifer

Erykah Badu

Nicole Scherzinger

Rihanna

Britney

Solange

Christina Aguilera

Alicia Keys

Mariah Carey

Kate Bush

Aretha Franklin

Janelle Monáe

Cyndi Lauper

Donna Summer

Céline Dion

Amy Winehouse

P!nk

Aaliyah (RIP)

Leona Lewis

Alanis Morissette

Brandy

Ke$ha

Ellie Goulding

Natasha Bedingfield

dramatic soprano
light lyric soprano
lyric soprano
soprano
spinto mezzo soprano
mezzo soprano
lyric contralto
coloratura contralto
contralto

Taylor
Swift

Critical acclaim
(Grammys per career year)

2 octaves

Vocal range

Adele

Cheryl Cole

Emeli Sandé

Lauryn
Hill

Jessie J

Nelly Furtado   Shakira

Avril Lavigne

Kylie

Katy Perry

Ciara

Joss
Stone

Alexandra
Burke

Björk

Enya

Lily Allen

AARGH!

HIGH

MEDIUM

Rumoured diva-ness

LOW

Sources: Last.FM.com, DivaDevotee.com, Wikipedia
data: bit.ly/KtB_Divas

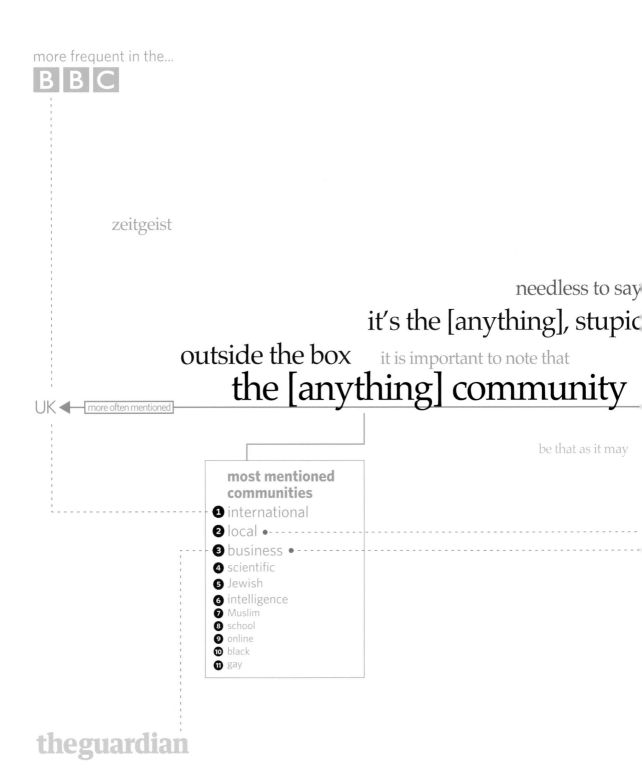

more frequent in the...

BBC

zeitgeist

needless to say

it's the [anything], stupid

outside the box   it is important to note that

the [anything] community

UK ← more often mentioned

be that as it may

most mentioned communities
1. international
2. local
3. business
4. scientific
5. Jewish
6. intelligence
7. Muslim
8. school
9. online
10. black
11. gay

theguardian

size of **text** = frequency

sparked debate

no silver bullet

hastily convened   kingmaker   situation is fluid

fevered speculation pre-dawn raid feeding frenzy stinging rebuke

charm offensive at a crossroads inside the beltway little-noticed

begs the question as a nation the narrative political theater

part and parcel out of the box grizzled veteran paradigm shift oft-cited

pundits say midwife critics say observers pushback

here, I said it going forward iconic redux the American people

increasingly any 'not-un' formulation

literally xxx is not alone [anything] 2.0

the other xxx call it xxx Hot-button issue

more often mentioned → US

that's just [person] being [person]

pity the poor xxx remains to be seen Mr. xx goes to Washington

ignominious end to be sure Gestalt shines a spotlight on underscored

xxx is no panacea

palpable sense of relief At first glance It is what it is

manicured lawns the proverbial xxx

the argument goes not unlike double down

rose from obscurity dizzying array demurred partisans on both sides

withering criticism Rorschach test

growing body of evidence the thinking goes

yes, Virginia, there is a xxx

tightly knit community a rare window

shifting dynamics

as a society

The New York Times

source: WashingtonPost.com, JimRomenesko.com
data: bit.ly/JournoCliches

SOLAR
2,750,000
exajoules

HYDRO
51

OCEAN
170

WIND
330

BIOFUEL
275

FOSSIL
FUEL
525

GEO-
THERMAL
775

NUCLEAR
NO DATA

USED AS FODDER,
BUILDING, TIMBER, ETC

POTENTIALLY USABLE AS ENERGY   exajoules ——————————— 1 exajoule will power humanity for 24 hours

Energy Flow Man

0.1

12

0.002

1

32 TRADITIONAL

8 MODERN

3.1 BIOFUEL

8.7 WASTE

52

PETROLEUM
167

COAL & PEAT
138

NATURAL GAS
106

SPARE
114

2.2

29

509
exajoules

TOTAL
HUMAN
ENERGY
HARVESTED

350
exajoules

TOTAL
FINAL
HUMAN
USAGE

ACTUALLY HARVESTED

LOST IN CONVERSION

ACTUALLY USED

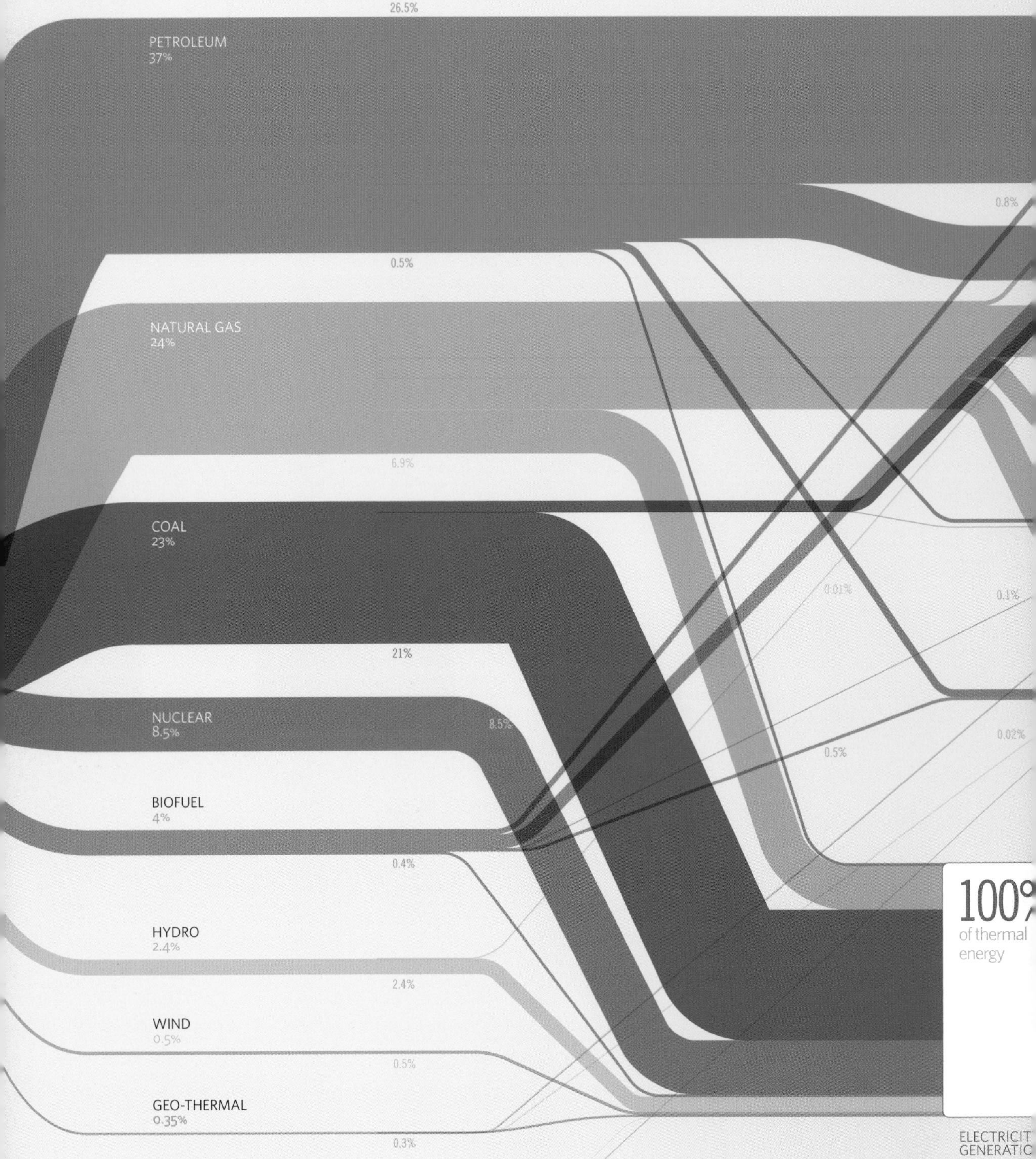

PETROLEUM
37%

26.5%

0.8%

NATURAL GAS
24%

0.5%

COAL
23%

6.9%

0.01%

0.1%

NUCLEAR
8.5%

21%

8.5%

BIOFUEL
4%

0.5%

0.02%

HYDRO
2.4%

0.4%

100%
of thermal
energy

WIND
0.5%

2.4%

GEO-THERMAL
0.35%

0.5%

ELECTRICITY
GENERATION

0.3%

SOLAR
0.1%

0.01%

TRANSPORT
39%

INDUSTRIAL
33%

0.7%

8.6%

1.8%

COMMERCIAL
12%

0.6%

0.01%

RESIDENTIAL
16%

1.2%

0.08%

%
COOKING 5
HOT WATER 6
HEATING 14

31%
of thermal
energy left

LIGHTING
& APPLIANCES 75

ELECTRIC
SUPPLY

77%   65%   66%   54%   68%
LOST IN CONVERSION

note: sample UK country data used for electricity generation figures
sources: International Energy Agency, US Department of Energy, REN21 Renewables Report 2012, BP Statistical Review World Energy
data: bit.ly/KIB_EnergyFlow

ABOVE AVERAGE

BELOW AVERAGE

The Prom Video

Phoebe's Ex-Partner

The Embryos   Ross's Wedding

Everybody Finds Out

The Invitation

The Contest

The Marine Biologist   The Opposite

Male Unbonding
The Robbery

The Ex-Girlfriend   The Baby Shower

The Dog   The Stranded

Black Tie

Cooter

Generalissimo   Apollo, Apollo   Kidney Now!

I Do Do

Live Show   100: Part 2

Pilot

Khonani

Queen of Jordan

Beloved Aunt

The Doll

The Grand Opening

The Ski Lift

The Christ Nail

Opening Night

Pilot

The Injury   Casino Night

The Job

Dinner Party   Goodbye, Toby

Stress Relief   Broke

The Spider Episode
Out of the Loco

Hank's Sex Tape

The Book

The Warmth Episode

The List   Being There

Would You Do
Me a Favor?   Doubt of the Benefit

The P.A.   0.409

Pain Equals Funny

Luckier Dip Best. Episode. Evah?

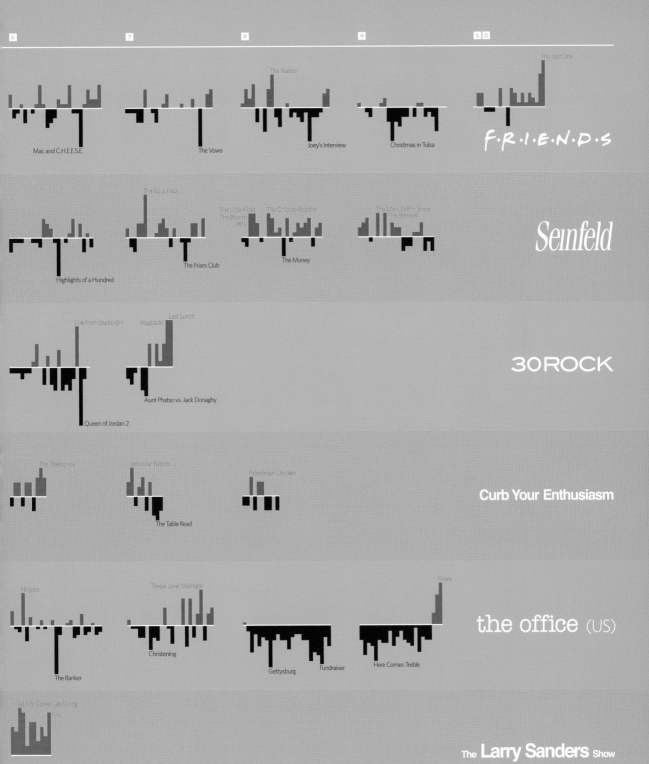

6   7   8   9   10

The Last One

F·R·I·E·N·D·S

Mac and C.H.E.E.S.E.

The Rumor

The Vows

Joey's Interview

Christmas in Tulsa

Seinfeld

The Soup Nazi

The Little Kicks
The Bizarro
Jerry

The Chicken Roaster

The Merv Griffin Show
The Betrayal

Highlights of a Hundred

The Friars Club

The Money

30ROCK

Live from Studio 6H

Hogcock!
Last Lunch

Aunt Phatso vs. Jack Donaghy

Queen of Jordan 2

Curb Your Enthusiasm

The Therapists

Vehicular Fellatio

Palestinian Chicken

The Table Read

the office (US)

Niagara

Threat Level Midnight

Finale

The Banker

Christening

Gettysburg

Fundraiser

Here Comes Treble

The Larry Sanders Show

As My Career Lay Dying
Flip

source: Internet Movie Database (IMDb.com)
data: bit.ly/KIB_BestEpisodes

the Simpsons

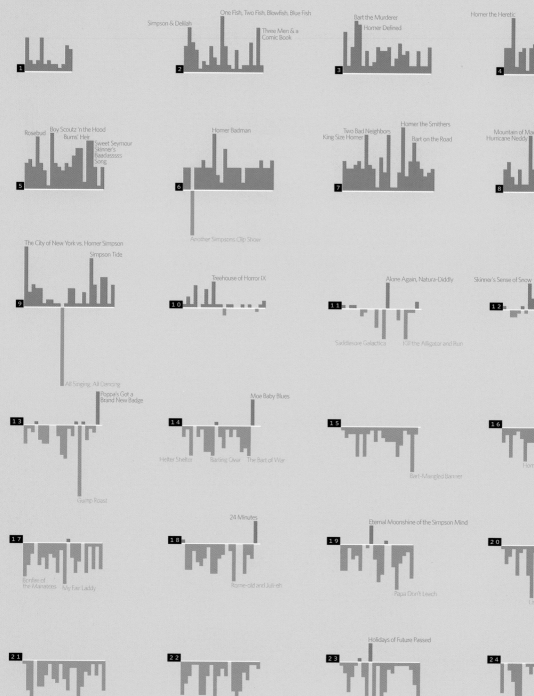

Simpson & Delilah

One Fish, Two Fish, Blowfish, Blue Fish

Three Men & a Comic Book

1

2

Bart the Murderer
Homer Defined

3

Homer the Heretic
Homer's Triple Bypass

4

Rosebud
Boy Scoutz 'n the Hood
Burns' Heir
Sweet Seymour Skinner's Baadasssss Song

5

Homer Badman

6

Another Simpsons Clip Show

King Size Homer
Two Bad Neighbors
Homer the Smithers
Bart on the Road

7

Mountain of Madness
Hurricane Neddy
Homer's Phobia
Homer's Enemy

8

The City of New York vs. Homer Simpson
Simpson Tide

9

All Singing, All Dancing

Treehouse of Horror IX

10

Alone Again, Natura-Diddly

11

Saddlesore Galactica
Kill the Alligator and Run

Skinner's Sense of Snow
Trilogy of Error

12

Bye Bye Nerdie

Poppa's Got a Brand New Badge

13

Gump Roast

Moe Baby Blues

14

Helter Shelter
Barting Over
The Bart of War

15

Bart-Mangled Banner

16

Homer and Ned's Hail Mary Pass

17

Bonfire of the Manatees
My Fair Laddy

24 Minutes

18

Rome-old and Juli-eh

Eternal Moonshine of the Simpson Mind

19

Papa Don't Leech

20

Lisa the Drama Queen

21

The Great Wife Hope
The Greatest Story Ever D'ohed

22

Moms I'd Like to Forget

Holidays of Future Passed

23

Lisa Goes Gaga

24

Gorgeous Grampa

source: Internet Movie Database (Imdb.com)
data: bit.ly/KIB_BestEpisodes

Should I Believe This Medical Study?

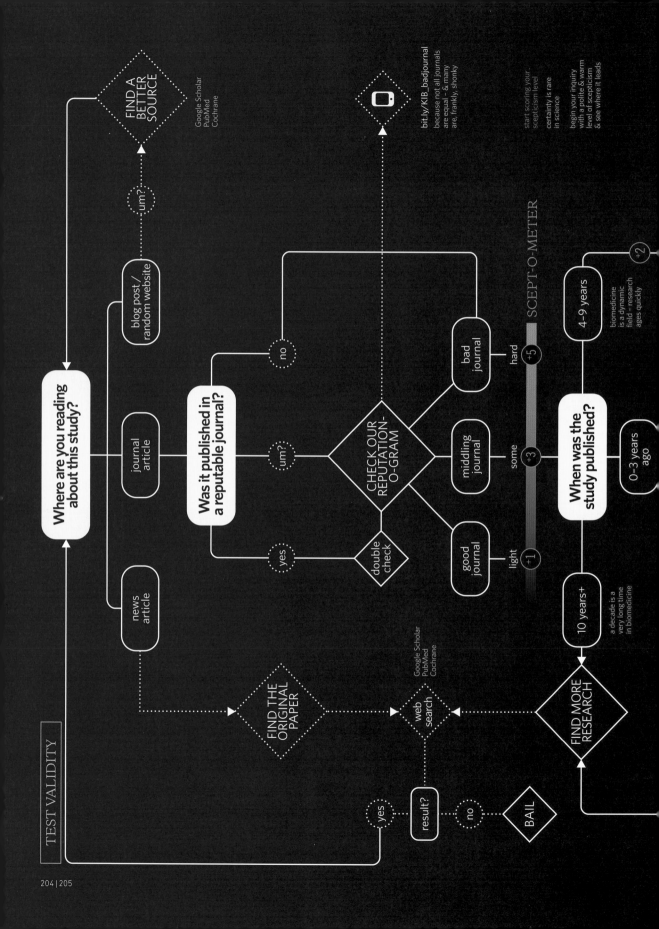

TEST VALIDITY

Where are you reading about this study?

news article

journal article

blog post / random website

FIND A BETTER SOURCE

Google Scholar
PubMed
Cochrane

um?

Was it published in a reputable journal?

yes

um?

no

CHECK OUR REPUTATION-O-GRAM

double check

good journal

middling journal

bad journal

light

+1

some

+3

hard

+5

bit.ly/KIB_badjournal
because not all journals are equal – & many are, frankly, shonky

SCEPT-O-METER

start scoring your scepticism level

certainty is rare in science

begin your inquiry with a polite & warm level of scepticism & see where it leads

When was the study published?

4–9 years

+2

0–3 years ago

10 years+

a decade is a very long time in biomedicine

biomedicine is a dynamic field – research ages quickly

FIND MORE RESEARCH

web search

Google Scholar
PubMed
Cochrane

result?

yes

no

BAIL

FIND THE ORIGINAL PAPER

Google Scholar
PubMed
Cochrane

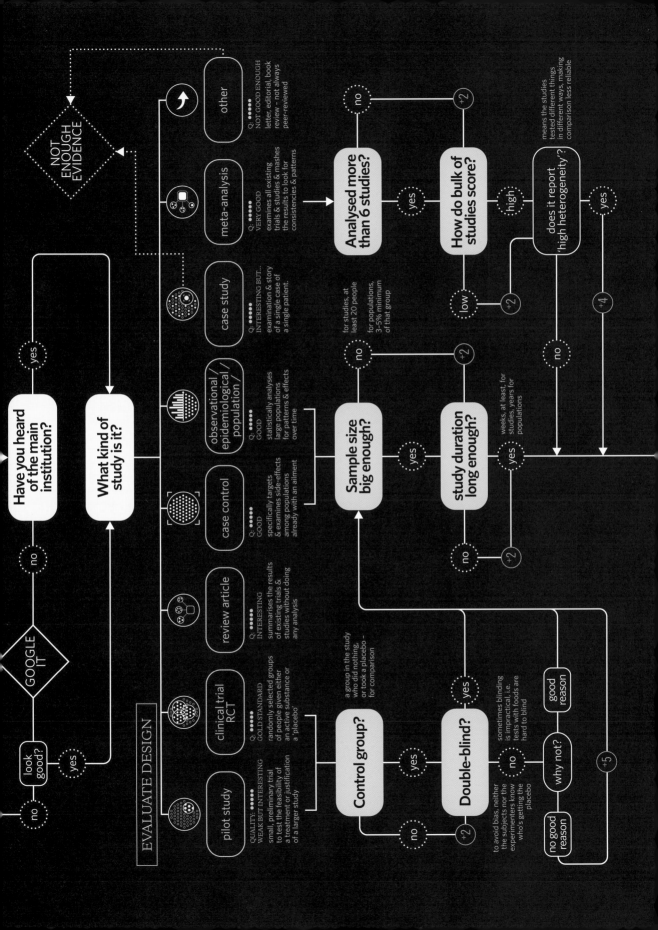

EVALUATE DESIGN

Have you heard of the main institution?

GOOGLE IT

look good?

yes — no

yes → NOT ENOUGH EVIDENCE

no

What kind of study is it?

pilot study
QUALITY: ●●●●●
WEAK BUT INTERESTING
small, preliminary trial
to test the feasibility of
a treatment or justification
of a larger study

clinical trial RCT
Q: ●●●●●
GOLD STANDARD
randomly selected groups
of people given either
an active substance or
a placebo

review article
Q: ●●●●●
INTERESTING
summarises the results
of existing trials &
studies without doing
any analysis

case control
Q: ●●●●●
GOOD
specifically targets
& examines side-effects
among populations
already with an ailment

observational / epidemiological / population /
Q: ●●●●●
GOOD
statistically analyses
large populations
for patterns & effects
over time

case study
Q: ●●●●●
INTERESTING BUT...
examination & story
of a single case of
a single patient.

meta-analysis
Q: ●●●●●
VERY GOOD
examines all existing
trials & studies & mashes
the results to look for
consistencies & patterns

other
Q: ●●●●●
NOT GOOD ENOUGH
letter, editorial, book
review - not always
peer-reviewed

Control group?
a group in the study
who did nothing,
or took a placebo -
for comparison

yes → **Double-blind?**
no → +2

to avoid bias, neither
the subjects nor the
experimenters know
who's getting the
placebo

Double-blind?
yes
no → sometimes blinding
is impractical, i.e.
tests with foods are
hard to blind

why not?
good reason → +5
no good reason

Sample size big enough?
for studies, at
least 20 people
for populations,
3-5% minimum
of that group
yes — no → +2

study duration long enough?
weeks, at least, for
studies, years for
populations
yes — no → +2

Analysed more than 6 studies?
yes — no → +2

How do bulk of studies score?
high
low → +2

does it report 'high heterogeneity'?
means the studies
tested different things
in different ways, making
comparison less reliable
yes → +4
no

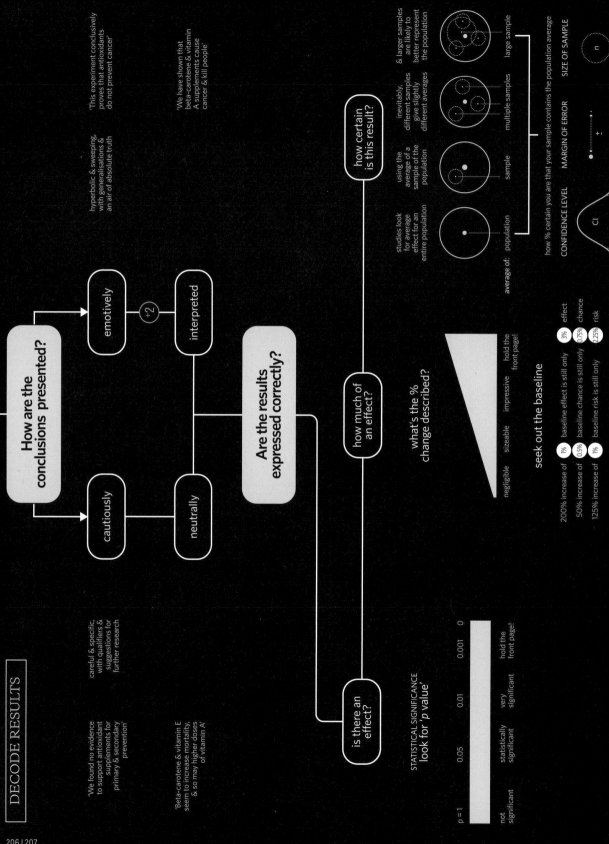

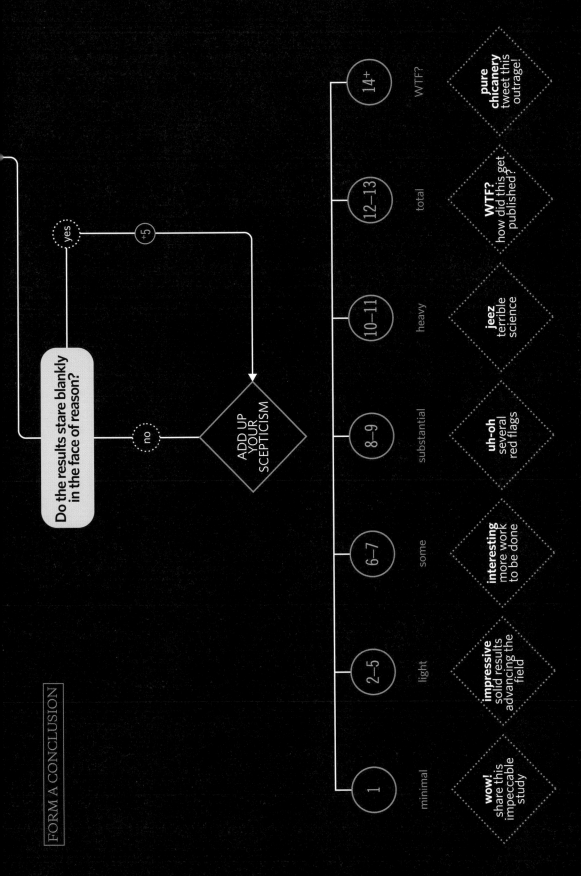

FORM A CONCLUSION

Do the results stare blankly in the face of reason?

yes

no

+5

ADD UP YOUR SCEPTICISM

1	2–5	6–7	8–9	10–11	12–13	14+
minimal	light	some	substantial	heavy	total	WTF?

wow! share this impeccable study

impressive solid results advancing the field

interesting more work to be done

uh-oh several red flags

jeez terrible science

WTF? how did this get published?

pure chicanery tweet this outrage!

sources: NYTimes, EigenFactor.org, Scholarlyoa.com, BioMed Central
data: bit.ly/KIB_StudyAid

Simple IV

Easy Metric
Only nations not using the metric system

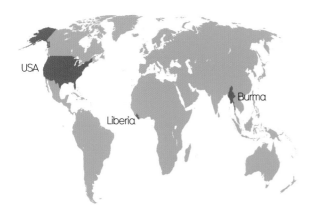

USA

Liberia

Burma

source: CIA World Factbook

Wealth Pyramids
The 0.7%

% of adult population   % of global wealth

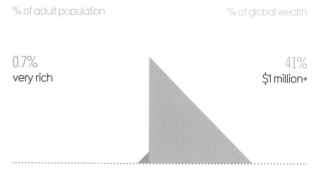

0.7%   41%
very rich $1 million+

7.7%   42%
rich $100k–$1m

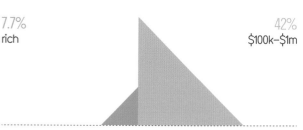

23%   14%
middle $10k–$100k

Out of Sight, Out of Mind
Location of people with mental health problems

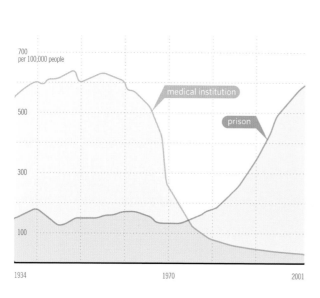

700
per 100,000 people

medical institution

prison

500

300

100

1934   1970   2001

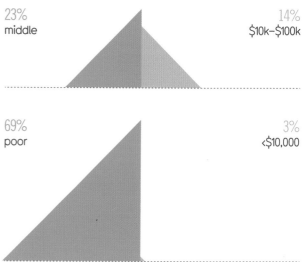

69%   3%
poor   <$10,000

source: 'An Institutionalization Effect', B.E. Harcourt (2007), US data

note: wealth = assets - debts // sources: Credit Suisse Global Wealth Databook 2013, Step Journ.

Dead Rich Presidents
Money stolen from government coffers

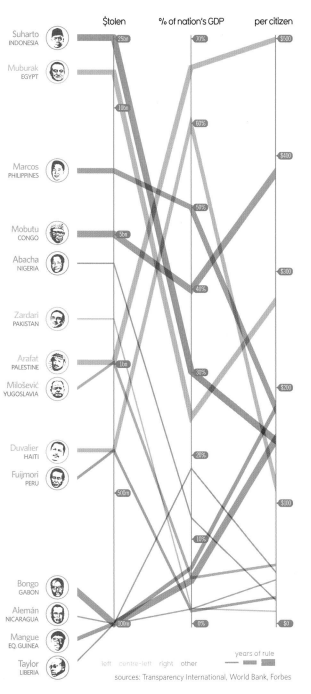

	$Stolen	% of nation's GDP	per citizen

Suharto — INDONESIA
Muburak — EGYPT
Marcos — PHILIPPINES
Mobutu — CONGO
Abacha — NIGERIA
Zardari — PAKISTAN
Arafat — PALESTINE
Milošević — YUGOSLAVIA
Duvalier — HAITI
Fuijmori — PERU
Bongo — GABON
Alemán — NICARAGUA
Mangue — EQ. GUINEA
Taylor — LIBERIA

years of rule
left   centre-left   right   other

sources: Transparency International, World Bank, Forbes

Kissing Cousins
Rules around first-cousin marriage

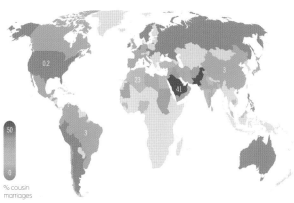

% cousin marriages

Famously married their first cousins

| Albert Einstein | Abraham Maslow | Saddam Hussein | Edgar Allan Poe | Greta Scacchi | H.G. Wells | Charles Darwin |

sources: Centre for Comparative Genomics (Murdoch University), Wikipedia

Birth-defect chances
Risky business

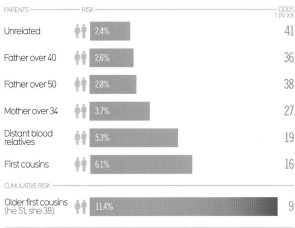

PARENTS	RISK	ODDS 1 IN XX
Unrelated	2.4%	41
Father over 40	2.6%	36
Father over 50	2.8%	38
Mother over 34	3.7%	27
Distant blood relatives	5.3%	19
First cousins	6.1%	16
CUMULATIVE RISK		
Older first cousins (he 51, she 38)	11.4%	9

sources: The Lancet, Sheridan et al (2013), Yang et al (2007)

data: bit.ly/KIB_Simple4

Live Long...
What will really extend your life?

Strength of science

male / female specific

Suggestive

Good

Strong

-10	-5	YEARS	+5	+10	+15	+20

7 hours ideal, but no more than 8 hours a night. Less sleep is better than 8 hours•   ⋯⋯ **Sleep too much**

Be optimistic ⋯⋯ Women with highest levels of cynical hostility are 16% more likely to die earlier

Get promoted ⋯⋯ Managers & those with more professional responsibility live longer than those with more 'routine' work

Live in a city

Live in the country

Eat less food ⋯⋯ Seen 10-20% lifespan boost in rats & monkeys...not yet proved in humans

Have a long-lived maternal grandfather

Men who spend a lot of time with women in their formative years ⋯⋯ **Hang out with women – a lot!**

Drink a little alcohol ⋯⋯ Those drinking a little a day (less than 2 units) do better than complete abstainers

Includes reliability, non-impulsivity & being neat & orderly ⋯⋯ **Be conscientious**

Have more orgasms ⋯⋯ Shoot for 350 a year!

And a little red wine

With close friends ⋯⋯ Loneliness equivalent to smoking 15 cigarettes a day

Men with more than one wife live 12% longer ⋯⋯ **Be polygamous, maybe**

Go to church regularly

No matter how much you exercise, sitting too much raises your risk of death ⋯⋯ **Sit down**

More pets ⋯⋯ Cat owners are 30% less likely to have a heart attack, especially in the elderly

Eat red meat

Avoid cancer

Avoid heart disease

Be alcoholic

Get health checks ⋯⋯ When aged 30–49 years

Get married!

Be rich ⋯⋯ Poorer people die 5–10 years earlier than their privileged peers

25 years shorter life expectancy ⋯⋯ **Be a woman**

Suffer severe mental illness

Become obese

Keep smoking / **Quit** ⋯⋯ 10 years gained if you quit age 25; 5 years gained if you quit between 45-59

Mediterranean- & Japanese-style diets ⋯⋯ **Eat healthy**

Live healthily ⋯⋯ Obviously, combine diet & exercise

If your siblings are long-lived, you probably will be too ⋯⋯ **Have a long-lived sibling**

Exercise more ⋯⋯ 150+ mins brisk walking per week

Live at a high altitude

RECIPE   married happy-go-lucky outdoors-loving sex-mad hippy party-girl in senior management with a cat

sources: British Medical Journal, PLOS Medicine, New Scientist
data: bit.ly/KIB_LiveLong

...and Prosper
Average annualised % return

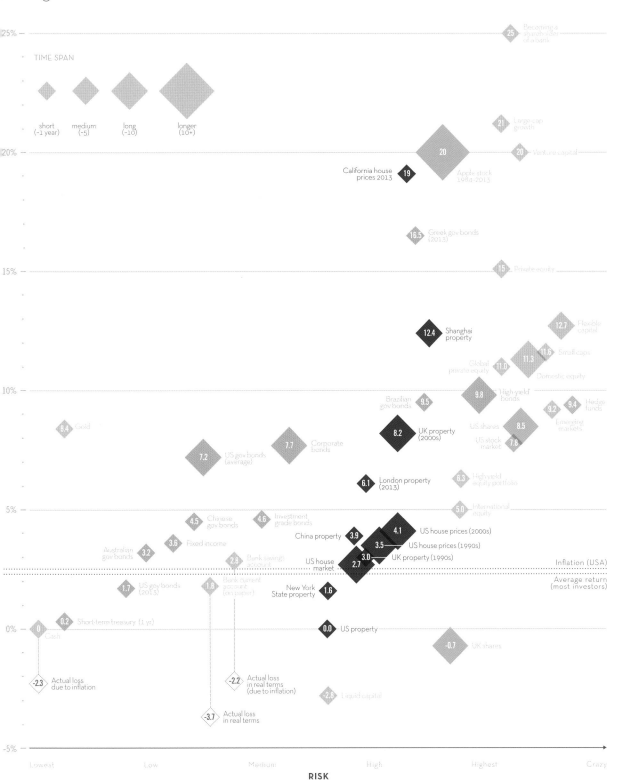

Bonds Stocks **Property** Others

25% — · **25** Becoming a shareholder of a bank

TIME SPAN

short (~1 year) | medium (~5) | long (~10) | longer (10+)

21 Large-cap growth

20% — · **20** · · · · · · **20** Venture capital

California house prices 2013 **19**   Apple stock 1984-2013

16.5 Greek gov bonds (2013)

15% — · **15** Private equity

12.7 Flexible capital

12.4 Shanghai property

11.6 Small-caps

11.0 Global private equity   **11.3** Domestic equity

10% — · **9.8** · · · 'High-yield' bonds

Brazilian gov bonds **9.5**   **9.2**   **9.4** Hedge funds

8.4 Gold   **9.8** US shares   **8.5** Emerging markets

7.7 Corporate bonds   **8.2** UK property (2000s)   US stock market **7.8**

7.2 US gov bonds (average)

6.1 London property (2013)   **6.3** High yield equity portfolio

5% — · **5.0** International equity

4.5 Chinese gov bonds   **4.6** Investment grade bonds   **4.1** US house prices (2000s)

China property **3.9**   **3.5** US house prices (1990s)

3.6 Fixed income   **3.0** UK property (1990s)

Australian gov bonds **3.2**   **2.7**

2.8 Bank savings account   US house market

Inflation (USA)

1.7 US gov bonds (2013)   **1.8** Bank current account (on paper)   New York State property **1.6**

Average return (most investors)

0.2 Short-term treasury (1 yr.)

0% — · **0** · **0.0** US property · · · · · · · · · · · ·

Cash   **-0.7** UK shares

-2.3 Actual loss due to inflation   **-2.2** Actual loss in real terms (due to inflation)

-2.8 Liquid capital

-3.7 Actual loss in real terms

-5% —

Lowest | Low | Medium | High | Highest | Crazy

RISK

sources: Forbes, TradingEconomics.com, The Economist. Yahoo! Finance, USA Today
data: bit.ly/KIB_Gambling

Superpower Showdown
Consumption

	China	EU	India	USA
ELECTRICITY PRODUCTION / CONSUMPTION KW/H, % OF WORLD TOTAL	22% 25%	16% 16%	4% 3%	20% 20%
FOSSIL-FUEL ENERGY % OF ELECTRICITY	74.3	56.8	69.9	75.5
RENEWABLE ENERGY % OF ELECTRICITY	9.1%	43.3%	4.7%	23.2%
CRUDE OIL PRODUCTION % OF WORLD TOTAL	5	15	1	11
CRUDE OIL IMPORT % OF WORLD TOTAL	10	21	7	22
CRUDE OIL EXPORT % OF WORLD TOTAL	0	5	0	0
NATURAL GAS PRODUCTION / CONSUMPTION % OF WORLD TOTAL	3 4	5 14	1 2	19 21
FUNCTIONING NUCLEAR REACTORS	14	185	19	104
NUCLEAR REACTORS PER 100 MILLION PEOPLE	1	37	2	33
CO_2 EMISSIONS % OF WORLD TOTAL	26	11	5	18
SCORE	1	6	3	2

THE EU GOBBLES ALL THE POINTS!

Superpower Showdown
Personal Consumption

	China	EU	India	USA
CARS PER 1,000 PEOPLE	44	475	12	627
CLOTHING & FOOTWEAR % OF HOUSEHOLD EXPENDITURE	10.5	5.7	6.5	3.5
HOUSING, WATER, ELECTRICITY, GAS & OTHER FUELS % OF HOUSEHOLD EXPENDITURE	10	27.7	14.8	19.5
FURNISHINGS, HOUSEHOLD EQUIPMENT & MAINTENANCE % OF HOUSEHOLD EXPENDITURE	6.4	5.5	4.1	4.3
HEALTH % OF HOUSEHOLD EXPENDITURE	7	3.4	4.1	20.2
TRANSPORT % OF HOUSEHOLD EXPENDITURE	13.7	11.9	15	9.1
TECHNOLOGY / COMMUNICATION % OF HOUSEHOLD EXPENDITURE	NO DATA	3.3	2	2.4
RECREATION / CULTURE % OF HOUSEHOLD EXPENDITURE	12	8.4	1.4	9.3
RESTAURANTS / HOTELS % OF HOUSEHOLD EXPENDITURE	NO DATA	5.3	2.5	6.2
FOOD KCAL PER PERSON/DAY	2,990	3,456	2,360	3,750
BEER / WINE LITRES PER PERSON/YEAR	1.5 / 0.2	3.8 / 4.3	0.06 / 0.02	4.5 / 1.4
TOTAL ALCOHOL CONSUMPTION LITRES OF PURE ALCOHOL PER PERSON/YEAR	5.9	10.3	2.6	9.4
SCORE	3	2	4	4

USA AND INDIA DRAW!

sources: CIA World Factbook, World Bank, Eurostat
data: bit.ly/KIB_Superpowers

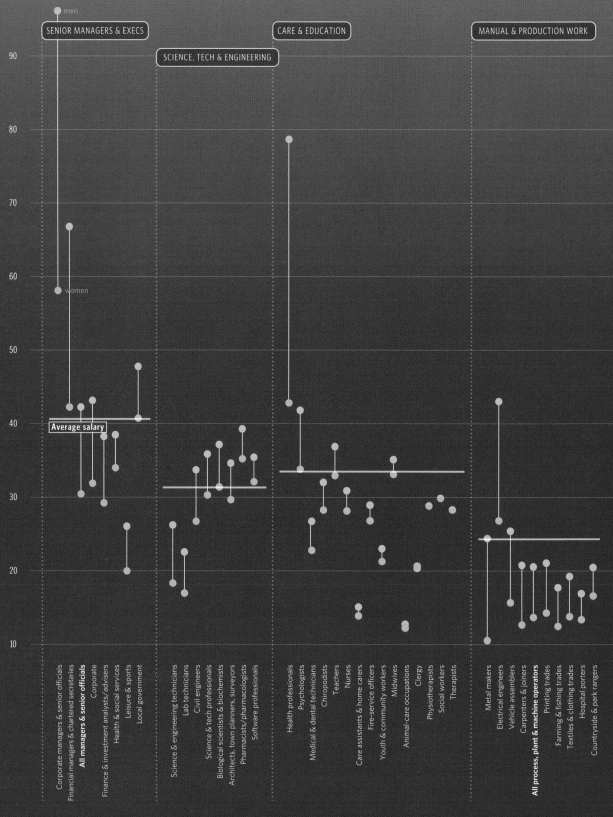

£100,000
typical salary

● men

SENIOR MANAGERS & EXECS

CARE & EDUCATION

MANUAL & PRODUCTION WORK

90

SCIENCE, TECH & ENGINEERING

80

70

60

● women

50

40

Average salary

30

20

10

Corporate managers & senior officials
Financial managers & chartered secretaries
All managers & senior officials
Corporate
Finance & investment analysts/advisers
Health & social services
Leisure & sports
Local government

Science & engineering technicians
Lab technicians
Civil engineers
Science & tech professionals
Biological scientists & biochemists
Architects, town planners, surveyors
Pharmacists/pharmacologists
Software professionals

Health professionals
Psychologists
Medical & dental technicians
Chiropodists
Teachers
Nurses
Care assistants & home carers
Fire-service officers
Youth & community workers
Midwives
Animal-care occupations
Clergy
Physiotherapists
Social workers
Therapists

Metal makers
Electrical engineers
Vehicle assemblers
Carpenters & joiners
All process, plant & machine operators
Printing trades
Farming & fishing trades
Textiles & clothing trades
Hospital porters
Countryside & park rangers

Gender Pay Gap UK

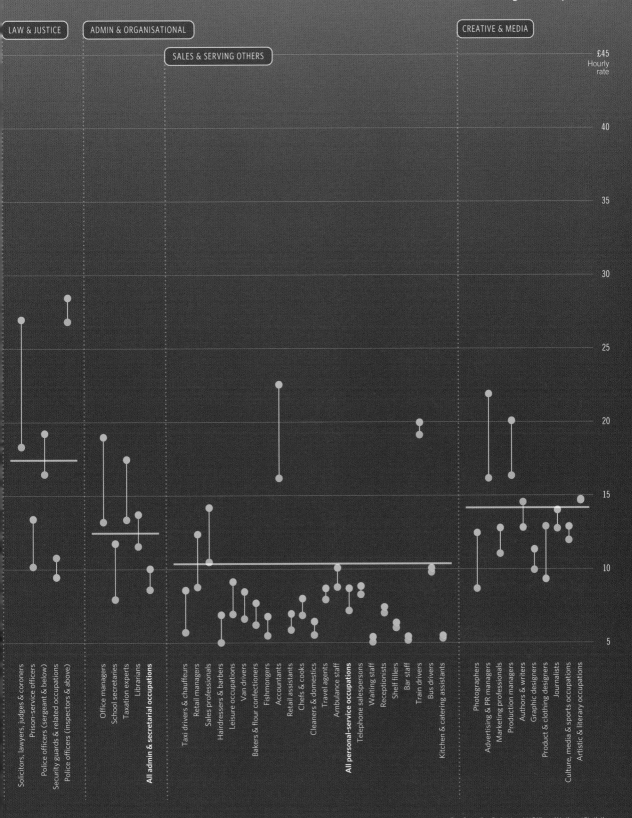

LAW & JUSTICE

ADMIN & ORGANISATIONAL

SALES & SERVING OTHERS

CREATIVE & MEDIA

£45
Hourly
rate

40

35

30

25

20

15

10

5

Solicitors, lawyers, judges & coroners
Prison-service officers
Police officers (sergeant & below)
Security guards & related occupations
Police officers (inspectors & above)

Office managers
School secretaries
Taxation experts
Librarians
All admin & secretarial occupations

Taxi drivers & chauffeurs
Retail managers
Sales professionals
Hairdressers & barbers
Leisure occupations
Van drivers
Bakers & flour confectioners
Fishmongers
Accountants
Retail assistants
Chefs & cooks
Cleaners & domestics
Travel agents
Ambulance staff
All personal-service occupations
Telephone salespersons
Waiting staff
Receptionists
Shelf fillers
Bar staff
Train drivers
Bus drivers
Kitchen & catering assistants

Photographers
Advertising & PR managers
Marketing professionals
Production managers
Authors & writers
Graphic designers
Product & clothing designers
Journalists
Culture, media & sports occupations
Artistic & literary occupations

sources: The Guardian Datablog, UK Office of National Statistics
data: bit.ly/KIB_GenderGap

$110,000
typical salary

men

SENIOR MANAGERS & EXECS

SCIENCE, TECH & ENGINEERING

CARE & EDUCATION

MANUAL

100

90

80

70

Average salary

60

50

40

women

30

20

10

Property & real-estate managers
Financial managers
Marketing & sales managers
Chief executives
Management jobs
Managers, all other
Medical & health-services managers

Biological scientists
Physical scientists, all other
Computer & mathematics jobs
Architecture & engineering occupations
Software developers
Life, physical & social sciences
Computer-support specialists
Lab technologists & technicians
Operations-research analysts
Pharmacists
Computer & IT systems managers
Medical scientists

Personal care & service jobs
Training & development specialists
Education, training & library
Physicians & surgeons
Physical therapists
Post-secondary teachers
Farming, fishing & forestry jobs
Community & social services
Healthcare practitioners & technical
Human-resource managers
Paramedics
Recreation & fitness workers
Nursing, psychiatric & home-health aides
Elementary & middle-school teachers
Counsellors
Clergy
Secondary-school teachers
Registered nurses
Special-education teachers

Construction & maintenance jobs
Driver/sales workers & truck drivers
Production, transportation & moving
Electromechanical assemblers

216 | 217

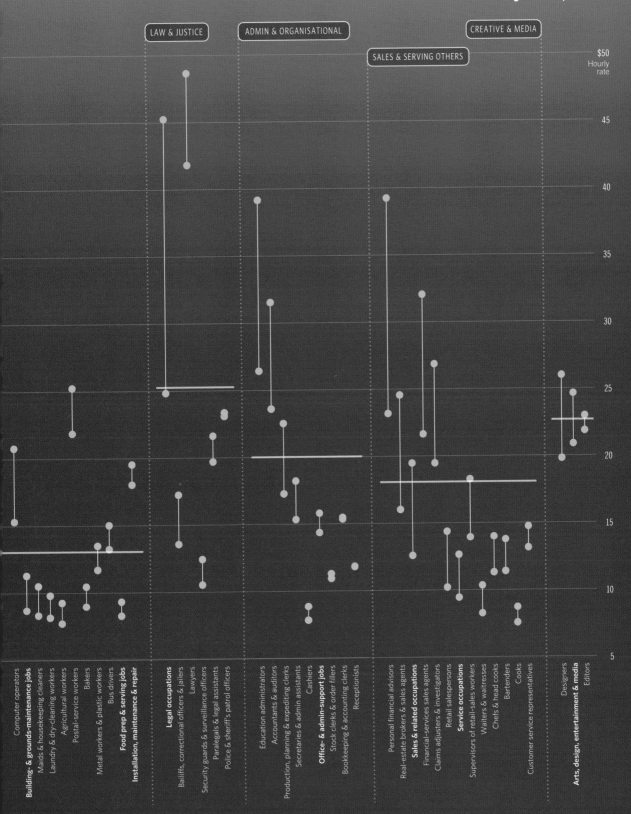

Gender Pay Gap US

LAW & JUSTICE

ADMIN & ORGANISATIONAL

CREATIVE & MEDIA

SALES & SERVING OTHERS

$50
Hourly rate

45

40

35

30

25

20

15

10

5

Computer operators
Building- & grounds-maintenance jobs
Maids & housekeeping cleaners
Laundry & dry-cleaning workers
Agricultural workers
Postal-service workers
Bakers
Metal workers & plastic workers
Bus drivers
Food prep & serving jobs
Installation, maintenance & repair

Legal occupations
Bailiffs, correctional officers & jailers
Lawyers
Security guards & surveillance officers
Paralegals & legal assistants
Police & sheriff's patrol officers

Education administrators
Accountants & auditors
Production, planning & expediting clerks
Secretaries & admin assistants
Cashiers
Office- & admin-support jobs
Stock clerks & order fillers
Bookkeeping & accounting clerks
Receptionists

Personal financial advisors
Real-estate brokers & sales agents
Sales & related occupations
Financial-services sales agents
Claims adjusters & investigators
Retail salespersons
Service occupations
Supervisors of retail-sales workers
Waiters & waitresses
Chefs & head cooks
Bartenders
Cooks
Customer service representatives

Designers
Arts, design, entertainment & media
Editors

source: US Bureau of Labor Statistics
data: bit.ly/KIB_GenderGap

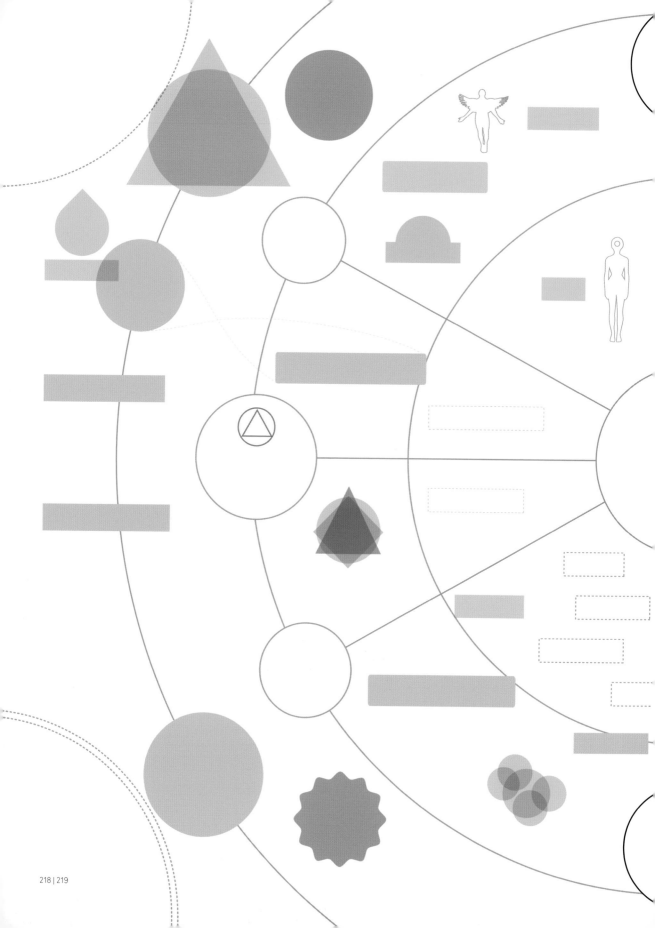

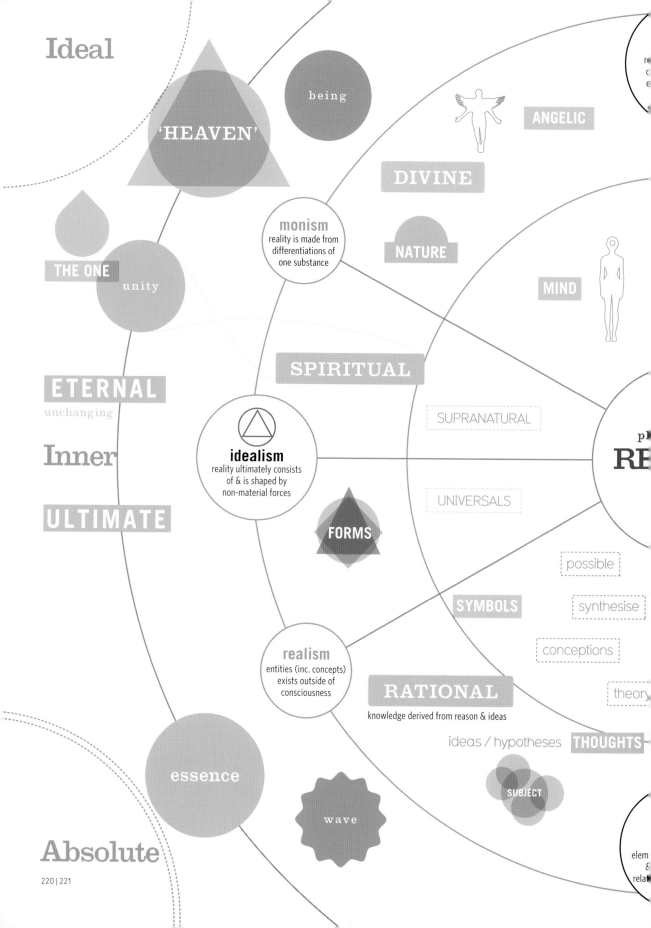

Ideal

being

'HEAVEN'

ANGELIC

DIVINE

monism
reality is made from
differentiations of
one substance

NATURE

THE ONE

unity

MIND

SPIRITUAL

ETERNAL

unchanging

SUPRANATURAL

Inner

idealism
reality ultimately consists
of & is shaped by
non-material forces

UNIVERSALS

ULTIMATE

FORMS

possible

synthesise

SYMBOLS

conceptions

p
RE

theory

realism
entities (inc. concepts)
exists outside of
consciousness

RATIONAL

knowledge derived from reason & ideas

ideas / hypotheses   THOUGHTS

essence

SUBJECT

wave

Absolute

elem
&
rela

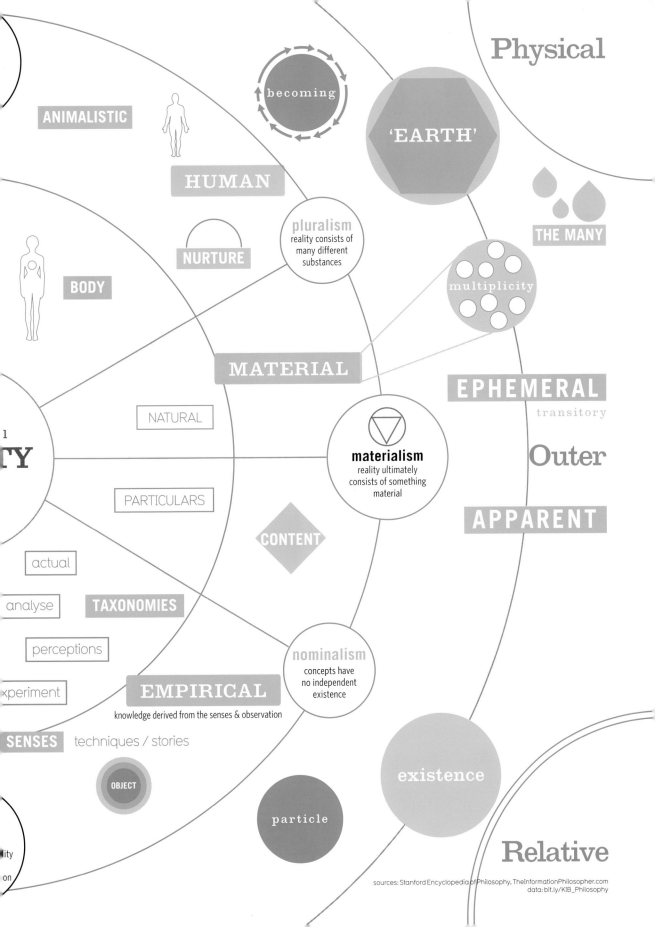

Physical

ANIMALISTIC

becoming

'EARTH'

HUMAN

pluralism
reality consists of
many different
substances

THE MANY

NURTURE

multiplicity

BODY

MATERIAL

EPHEMERAL
transitory

NATURAL

materialism
reality ultimately
consists of something
material

Outer

1
TY

PARTICULARS

APPARENT

actual

CONTENT

analyse

TAXONOMIES

perceptions

nominalism
concepts have
no independent
existence

xperiment

EMPIRICAL

knowledge derived from the senses & observation

SENSES   techniques / stories

OBJECT

existence

particle

ity

on

Relative

sources: Stanford Encyclopedia of Philosophy, TheInformationPhilosopher.com
data: bit.ly/KIB_Philosophy

World Dashboard

Average wealth per person

+**180**%

$11,070

$6,140

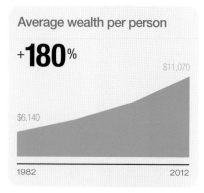

1982 — 2012

Those on less than $1.25 / day

47% **21**%

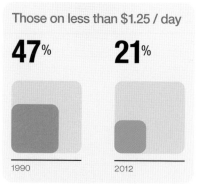

1990 2012

Global deficit

$**1** trillion

$71.8 $72.8

global earnings global debt

Land used for crops
% Earth's surface

safe planetary limit 15%

11.7% current value

78% of limit

Ocean phosphorus
million tonnes

11

9

82%

Atmospheric CO$_2$
parts per million

350

393

112%

Freshwater usage
km³

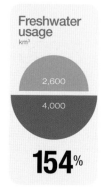

2,600

4,000

154%

Atmospheric nitrogen removal
million tonnes

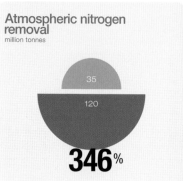

35

120

346%

Insecure jobs poorly paid
% of all employment

0% GOAL

67% 1991

58% 2011

Worldwide hunger
■ % undernourished people

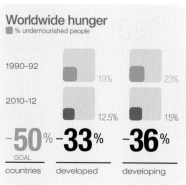

1990–92   19%   23%

2010–12   12.5%   15%

−**50**% GOAL   −**33**%   −**36**%

countries developed developing

Primary education
% children enrolling

100% 82% 90%

GOAL 1991 2001

Global obesity

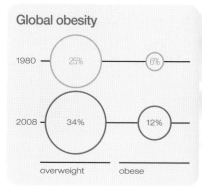

1980 25% 6%

2008 34% 12%

overweight obese

Access to sanitation
% global population

1990 36%

GOAL 68%

2010 50%

Access to drinking water
% global population

1990 76%

GOAL 88%

2010 89%

Child deaths
goal: reduce by 66%

−**35**%

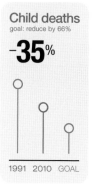

1991 2010 GOAL

Literate young women
for every 100 literate young men

90   **95**

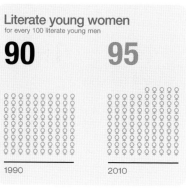

1990   2010

Girls@school
% relative to boys

100% 97%

GOAL 2010

Ownership of the world's wealth

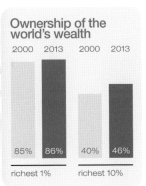

2000	2013	2000	2013

85% | 86% | 40% | 46%

richest 1%   richest 10%

On Facebook
% global population

+400%

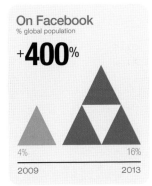

4%   16%

2009   2013

Average global life expectancy

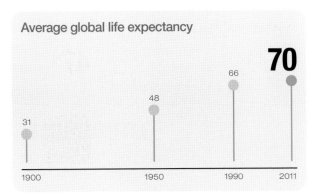

31   48   66   **70**

1900   1950   1990   2011

Forest loss
million hectares
lost per year

8.3   5.2   0

1991   2001   GOAL

Rainforest loss
square kilometres

5,000

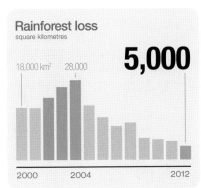

18,000 km²   28,000

2000   2004   2012

Ocean acidity
parts per million

+30%

298ppm   388ppm

1990   2010

Global temperature

+0.8°C

1850   2012

Sea levels

+6cm   +38cm

1993–2012   2050

Maternal mortality
goal: reduce by 75%

−45%

440 deaths per 100,000 live births

240

110

1990   2010   GOAL

HIV sufferers
% of population

+280%

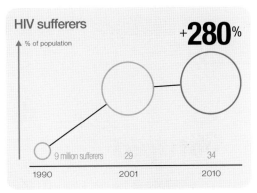

9 million sufferers   29   34

1990   2001   2010

HIV new cases

−23%   # −0%

Malaria

−17%

developing   developed   global

Species extinction
% of species threatened

13%   # 25%   # 41%

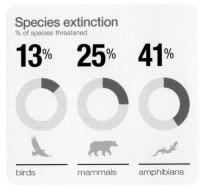

birds   mammals   amphibians

Energy usage

+116%   KWh per person / day

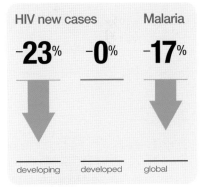

58   60   61   73

2005   2009   2013   2040

sources: Forbes, World Bank, UN, CIA World Factbook, Credit Suisse, OECD, World Health Organisation, Stevens (2012), EIA.org, Scientific American
data: bit.ly/KIB_Arrggg

A Taxonomy of Ideas
Structure + functionality + unpredictability?

[

IMPOSSIBLE

inspiring

abstract

over-cooked **over-worked**

clever

funny elaborate

DYSFUNCTIONAL ···································· | dys- | ·············· | sub- | ·············· | non- | ················ | less | ····················

early

half-baked

dumb

stupid bad

terrible

crap

the worst

genius

incredible

brilliant

beautiful

great

sweet

SMART

elegant

fantastic

...ool

WONDERFUL

nice   good

novel

awesome!

NEAT

...eresting   *COMPELLING*

boring

CRAZY

slightly   pretty   super   trans-   FUNCTIONAL

...illy

ODD

STRANGE

UNUSUAL

INSANE

weird

woolly

OBVIOUS

PREDICTABLE

INEVITABLE

UNEXPECTED

UNPREDICTABLE

OTHERWORLDLY

sources: Author's curiosity, IIB crowdsourcers

Life Scape

events

cosmic

planetary

mass extinctions

evolutionary

continental

bio innovations

mammals

reptilia

amphibians

fish

invertebrates

plants & fungi

microbial

time

million years ago

geological period

era

eon

sources: too many to list
See : bit.ly/KIB_Lifescape

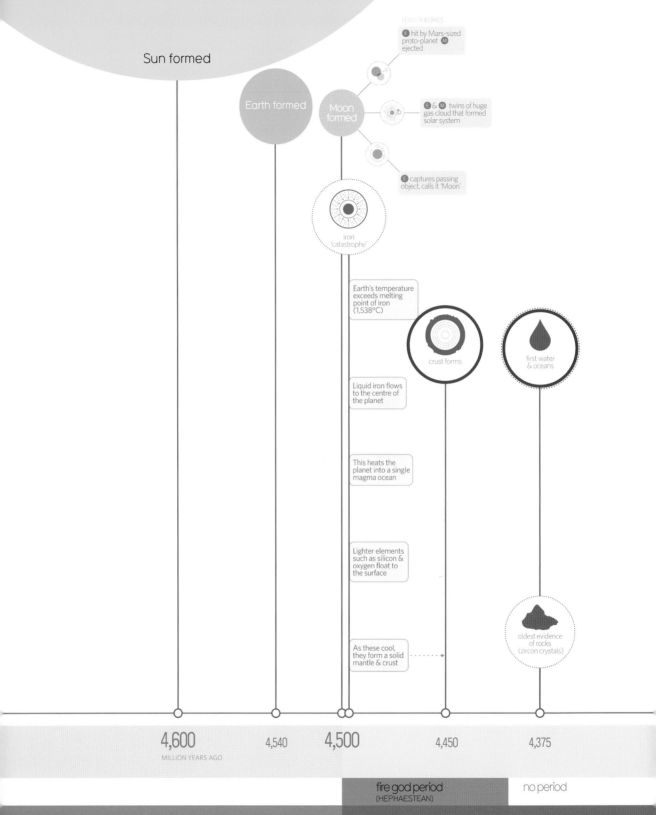

Sun formed

Earth formed

Moon formed

LEAD THEORIES

E hit by Mars-sized proto-planet **M** ejected

E & **M** twins of huge gas cloud that formed solar system

E captures passing object, calls it 'Moon'

iron 'catastrophe'

Earth's temperature exceeds melting point of iron (1,538°C)

Liquid iron flows to the centre of the planet

This heats the planet into a single magma ocean

Lighter elements such as silicon & oxygen float to the surface

As these cool, they form a solid mantle & crust

crust forms

first water & oceans

oldest evidence of rocks (zircon crystals)

4,600
MILLION YEARS AGO

4,540

4,500

4,450

4,375

fire god period
(HEPHAESTEAN)

no period

new chaos era (NEOCHOATIAN)

early hell (PALAEOHADEAN)

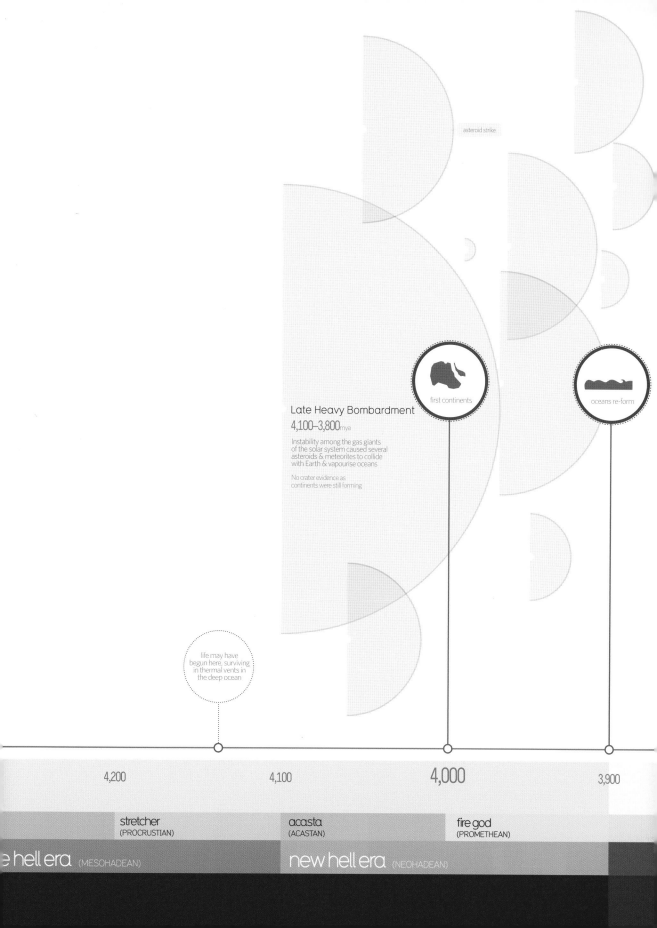

asteroid strike

first continents

oceans re-form

Late Heavy Bombardment
4,100–3,800mya

Instability among the gas giants
of the solar system caused several
asteroids & meteorites to collide
with Earth & vapourise oceans

No crater evidence as
continents were still forming

life may have
begun here, surviving
in thermal vents in
the deep ocean

4,200

4,100

4,000

3,900

stretcher
(PROCRUSTIAN)

acasta
(ACASTAN)

fire god
(PROMETHEAN)

e hell era (MESOHADEAN)

new hell era (NEOHADEAN)

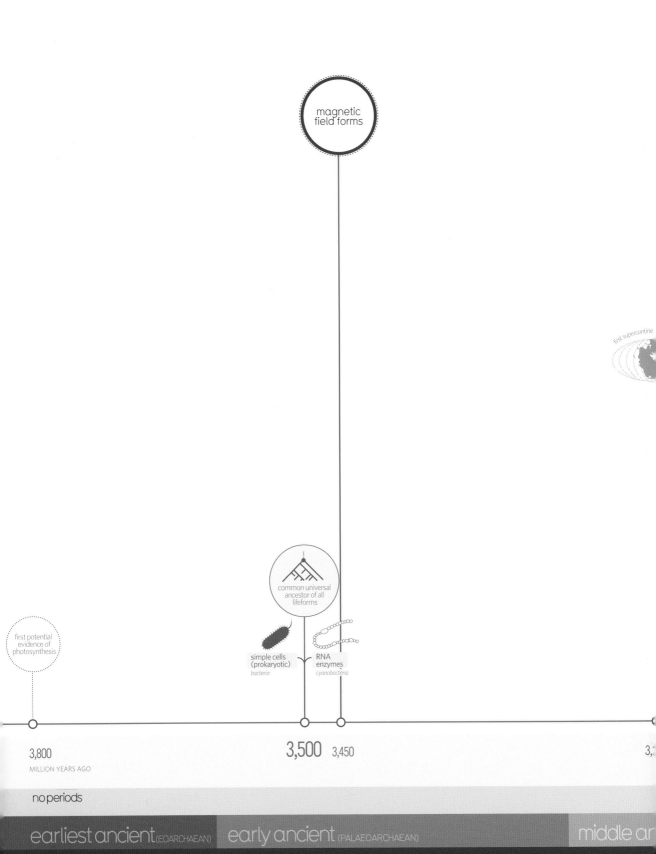

magnetic
field forms

first supercontine

common universal
ancestor of all
lifeforms

first potential
evidence of
photosynthesis

simple cells
(prokaryotic)
bacteria

RNA
enzymes
cyanobacteria

3,800
MILLION YEARS AGO

3,500   3,450

3,

no periods

the beginning eon (ARCHAEAN)

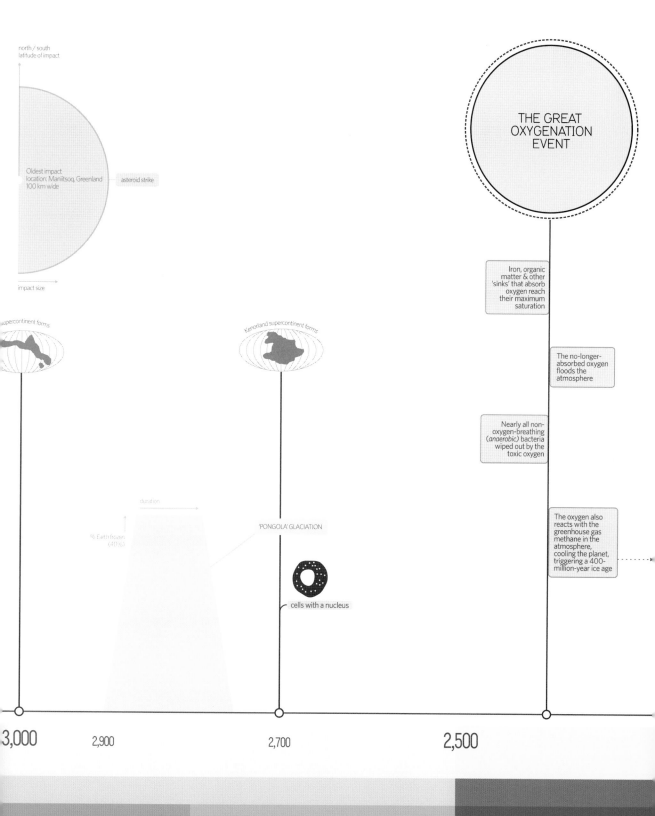

north / south
latitude of impact

Oldest impact
location: Maniitsoq, Greenland
100 km wide

asteroid strike

impact size

supercontinent forms

Kenorland supercontinent forms

THE GREAT
OXYGENATION
EVENT

Iron, organic
matter & other
'sinks' that absorb
oxygen reach
their maximum
saturation

The no-longer-
absorbed oxygen
floods the
atmosphere

Nearly all non-
oxygen-breathing
(*anaerobic*) bacteria
wiped out by the
toxic oxygen

duration

% Earth frozen
(40%)

'PONGOLA' GLACIATION

The oxygen also
reacts with the
greenhouse gas
methane in the
atmosphere,
cooling the planet,
triggering a 400-
million-year ice age

cells with a nucleus

3,000   2,900   2,700   2,500

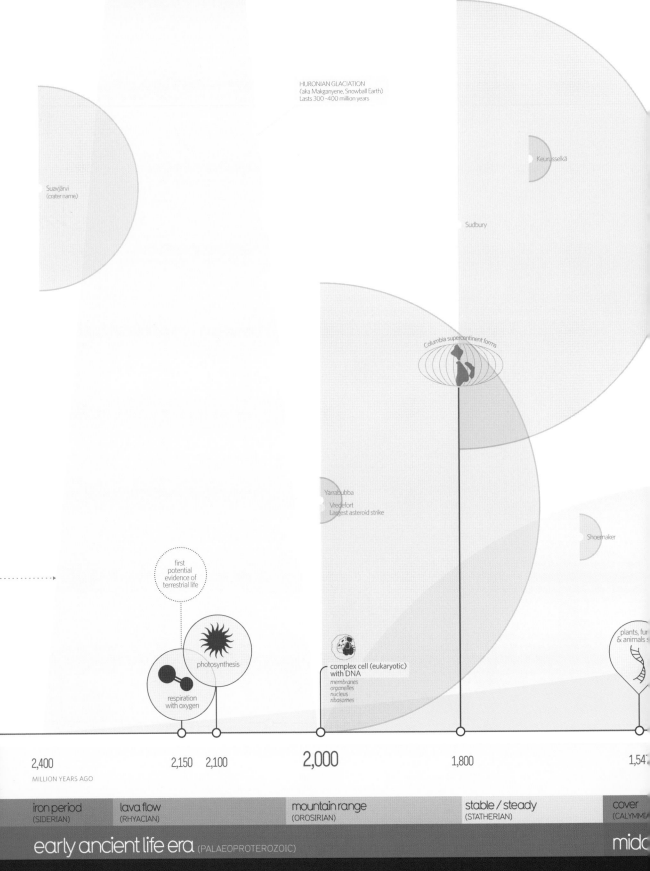

HURONIAN GLACIATION
(aka Makganyene, Snowball Earth)
Lasts 300 –400 million years

Keurusselkä

Suavjärvi
(crater name)

Sudbury

Columbia supercontinent forms

Yarrabubba
Vredefort
Largest asteroid strike

Shoemaker

first
potential
evidence of
terrestrial life

plants, fun
& animals s

photosynthesis

complex cell (eukaryotic)
with DNA
membranes
organelles
nucleus
ribosomes

respiration
with oxygen

2,400   2,150   2,100   2,000   1,800   1,54

MILLION YEARS AGO

| iron period (SIDERIAN) | lava flow (RHYACIAN) | mountain range (OROSIRIAN) | stable / steady (STATHERIAN) | cover (CALYMMI |

early ancient life era (PALAEOPROTEROZOIC)   mid

eon of ancient life (PROTEROZOIC)

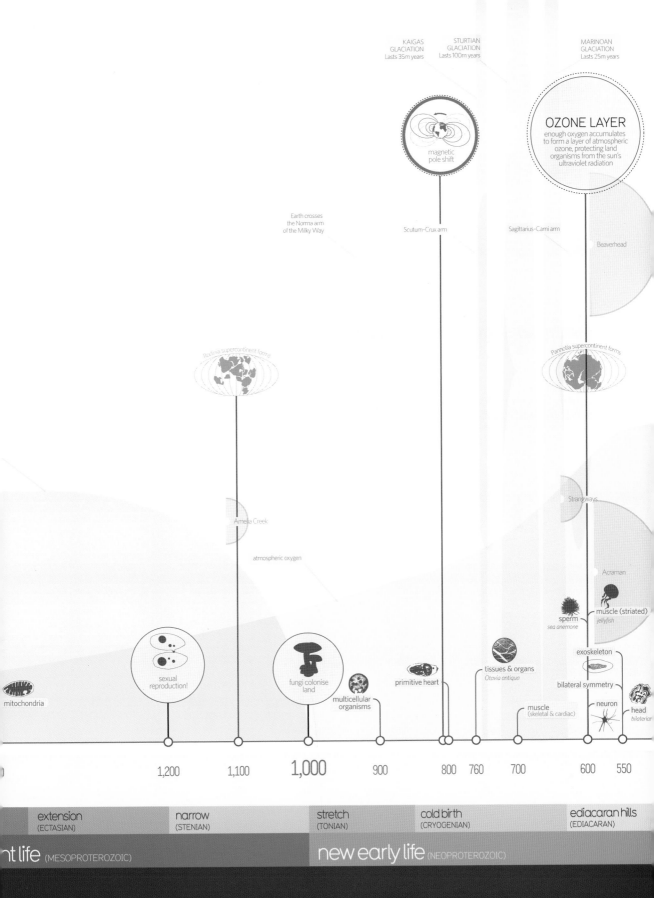

KAIGAS
GLACIATION
Lasts 35m years

STURTIAN
GLACIATION
Lasts 100m years

MARINOAN
GLACIATION
Lasts 25m years

OZONE LAYER
enough oxygen accumulates
to form a layer of atmospheric
ozone, protecting land
organisms from the sun's
ultraviolet radiation

magnetic
pole shift

Earth crosses
the Norma arm
of the Milky Way

Scutum–Crux arm

Sagittarius–Carni arm

Beaverhead

Rodinia supercontinent forms

Pannotia supercontinent forms

Amelia Creek

Strangways

atmospheric oxygen

Acraman

sperm
sea anemone

muscle (striated)
jellyfish

sexual
reproduction!

fungi colonise
land

multicellular
organisms

primitive heart

tissues & organs
Otavia antiqua

exoskeleton

bilateral symmetry

neuron

head
bilaterian

mitochondria

muscle
(skeletal & cardiac)

1,200   1,100   **1,000**   900   800 760   700   600   550

extension
(ECTASIAN)

narrow
(STENIAN)

stretch
(TONIAN)

cold birth
(CRYOGENIAN)

ediacaran hills
(EDIACARAN)

nt life (MESOPROTEROZOIC)

new early life (NEOPROTEROZOIC)

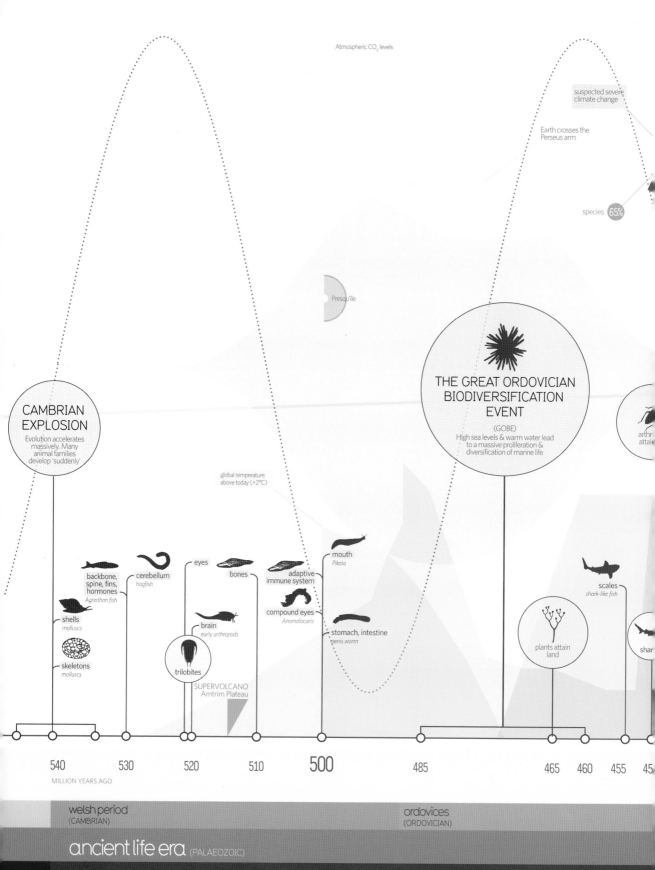

Atmospheric CO₂ levels

suspected severe
climate change

Earth crosses the
Perseus arm

species 65%

Presqu'île

THE GREAT ORDOVICIAN
BIODIVERSIFICATION
EVENT
(GOBE)
High sea levels & warm water lead
to a massive proliferation &
diversification of marine life

CAMBRIAN
EXPLOSION
Evolution accelerates
massively. Many
animal families
develop 'suddenly'

global temperature
above today (+2°C)

mouth
Pikaia

eyes

bones

backbone,
spine, fins,
hormones
Agnathan fish

cerebellum
hagfish

adaptive
immune system

scales
shark-like fish

shells
molluscs

brain
early arthropods

compound eyes
Anomalocaris

skeletons
molluscs

stomach, intestine
penis worm

plants attain
land

shar

trilobites

SUPERVOLCANO
Amtrim Plateau

arthr
attai

540   530   520   510   500   485   465 460 455 45

MILLION YEARS AGO

welsh period
(CAMBRIAN)

ordovices
(ORDOVICIAN)

ancient life era (PALAEOZOIC)

eon of visible life (PHANEROZOIC)

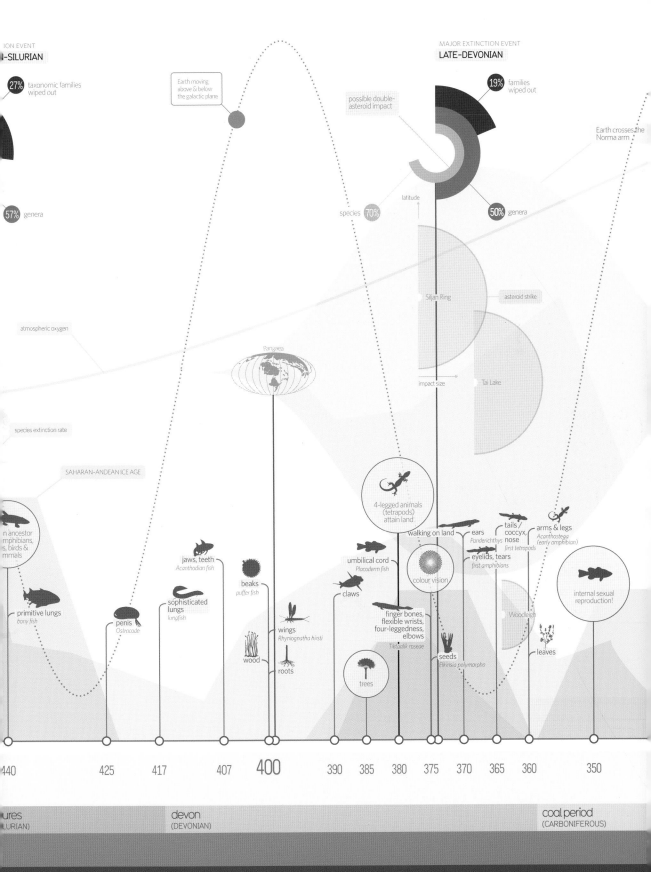

27% taxonomic families wiped out

19% families wiped out

Earth moving above & below the galactic plane

possible double-asteroid impact

Earth crosses the Norma arm

57% genera

species 70%

50% genera

latitude

atmospheric oxygen

Siljan Ring

asteroid strike

Pangaea

impact size

Tai Lake

species extinction rate

SAHARAN-ANDEAN ICE AGE

4-legged animals (tetrapods) attain land.

n ancestor mphibians, s, birds & mmals

walking on land

ears
Panderichthys

tails / coccyx, nose
first tetrapods

arms & legs
Acanthostega
(early amphibian)

jaws, teeth
Acanthodian fish

umbilical cord
Placoderm fish

eyelids, tears
first amphibians

beaks
puffer fish

claws

colour vision

primitive lungs
bony fish

sophisticated lungs
lungfish

wings
Rhyniognatha hirsti

finger bones, flexible wrists, four-leggedness, elbows
Tiktaalik roseae

internal sexual reproduction!

penis
Ostracode

Woodleigh

wood

seeds
Elkinsia polymorpha

leaves

roots

trees

440   425   417   407   **400**   390   385   380   375   370   365   360   350

ures
ILURIAN)

devon
(DEVONIAN)

coal period
(CARBONIFEROUS)

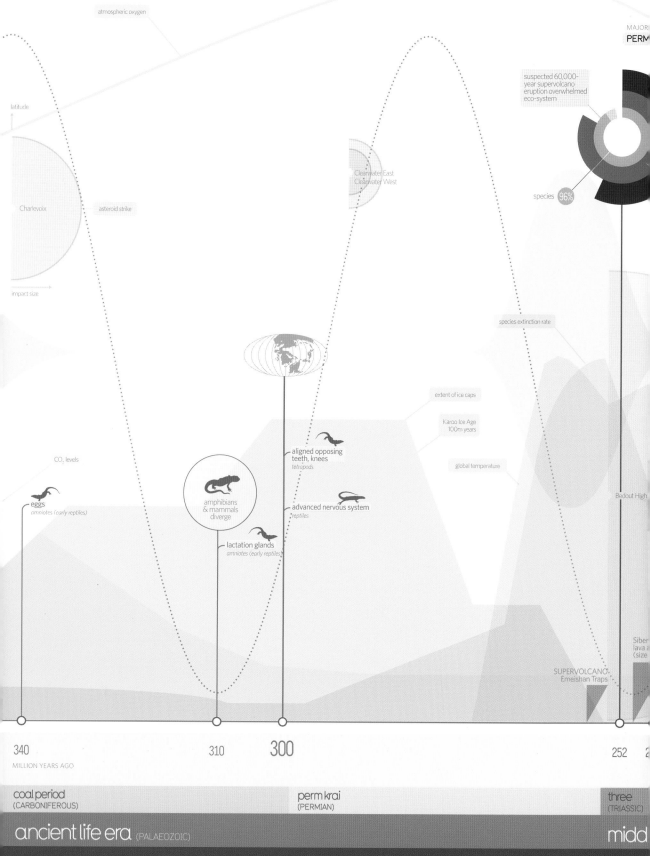

latitude

suspected 60,000-
year supervolcano
eruption overwhelmed
eco-system

Charlevoix

asteroid strike

Clearwater East
Clearwater West

species 96%

impact size

species extinction rate

CO₂ levels

extent of ice caps

Karoo Ice Age
100m years

aligned opposing
teeth, knees
tetrapods

global temperature

Bedout High

amphibians
& mammals
diverge

advanced nervous system
reptiles

eggs
amniotes (early reptiles)

lactation glands
amniotes (early reptiles)

Siber
lava a
(size

SUPERVOLCANO
Emeishan Traps

340

310

300

252

2

MILLION YEARS AGO

coal period
(CARBONIFEROUS)

perm krai
(PERMIAN)

three
(TRIASSIC)

ancient life era (PALAEOZOIC)

midd

eon of visible life (PHANEROZOIC)

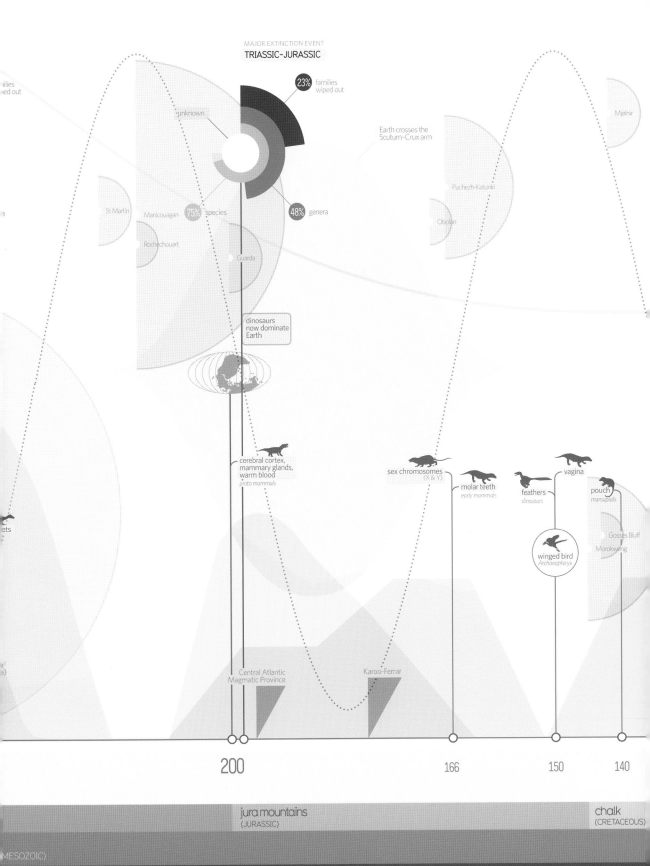

MAJOR EXTINCTION EVENT
TRIASSIC–JURASSIC

23% families
wiped out

unknown

Earth crosses the
Scutum–Crux arm

ilies
ed out

Mjølnir

St Martin

a

75% species

48% genera

Puchezh-Katunki

Manicouagan

Obolon

Rochechouart

Guarda

dinosaurs
now dominate
Earth

cerebral cortex,
mammary glands,
warm blood
proto mammals

sex chromosomes
(X & Y)

vagina

molar teeth
early mammals

feathers
dinosaurs

pouch
marsupials

ets

winged bird
Archaeopteryx

Gosses Bluff

Morokweng

Central Atlantic
Magmatic Province

Karoo-Ferrar

200   166   150   140

jura mountains
(JURASSIC)

chalk
(CRETACEOUS)

MESOZOIC)

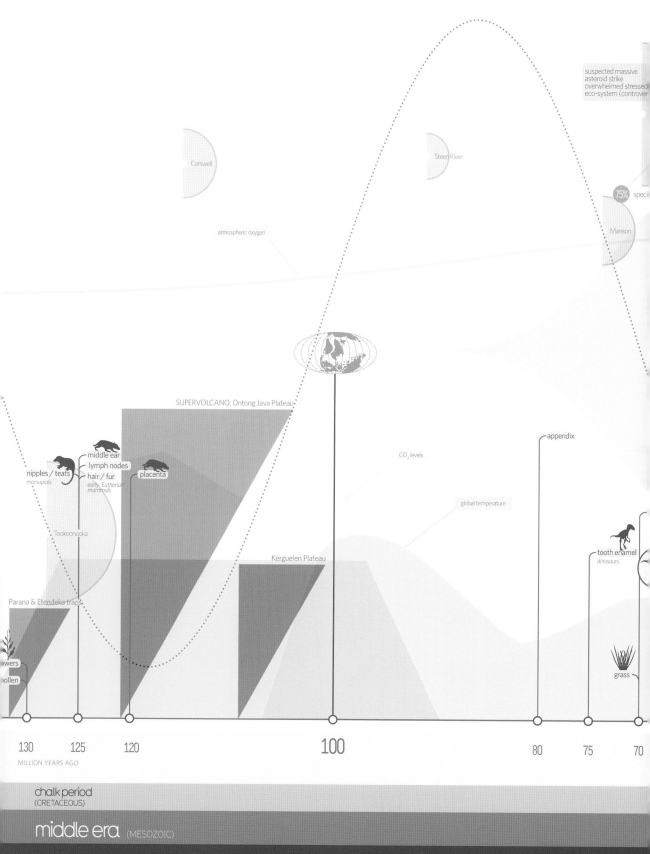

suspected massive
asteroid strike
overwhelmed stressed
eco-system (controver...

Carswell

Steen River

75% speci...

Manson

atmospheric oxygen

SUPERVOLCANO: Ontong Java Plateau

appendix

CO₂ levels

middle ear
lymph nodes
hair / fur
*early 'Eutherian'
mammals*

nipples / teats
marsupials

placenta

global temperature

tooth enamel
dinosaurs

Tookoonooka

Kerguelen Plateau

Parana & Etendeka traps

...wers

...pollen

grass

130   125   120   100   80   75   70

MILLION YEARS AGO

chalk period
(CRETACEOUS)

middle era (MESOZOIC)

eon of visible life (PHANEROZOIC)

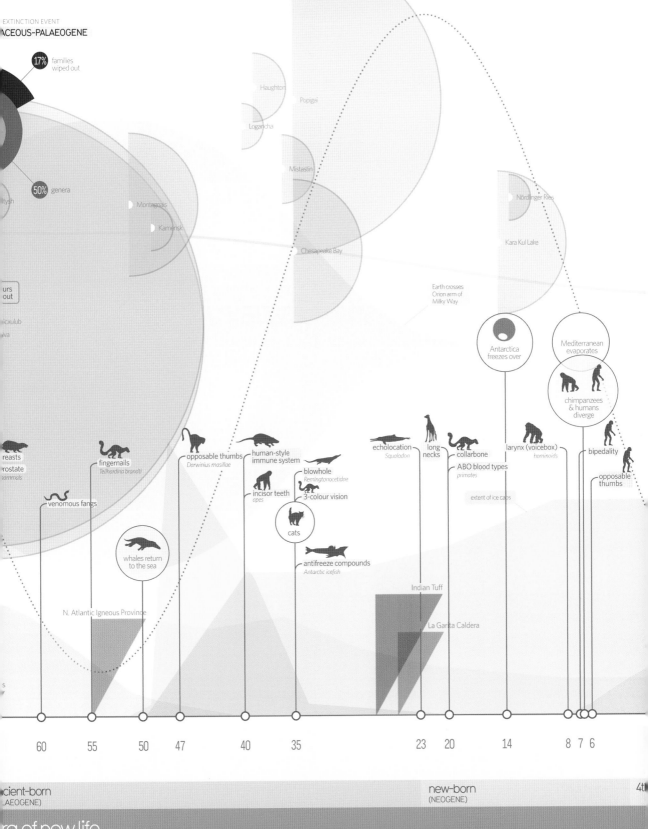

EXTINCTION EVENT
ACEOUS–PALAEOGENE

17% families
wiped out

50% genera

Haughton

Popigai

Logancha

Mistastin

Nördlinger Ries

Montagnais

Kamensk

Chesapeake Bay

Kara Kul Lake

urs
out

icxulub
iva

Earth crosses
Orion arm of
Milky Way

Antarctica
freezes over

Mediterranean
evaporates

chimpanzees
& humans
diverge

reasts
rostate
ammals

fingernails
Teilhardina brandti

opposable thumbs
Darwinius masillae

human-style
immune system

echolocation
Squalodon

long
necks

collarbone

larynx (voicebox)

bipedality
hominoids

venomous fangs

incisor teeth
apes

blowhole
Remingtonocetidae

3-colour vision

ABO blood types
primates

opposable
thumbs

cats

extent of ice caps

whales return
to the sea

antifreeze compounds
Antarctic icefish

Indian Tuff

N. Atlantic Igneous Province

La Garita Caldera

s

| 60 | 55 | 50 | 47 | 40 | 35 | | 23 | 20 | 14 | 8 7 6 |

cient-born
(PALAEOGENE)

new-born
(NEOGENE)

4t

ra of new life (CENOZOIC)

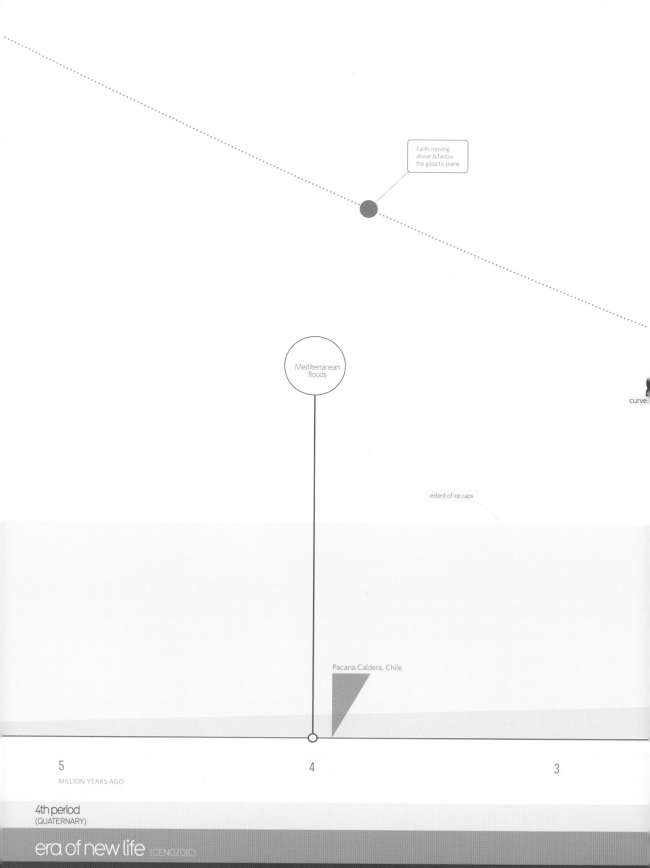

Earth moving
above & below
the galactic plane

Mediterranean
floods

curve

extent of ice caps

Pacana Caldera, Chile

5   4   3

MILLION YEARS AGO

4th period
(QUATERNARY)

era of new life (CENOZOIC)

eon of visible life (PHANEROZOIC)

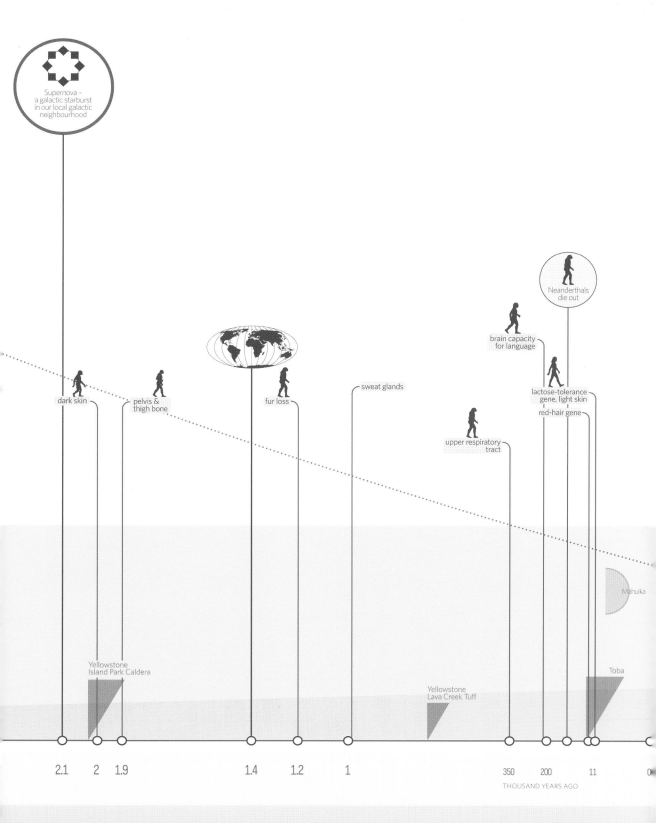

Supernova –
a galactic starburst
in our local galactic
neighbourhood

Neanderthals
die out

brain capacity
for language

dark skin

pelvis &
thigh bone

fur loss

sweat glands

lactose-tolerance
gene, light skin

red-hair gene

upper respiratory
tract

Yellowstone
Island Park Caldera

Yellowstone
Lava Creek Tuff

Mahuika

Toba

2.1   2   1.9   1.4   1.2   1   350   200   11   0

THOUSAND YEARS AGO

sources: too many to list
See : bit.ly/KIB_Lifescape

What Makes a Good Visualisation?

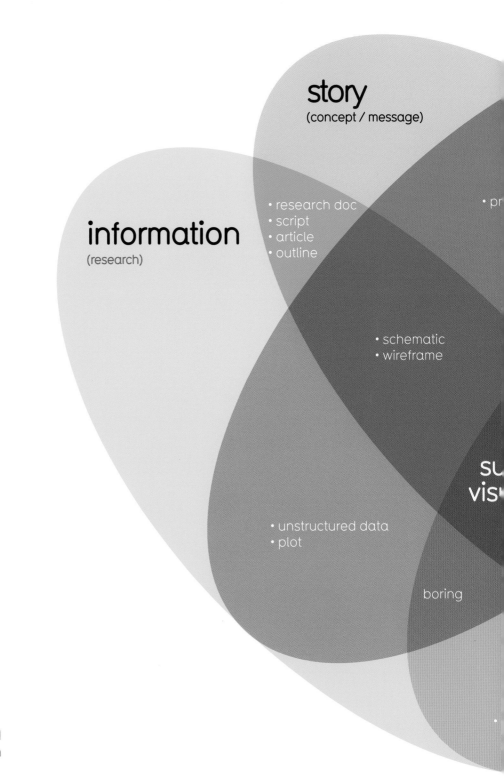

story
(concept / message)

information
(research)

• research doc
• script
• article
• outline

• pr

• schematic
• wireframe

su
vis

• unstructured data
• plot

boring

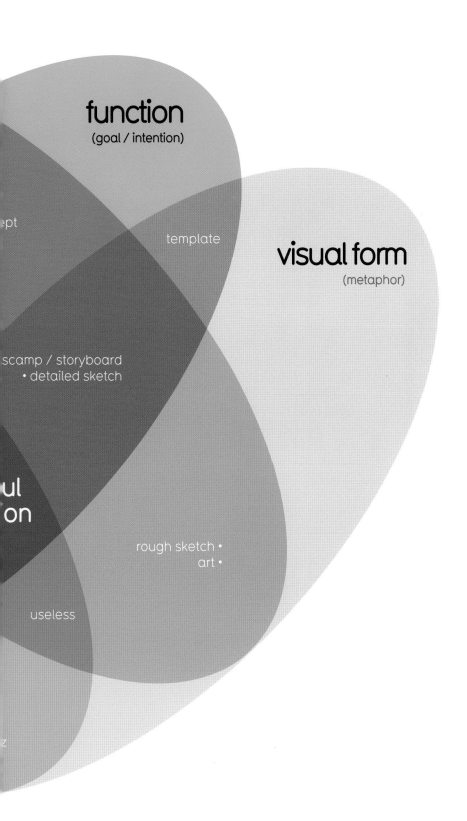

explicit
(implicit)

function
(goal / intention)

...ept

template

visual form
(metaphor)

scamp / storyboard
• detailed sketch

...ul
...on

rough sketch •
art •

useless

...z

visualisation
art of design
structuring visual elements

TYPE	**data**	structured data	information
ART	VISUALISATION		DESIGN

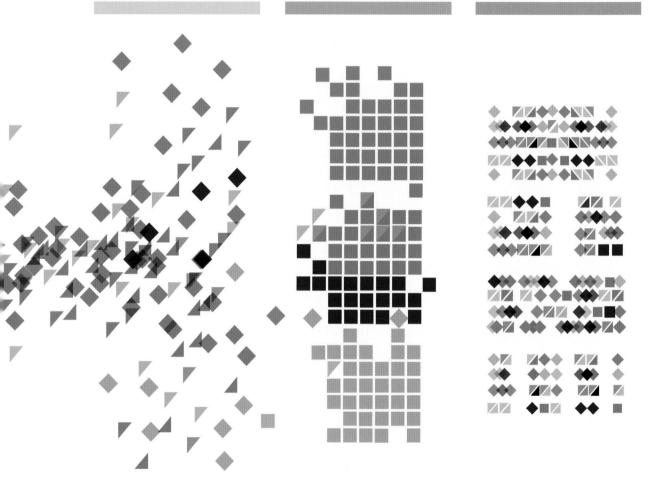

PROCESSES	mine, direct, stream capture, gather, collect measure, quantify, weigh	recognise, discriminate, categorise examine, analysis, separate evaluate, tabulate, structure classify, label, index	recall, identify, associate arrange, order, frame filter, compare, contrast, assess, interpret, file
FORMS	POINTS, SETS, STREAMS, NUMBERS	TABLES, DATABASES, COLLECTIONS, WORDS	TEXT, SENTENCES, PARAGRAPHS
METAPHOR	atoms	molecules	DNA

linked
information

knowledge

MAPPING

inter-connected
knowledge

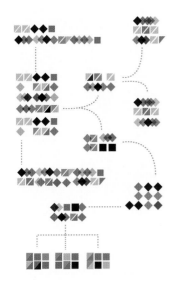

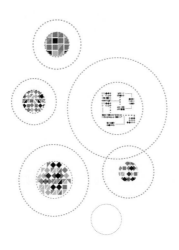

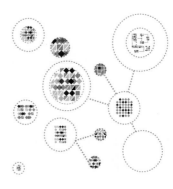

combine, mash, emphasise
connect, frame, inter-link
sequence, prioritise flow
condense, optimise, summarise

relate, inter-relate, contextualise
interpret, rank, qualify
evaluate, deconstruct, recombine
explain, illustrate, map

organise, weave, integrate
extrapolate, predict, model
hyper-structure, generate

WEBS, HYPERTEXT, CHAPTERS, BOOKS

BODIES, SCHOOLS, ENCYCLOPEDIAS

FIELDS, DOMAINS

chromosomes

cells

organisms

Acknowledgemap

DESIGN

Jack Hagley

Andrew Park

Philippa Thomas

Fabio Bergamaschi

Piero Zagami

Omid Kashan

Paulo Estriga

Theo Deutinger

Paul Butt

Lily Tidhar

Tatjana Dubovina

Phil South

ART DIRECTION

Duncan Swain

Kathryn Ariel

RESEARCH

Kesta Desmond

Marley Whiteside

Andrew Key

Miriam Quick

Pearl-Doughty White

James Kennedy Monash

Christian Miles

Dan Hampson

Alex Lemon

Laurin Janes

Ella Hollowood

IIB Crowd Sourcers

SOFTWARE

VizSweet

Adobe Illustrator

Adobe InDesign

HARPER COLLINS U.S.

Julia Abramoff
Martin Wilson
Stephanie Cooper
Paige Doscher
Marta Schooler

WILLIAM COLLINS U.K.

Hannah MacDonald
Helena Nicholls
Agnes Rigou
Katherine Patrick
Jamie Joseph
Chris Wright
Kate Tolley
Simon Trewin
Mark Bolland
Martin Redfern
Mary Thompson
Charlotte Wheeler

SUPPORT TEAM

Rebecca Conroy
Kesta Desmond
Michelle
Kathryn Ariel
Holly McCandless-Desmond
Ruth Jobey
David
Duncan Swain
Christianne

CODE

Tom Evans

Thank you! Toby Slater, Sister Kovida, Ajahn Sucitto, Rejina Sabur-Cross, Stefanie Posavec, Robert Downes, Aziz Cami, Jo Hutchinson, Peter McInnery, Steve Beckett, Anna Brunoro, Ian Webster, Nick Berry

Icon Art

Thanks to thenounproject.com

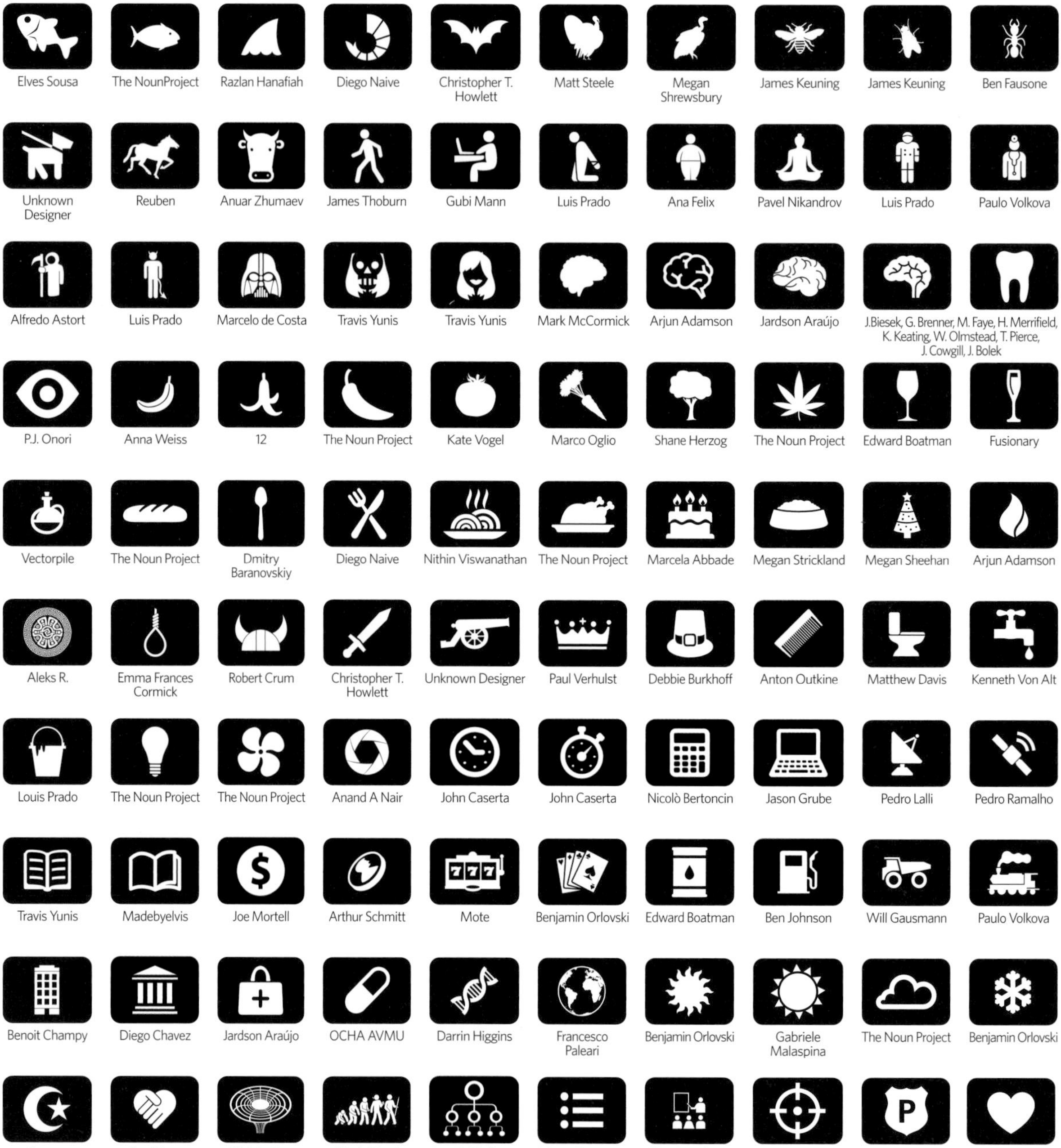

Elves Sousa	The NounProject	Razlan Hanafiah	Diego Naive	Christopher T. Howlett	Matt Steele	Megan Shrewsbury	James Keuning	James Keuning	Ben Fausone
Unknown Designer	Reuben	Anuar Zhumaev	James Thoburn	Gubi Mann	Luis Prado	Ana Felix	Pavel Nikandrov	Luis Prado	Paulo Volkova
Alfredo Astort	Luis Prado	Marcelo de Costa	Travis Yunis	Travis Yunis	Mark McCormick	Arjun Adamson	Jardson Araújo	J.Biesek, G. Brenner, M. Faye, H. Merrifield, K. Keating, W. Olmstead, T. Pierce, J. Cowgill, J. Bolek	
P.J. Onori	Anna Weiss	12	The Noun Project	Kate Vogel	Marco Oglio	Shane Herzog	The Noun Project	Edward Boatman	Fusionary
Vectorpile	The Noun Project	Dmitry Baranovskiy	Diego Naive	Nithin Viswanathan	The Noun Project	Marcela Abbade	Megan Strickland	Megan Sheehan	Arjun Adamson
Aleks R.	Emma Frances Cormick	Robert Crum	Christopher T. Howlett	Unknown Designer	Paul Verhulst	Debbie Burkhoff	Anton Outkine	Matthew Davis	Kenneth Von Alt
Louis Prado	The Noun Project	The Noun Project	Anand A Nair	John Caserta	John Caserta	Nicolò Bertoncin	Jason Grube	Pedro Lalli	Pedro Ramalho
Travis Yunis	Madebyelvis	Joe Mortell	Arthur Schmitt	Mote	Benjamin Orlovski	Edward Boatman	Ben Johnson	Will Gausmann	Paulo Volkova
Benoit Champy	Diego Chavez	Jardson Araújo	OCHA AVMU	Darrin Higgins	Francesco Paleari	Benjamin Orlovski	Gabriele Malaspina	The Noun Project	Benjamin Orlovski
Saman Bemel-Benrud	Ben Rizzo	Christopher McDonnell	Jakob Vogel	Juan Pablo Bravo	Mauro Fontanari	Chris Matthews	Laurent Patain	OCHA AVMU	Bruno Gätjens González

Fonts

Akkurat Lineto.com
ABCDEFGHIJKLMNOPQRTSUVWXYZabcedfghijklmnopqrstuvwyz1234567890

Type 1451 Lineto.com
ABCDEFGHIJKLMNOPQRTSUVWXYZabcedfghijklmnopqrstuvwyz1234567890

Helvetica Neue Linotype
ABCDEFGHIJKLMNOPQRTSUVWXYZabcedfghijklmnopqrstuvwyz1234567890

Copernicus Klim.co.nz
ABCDEFGHIJKLMNOPQRTSUVWXYZabcedfghijklmnopqrstuvwyz1234567890

Domaine Klim.co.nz
ABCDEFGHIJKLMNOPQRTSUVWXYZabcedfghijklmnopqrstuvwyz1234567890

Whitney Hoefler & Co.
ABCDEFGHIJKLMNOPQRTSUVWXYZabcedfghijklmnopqrstuvwyz1234567890

Trade Gothic Condensed Linotype
ABCDEFGHIJKLMNOPQRTSUVWXYZabcedfghijklmnopqrstuvwyz1234567890

Claimcheck Hoefler & Co.
1234567890

Caslon Pro Adobe
ABCDEFGHIJKLMNOPQRTSUVWXYZabcedfghijklmnopqrstuvwyz1234567890

Univers Linotype
ABCDEFGHIJKLMNOPQRTSUVWXYZabcedfghijklmnopqrstuvwyz1234567890

Neutra House Industries
ABCDEFGHIJKLMNOPQRTSUVWXYZabcedfghijklmnopqrstuvwyz1234567890

Egyptian Slate Linotype
ABCDEFGHIJKLMNOPQRTSUVWXYZabcedfghijklmnopqrstuvwyz1234567890

Keep the Knowledge

InformationisBeautiful.net

- explore our collection of beautiful visualisations
- access all the data & research from this book
- get involved with commenting & crowdsourcing
- buy posters & prints of your favourite images
- find all our latest infographics and updates

🐦 @infobeautiful
📘 facebook.com/informationisbeautiful
📌 pinterest.com/infobeauty
g+ bit.ly/IIB_GooglePlus

VIZsweet.com

- see live examples of our dataviz app
- play with interactive versions of the images in this book

iibstudio.co

- explore our collaborations and commissio
- work with us!

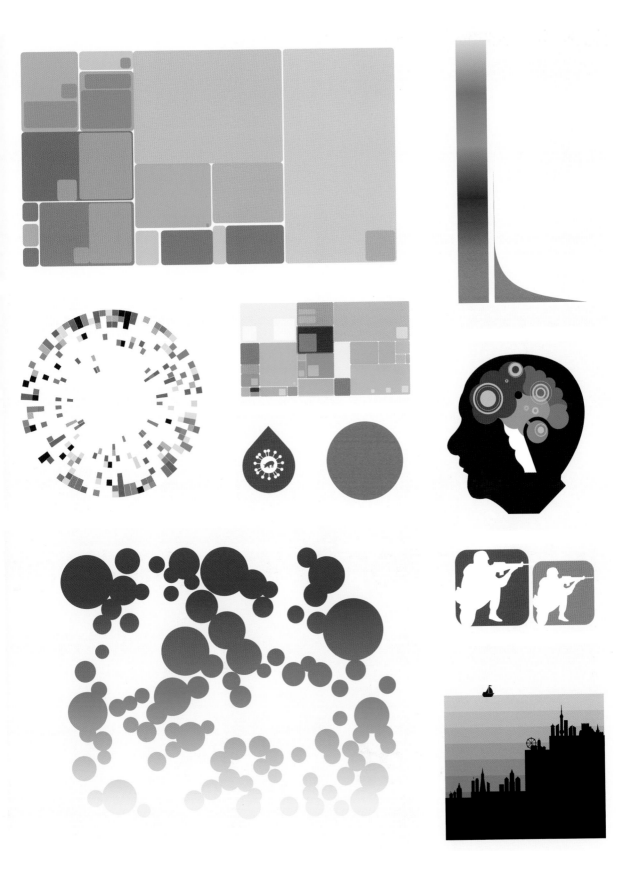

How Many Gigatonnes of CO₂...?
014

Best in Show
016

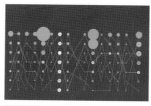

Train Wrecks
018

Recycling
020

Movie Lens
021

Save The Cat! Applied
022

Rhetological Fallacies
024

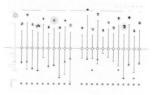

Oil Well
028

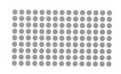

Common Mythconceptions I
030

Senseless
032

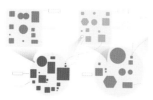

Big Data
034

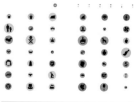

Mavericks & Heretics
038

Superpower Showdown: Demographics 043

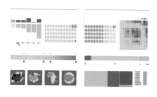

Simple I
044

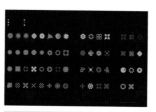

The Stellar Nursery
046

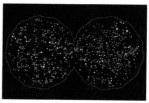

Stellar Constellations
048

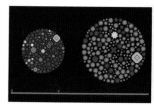

The Milky Way
050

Richest Churches
052

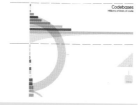

Codebases
054

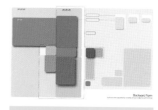

Backyard Farm
056

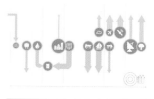

Crazy Global Warming Solutions
058

Top 500 Passwords
060

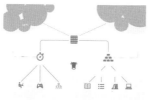

How Passwords are Hacked
062

Tooth & Law
064

Murder Stories
065

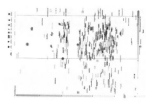

In Good Company?
066

Meditation
069

Types of Meditation
072

Meditation: Evidence 076

Water World 077

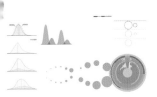
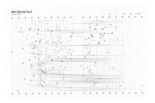

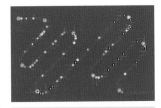
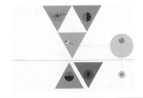

Maps
078

Superpower Showdown: Law & Order 079

One in...
080

True Genius
082

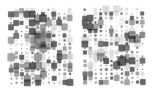
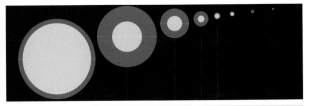
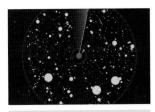

Simple II
086

Non-Fiction Books Everyone Should Read 88

Veg Table Bedfellows
090

Are We Alone in the Galaxy?
092

Astro Killers
095

Astro Attempted Killers 098

Astro-Killer Killers 099

Astro Would-be Killers
100

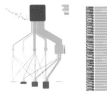

(Un) Surprising Studies
102

Who Old Are You?
104

Plane Truth
106

Crash Cause
108

Table Sugar
110

Glycaemix
112

Teaspoons
113

Superpower Showdown: Social Economics 114

Superpower Showdown: Economics 115

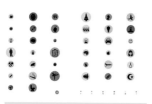

Common Mythconceptions II
116

The Point
118

Which Sandwich? 119

Person Years
124

Personal Transport 126

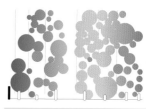

Snake Oil Baddies?
128

Pole Position
130

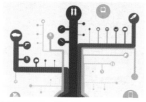

Buddhism
131

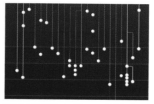

Buddhism: States of Consciousness 134

Cycle of Rebirth
136

Daily Bread UK
138

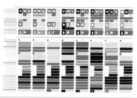

Daily Bread US
140

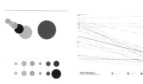

House Edges
142

Superpower Showdown: Education 143

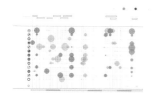

The Antibiotic Abacus
144

The Etiquettrix
146

Simple III
148

Natal Depression 150

Timeline of the Far Future
152

Superpower Showdown: Business 156

Disappearing Varieties
157

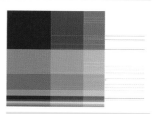

Human Cost
165

Drug Deal
166

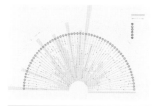

Age of Empires
168

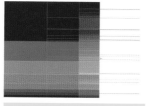

Counting the Cause UK
170

Counting the Cause US
172

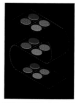

You Never Do Anything... 174

Action Movie Badasses 175

Box Rating
176

Influ-Venn-Za
177

Prison Bars
178

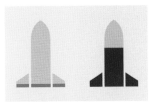

Superpower Showdown : War & Peace 182

Walled World
183

Good Relationtips
184

PIN Point
186

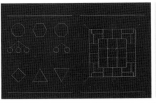

Ruling Casts
187

Divas
192

Journalistic Clichés 194

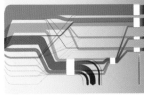

Energy Flow Man
196

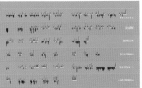

Luckier Dip
200

Luckier Dip: The Simpsons 202

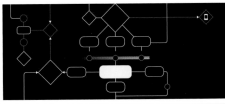

Should I Believe This Medical Study?
203

Simple IV
208

Live Long...
210

Live long...and Prosper
211

Superpower Showdown: Consumption 212

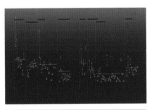

Gender Pay Gap UK
214

Gender Pay Gap US
216

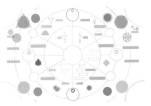

Philosophical Reality
218

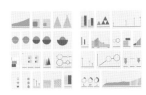

World Dashboard
222

A Taxonomy of Ideas
224

Life Scape
226

What Makes a Good Visualisation?
242

Data - Information - Knowledge
244